EVOLUTION IS NOT SCIENTIFIC: 32 REASONS WHY

(First Edition Entitled)
FROM ETERNITY TO ETERNITY

THE SONG OF ETERNITY

The Prelude, The Interlude and The Postlude
(An Enlarged Edition)

A Treatise on Why Evolution Is Contrary To
Theories and Laws of Science

(Written in the Language of the Average Person)

Copyright © 1995

Albert Sippert

Title for First Printing
FROM ETERNITY TO ETERNITY
EVOLUTION IS NOT A SCIENCE
Copyright © 1989
Library of Congress Catalog Card No. 89-092671
ISBN Number   0-9623872-0-7 - First Printing

Title for Second Printing
(An Enlarged Edition)

**EVOLUTION IS
NOT SCIENTIFIC:
32 REASONS WHY**
Copyright © 1995
Library of Congress Catalog Card No. 94-092301
ISBN Number   0-9623872-1-5

To Order Books
contact

Sippert Publishing Company
P.O. Box 1913 (330 Wheeler Ave.)
N. Mankato, MN 56002

REGARDING SECOND PRINTING

Additional pages were added at the end of the book, following page 404. Added there are:

1. Three major strikes against evolution with Thirty-two reasons why evolution is not scientific.
2. Six very evil, harmful, devastating effects that evolution has upon mankind.
3. Contacts I had with propagators of the evolution religion.
4. Discussions and debates with evolutionists on secular radio talk shows.

PREFACE

FOR WHOM IS THIS BOOK WRITTEN?

Primarily for Christians and others who are wondering if evolution is really a fact as is claimed by the evolutionists.

For evolutionists who are looking in vain for answers in their search for the origin of the universe, earth and mankind.

For anyone who is seeking an answer to the many questions that have arisen in any particular problem regarding the origin of all things.

For people who are seeking answers to the problem of the Separation of Religion and Anti-religion and State.

For all people who have been seeking answers to other questions that have been asked regarding origins, such as:

Why does the solar system and the entire universe move along in such an orderly and precise manner? A Big Bang could not cause such orderliness and precision.

What is the origin of all matter and materials?

What is the origin of coal, oil, natural gas, the elements and minerals?

On the basis of geology what was this earth like originally?

What is the explanation for layers after layers of sedimentary rock strata and fossils found in them?

What caused the dinosaurs to die suddenly in masses all over the earth? Why are the evolutionists confused regarding the sudden end of the dinosaurs?

Was there an ice age at one time and what are some problems regarding an ice age?

How did the various extremely complex parts of living creatures develop all at once, such as the eyes, ears, nose, lungs, hearts, stomach, blood vessels, brains, feet, legs, arms, reproductive systems, so that functional bodies could suddenly develop and live?

Why can't different kinds of animals be interbred so that cats and dogs and sheep and apes could produce still different kinds of animals: half cats, half dogs, half or quarter sheep, half apes, etc?

Could there ever have been any half or quarter apes and human creatures?

Who really are the Neanderthal and Cro-Magnon people?

What is the explanation for civilizations arising SUDDENLY all over the world at one time about 5,000 years ago, with the suddenness of a sunrise?

Why did these civilizations speak different languages?

Is evolution a fact or merely an anti-creation IDEA?

Does evolution have a scientific foundation?

Does Darwin's idea of evolution have any scientific foundation?

Why is evolution SCIENTIFICALLY NOT POSSIBLE?

If evolution is true, why does it go counter to the scientific Laws of Thermodynamics?

What is science and on what is true and complete science based?

To be scientific why must a non-material force greater than the material things of the universe be considered?

What is the religious and antireligious nature of evolution?

What are the court cases that have dealt with the antagonism that exists between evolutionists and creationists?

What wrong logic was used in the "Monkey Trial" of 1925?

COMMENTS MADE BY REVIEWERS AND READERS

Dr. (Ph.D.) Neelak Tjernagel: "In my opinion your book makes most other books on the same subject irrelevant."

The Sword of the Lord: "The book categorically devastates with truly scientific facts, the falsity of the evolution claims."

Dr. Henry Morris: "We do appreciate the excellent work you have put into this book."

Dr. Duane Gish: "It certainly is an excellent book. It is comprehensive and well written. It is especially good for the general layman, since you wrote it in non-technical language."

A reader: "I thoroughly enjoyed your remarkable treatise. I emphasize remarkable because the subject matter and its sequence is planned to guide the reader smoothly through diverse information from ancient history through pure science to legal aspects."

"It is THE best book on this subject that I have seen."

"A most powerful book."

"Your book is so very well written and so easy to follow. It covers all bases.

A president of a college: "I found the book to be more than excellent."

A dentist: "Your book is the best tool we have available to counter the evolution lie."

This book is an encyclopedia of information on the evolution - creation controversy."

"You have erected a tombstone, whose inscription will be read for centuries." "It is a dynamic piece of literature."

Readers from all walks of life have called the book amazing, astounding, extraordinary, fascinating, even a masterpiece.

An editor: "Many reliable reviewers applaud the rich content and powerful thrust of the book."

"Congratulations on an outstanding job of exposing the satanic lie of evolution. Few can boast of authoring a book at the age you authored yours. And I know of none who at the age authored a book on so complex a subject."

Reading your book was like taking a good year trip through the world."

Ibert Siegler, author of EVOLUTION OR DEGENERATION - WHICH? wrote: "I finished reading your tremendous book."

THE PRELUDE

     ANSWERS THAT HAVE BEEN GIVEN
     REGARDING THE ORIGIN OF ALL THINGS

     1. Questions that have been asked   18
     2. What school history books teach   18

II. TAKING THE HISTORY OF MANKIND
     BACKWARDS, or THE FACTS of History Over
     Against THE IDEAS of Evolution   21

(The Highly Advanced, Highly Technical and Highly Skilled
Civilizations at the Very Beginning of Recorded History)

     1. The Egyptians   21
     2. The Sumerians and Babylonians   25
     3. The city of Jericho in the Jordan Valley   28
     4. The people of the Indus Valley of India   28
     5. China   29
     6. Easter Island   29
     7. Asia Minor   30
     8. The island of Crete   31
     9. The ancient Greeks   32
    10. Europe proper   32
    11. England   33
    12. Africa   34
    13. The Americas   34
    14. The United States   35
    15. Mexico   35
    16. The Incas of Peru   36
    17. The southern tip of South America   3

III. COMPARING THE ASSUMPTIONS OF
     EVOLUTION WITH THE FACTS OF
     ARCHEOLOGY

IV. THE EARLIEST HISTORY OF MANKIND
     ACCORDING TO THE BIBLE   41

     1. The first chapters of Genesis and Adam and Eve   41
     2. The earth between the fall of man and the Flood   45

THE INTERLUDE   124

The Turmoil the Evolutionist Have Created With Their No-God
and Anti-God Ideas

XI.   TEACHINGS OF THE EVOLUTIONISTS   124

XII.   THE BEGINNING OF ALL THINGS   154

XXI. EVOLUTION IS NOT SCIENTIFIC   311

XXII. EVOLUTION IS AN ANTI-RELIGIOUS CREED, AND AT THE SAME TIME A RELIGION IN ITSELF   325

XXIII. THE EFFECTS OF TEACHING EVOLUTION   341

THE POSTLUDE

DEVASTATING FACTS ADDED TO A
REVISED BOOK   **404**

THE PRELUDE

I. QUESTIONS THAT HAVE BEEN ASKED AND ANSWERS THAT HAVE BEEN GIVEN REGARDING THE ORIGIN OF ALL THINGS

1. QUESTIONS THAT HAVE BEEN ASKED

What is the origin of mankind? Why is mankind superior to all other creatures? From where did all the animals (fauna) and all the plants and vegetation (flora) of the world come? How did the sun and other stars originate? What is the origin of the earth and its sister planets? From where did the universe and all its elements, material, energy and super clock-like precision come? Why and how did death, decay and all the degeneration (entropy) come upon this earth? What is the final destiny of all things? These are some of the questions that confront all of us. The sharpest minds in the history of mankind have tried to find the answers to these questions the past 4,000 to 6,000 years of recorded history.

2. WHAT SCHOOL HISTORY BOOKS TEACH

(Throughout this book, I will cite numerous quotations in order to let the evolutionists and others speak for themselves in regard to what they believe and teach.)

I will start with the beginning of mankind as given in the ancient history books our children have used and still use in school. *The World Book Encyclopedia* (Volume E, p. 12) states in regard to the earth:

How old is the earth? Geologists say the earth is 4,500,000,000 years old. . . .You will understand better how old this is when you realize that the earliest records we have of human history go back only about 5,000 years.

And even the first 1,000 years or so of those records are not clearly known.

The history book I used in high school, *The Story of Man's Early Progress* (1920) by W. West, begins history with these words, p. 3:

The first men were more helpless and brute-like than the lowest savages in the world today. Their only clothing was the coarse hair that covered their bodies. They had neither fire nor knife - no tools or weapons except their hands and their formidable apelike teeth and chance clubs and stones. The first marked gain was the discovery by some savage that he could chip off flakes from a flat stone by striking it with other stones, so as to give it a sharp edge, a keen point, and a convenient shape for the hand to grasp. This invention lifted man into the first stone age. In Europe the stone age began at least 100,000 years ago.

Then a few pages later West writes:

> Finally some 10,000 years ago, some ingenious barbarian discovered he could grind his stone knife with certain stones, and so get a keener edge and sharper point than merely by chipping at it. This invention began a new era. The *Old Stone Age* or age of chipped stone gave way to the *New Stone Age*.

It is truly amazing that it would take an *ingenious barbarian* 90,000 years to finally make a better stone to cut and chip. Would a barbarian really be that mentally handicapped? Laziness and need are the mother of invention. Certainly the mother of invention must have gotten to them sooner than that.

A recent history book, *People and Our World — A Study of World History* (1977-1984) by Allen Kownslar and Terry Smart, states in its Introduction:

> People have always wondered about the first inhabitants on the earth. It is difficult to know much about *prehistoric* people, because they had no system of writing. Therefore they were not able to leave any written records. This is called *prehistory* — a time before written history.

Then they write about the three different stone ages: the Old Stone Age, the Middle Stone Age, and the New Stone Age. They think these people were nomads or wanderers who lived by hunting animals and gathering wild plants and fruits. They write about the discoveries of so-called very ancient human fossils which Louis and Mary Leakey and now their son, Richard, have found in Africa, and which others have found there and in other parts of the earth, and which they have assumed to be from 1,750,000 to 3,750,000 years old.

Another school history book, *Men and Nations — A World History* (1975) by Anatole Mazour and John People states, p. 5:

> Recent discoveries of bones have led scientists to believe that manlike creatures appeared in Africa sometime between 500,000 and 1,750,000 years ago. . .Although in many ways these creatures bore little resemblance to modern man, they walked erect and had the physical characteristics of human beings. It is also thought that they used stones and pieces of wood as tools and weapons. We

know little of man's development during most of these hundreds of thousands of years. His way of life was much like that of the animals. He hunted as did the hunting animals, and like many other animals, he gathered edible berries and roots. But three important characteristics helped set man apart from the animals and enabled him to progress. First, his erect posture allowed him to use his hands to hold weapons for hunting and defense. Second, he could speak, so that he could give and receive information through language. Third, he had a large brain to make use of the information and to gather more.

If evolution is true, would it take such a creature hundreds of thousands of years and even over 1,000,000 years to progress to where man is today, or was 6,000 years ago? What made it possible for man to appear on the scene of human history all at once 6,000 to 8,000 years ago? What made it possible for mankind to speak, which no animal can do? What caused him to have a larger brain and an analytical mind?

The Epic of Man (1961) in *Life* magazine, p. 8, states about the same:

The history of man's evolution. . .covers approximately 15 million years of time. Five thousand years of intermittent written records cover man's known history, then trails off into the silence of the Stone Age hunter's world. For the rest of the 15 million years of human evolution, during which our bodies and our brains were drastically altered, we have today only a few handfuls of broken teeth, a few battered skulls, the magical carvings and paintings of dead hunters, and a paucity of rude tools to tell the story of the way we crawled upward from the jungle darkness.

Did it take these people millions of years to learn to use fire and tools?

II. TAKING THE HISTORY OF MANKIND BACKWARDS, or The FACTS of History Over Against The IDEAS of Evolution.

Taking the history of early mankind backwards, we find a different account of man. Actually written records of mankind go back only to about 3000 B.C., and perhaps less, depending on how much the Egyptian list of the kings in its first dynasty, 3500 to 2300 B.C., is exaggerated. If mankind is millions of years old, why are there no historical records before 3500 B.C., and why do these records appear in numerous places all at once, in many different languages throughout the world? Writing began simultaneously 3,000 to 4,000 B.C. in Mesopotamia, Egypt, the Indus Valley and other places. By then these records show that man is already highly advanced and civilized. Many of the achievements of the early Egyptians and other people have not been surpassed to this day. Did these highly advanced people just jump forward, all at once, from nowhere without any prior civilization? This is totally impossible! Outside of the Bible there is no record of civilization before 3000 B.C.

1. THE EGYPTIANS

Looking backwards in history, let us consider some of these civilizations that appeared suddenly in history, almost out of the blue sky. One of the most remarkable civilizations that appeared suddenly is that of the ancient Egyptians. I cannot stress too much the fact that civilizations appeared all over this earth with a *SUDDENNESS* that is almost unbelievable over against the evolutionary assumption that man progressed upwardly very slowly over millions of years. *Reader's Digest* (June, 1975, p. 86), had a condensation of a television script by Kenneth Clark, *In the Beginning: The Mystery of Ancient Egypt:*

These things, which we think of as essential to our very definition of civilization seem to have appeared with the suddenness of a sunrise, in the Nile Valley, between 3000 and 2800 B.C. It was as though after half a million years of semi-conscious existence, man leaped into full awareness of himself and his surroundings in the course of about 200 years. Science has uncovered fascinating evidence of fragments of civilized life in many other lands, but Egypt was the first great home of civilization.

Although Kenneth Clark states clearly that civilization appeared suddenly in Egypt and elsewhere, he cannot get away from the evolutionary millions of years that were assumed to precede it, "AFTER

HALF A MILLION YEARS." Numerous other writers with an evolutionary background have made similar statements. I shall quote one more from *Time-Life* magazine (1965) "Ancient Egypt," by Lionel Casson, p. 51:

> Some 7,000 or 8,000 years before the birth of Christ, civilization was emerging in scattered areas of the Near East. Man the hunter had become man the settler. He had ceased to depend on the luck of the chase for his food and now fed himself by herding flocks and raising crops instead. Then suddenly within a few centuries between 3200 and 3000 B.C. the scattered tribes that lived along the Nile were united under one head, ruled by a formal government.

And then he goes on and writes of the marvelous Egyptian civilization. It is simply amazing that Egyptian civilization with its kings and governments and pyramids, with its highly advanced architecture, sphinxes, engineering feats hardly matched today, tools, techniques, art, science, medicine, organizations, etc. just simply occurred suddenly as if they had been imported from some other region of the earth. Or still more silly, that they came from distant planets and outer space, as some otherwise intelligent people suggested to me. However, as I shall show later on they were imported or rather migrated from the highly civilized descendants of Noah who were dispersed at the Tower of Babel. But it is a sad fact of history that many civilizations after about 1900 B.C. degenerated in the course of time as happened to the Egyptians themselves, to people in Mesopotamia, Europe in the Dark Ages, the early people of Central and South America, and so on. It is important to stress that advanced civilizations did not evolve in Egypt but just occurred. In fact no remains of savage or primitive people are found in Egypt or Mesopotamia.

Egyptian history begins about 3400 B.C. to 3200 B.C. The first king of Egypt is believed to be Menes who united Lower and Upper Egypt into one kingdom about 3000 B.C., according to Manetho, an Egyptian priest who lived about 250 B.C. Others consider King Narmer as the first king or that he was the same as Menes. There are German historians who date Menes' reign as starting anywhere from 3623 B.C. to 5702 B.C.

Early in their history we find the Egyptians writing and keeping records. They made the world's first paper out of papyrus reeds and invented ink to go with it. They were able to measure distances and weights with standard measures, reckon time, survey the land and compute their taxes. They took advantage of the Nile floods by building canals and irrigation projects. With amazing *SUDDENNESS* we find these people using gold, silver, copper, bronze, turquoise, precious stones like lapis lazuli, gold jewelry, carvings in rare woods, ivory and stone, ostrich plumage, rare animal skins, myrrh and spices. Medicine was used early in their history.

With surprising suddenness they were quarrying granite and transporting it many miles down the Nile river, instead of using sunbaked bricks as the Sumerians did in Mesopotamia. Their architects built royal sepulchers, pyramids and stone monuments that rank in splendor with the most noble and artistic of any later age and region. Their art, paintings, architecture, artistic pillars and columns and sphinxes were centuries ahead of the ancient Greek artists and sculptors even though some were prehistoric structures, or before any historic records were kept.

Their sculptors in those early centuries carved huge heads of their kings in stone that match the faces of the presidents in the Black Hills of South Dakota. Their important buildings were painted in brilliant colors. These were industrious and intelligent people who appeared in history in almost instant abruptness, with no primitive forefathers.

Their tools also were highly advanced. Numerous histories give the impression that these people built the pyramids and other structures of granite and other stone almost with bare hands. But they did use very surprisingly advanced tools. Very early in their existence, the Egyptians knew how to make saws and tubular crown drills with fixed teeth of corundum or gemstones for cutting their quarried rock. These people were as advanced, if not more so, as the most gifted people today. It is true that more knowledge has been accumulated for the people of today, but we can hardly claim to be superior to them or more sophisticated. But in the course of time instead of evolution taking place, degeneration or loss of scientific knowledge took place according to the "History of Tools," Smithsonian Institution Report (1913), p. 566. In many cases advanced know-how and knowledge disappeared completely for centuries and centuries. The knowledge of how to cut through quartz rock was lost until it was reinvented when tunnel building was in progress in the last century.

The amazing abilities of those early Egyptians become especially evident when we behold those immense pyramids that they erected. Their very existence has baffled scholars for thousands of years. Even Napoleon and his army stood in awe of them when they first saw them.

How did those ancient Egyptians build them? Mathematicians of all ages have marvelled that elements of Pythagorean geometry were used thousands of years before Pythagoras lived.

The Great Pyramid of Giza covers 13 acres, which is as large as three city blocks. Its peak was 481 feet above the ground or as high as a 40 story skyscraper. It took about 2,000,000 blocks of limestone and granite, each weighing from two to seventy tons, rising on 201 stepped tiers, to complete the structure. It contains more stone than all the cathedrals, churches and chapels built in England since the days of Christ. Napoleon calculated that the three large pyramids of Giza contained enough stone to raise a wall ten feet high and three feet wide around all of France, or if they were lined up end to end they would reach one and one-half times across the United States. It has been figured that if those over two million blocks were quarried, transported up to 500 miles, polished and lifted in place, in 20 years, at the unbelievable rate of 315 blocks a day, to as high as 480 feet, 26 blocks per hour would have to be placed each 12 hour day and seven days a week. With 100,000 men using the most modern equipment, our construction workers today would not be able to accomplish this feat in the same period of time. And these are some of the people who appeared suddenly on the scene of human history, out of what is called prehistory by evolutionists!

Not only was the amount of stone and the amount of work amazing but so was also the accuracy of their extraordinary architectural abilities. The stones were cut and polished so accurately that a sheet of paper could hardly be inserted between the stones. Still more amazing is that the four sides slope smoothly up to the point. When the work was started, this point was difficult to check as the work progressed upward, because there was no point to refer to. If one side of the pyramid was laid a little too steep it would shoot over the others. Wherever the work is checked, there is unbelievable accuracy. And how did those Egyptians cut, polish and place those immense stones so perfectly and in such little time? Some investigators quite seriously suggest that the Great Pyramid could have been erected only with the help of computers or perhaps superminds from another planet using laser beams to cut the blocks and anti-gravity devices to raise them. On December 4, 1986, the *Minneapolis Tribune* printed an article, "Experts work on a new way to measure intelligence." The first question asked in the article was "Who built the pyramids - ancient Egyptians or extra-terrestrials?" Even if there were extra-terrestrials, why should they be smarter than we terrestrials, unless they were angels sent by God. But that does not fit in with the idea of evolution.

Another amazing feat in the construction of the Great Pyramid was the planning of the structure, supervising the construction and providing for all the labor necessary. To feed and house all the workers, to take care of the injured and the sick would tax the mind and abilities of the ablest organizers that ever lived. Another feat connected with the pyramids is the embalming techniques that were used to preserve the bodies of the deceased. These techniques have never been excelled.

To sum it all up, those early first Egyptians with all their outstanding feats and accomplishments were far from ascending from "primitive?" ancestors. I am sure you will find their ancestors from among the dispersed and highly advanced people at the Tower of Babel, of whom we shall hear further on. One further remark should be made here: Where are there any buildings or structures made by men 10,000 to 100,000 years before this if men evolved? There should be some prior buildings, at least in Egypt.

2.   THE SUMERIANS AND BABYLONIANS

The next outstanding civilization that must be considered is the Sumerian civilization in the Tigris and Euphrates valleys. Their history began about the same time as that of the Egyptians. The *Reader's Digest* (September 1977, p. 131), mentions that:

According to the king-lists, the First Dynasty was started after the Flood. . .Woolley [An English archeologist] believed that a highly advanced civilization must have preceded the First Dynasty. But other than the king-lists that spoke of a pre-Flood dynasty, there is no physical evidence to indicate that the Sumerians had not simply sprung up out of the desert like seeds sprouting after a rain.

How beautifully that was expressed! Just as the Egyptians did! The Sumerians also rose about 3500 B.C. There are no signs anywhere that these civilizations slowly evolved upward from cave men and above all, not from apes. Where did these people come from? No doubt the beginning of these civilizations took place some hundreds of years after the Flood and some time after the Tower of Babel.

These Sumerians appear suddenly to have developed a brilliant civilization between the Tigris and Euphrates rivers in Mesopotamia (which means between rivers). They developed an irrigation system with many canals, and they grew all kinds of vegetables, fruits, grain and date palms. They domesticated animals such as donkeys, goats and sheep. They developed a complex society with merchants and traders going between cities and traveling to other regions, soldiers, priests, rulers, freemen and slaves. They were able to put their language into writing before 3000 B.C., which is about the time just after the confusion of tongues at the Tower of Babel. Thousands of clay tablets and inscriptions have been found which tell about their business practices, government, law and religion. These tablets show that they had a knowledge of medicine, mathematics and astronomy. They created a calendar based on the movements of the sun. They had learned to divide the circle into 360 degrees, which we copied. They wrote thousands of literary works, including myths, epics, narrative poems, and songs to their gods and heroes. They wrote proverbs, fables, essays and wisdom on many subjects. One of their more interesting works was the Epic of Gilgamesh, which writes of the Flood as the Bible does and as many nationalities of the world do.

All this could not have happened in a few years unless they had been endowed by the Creator with knowledge and skill. At the ruins of Ur, the British Museum and the Museum of the University of Pennsylvania, between 1919 and 1929 excavated layers of three different civilizations, down to virgin soil, and they found that throughout all of Ur's entire history from its very beginning the people were endowed with a high degree of culture, talents, abilities and civilization.

Their craftsmen were skillful in producing things out of gold, silver, copper, bronze and stone. They produced fabulously beautiful objects of art, fashioned out of gold, silver and precious stone. They knew how to make bronze out of copper and tin, which gave them a stronger metal to work with. Out of bronze they made cups, vases, knives, helmets, battle axes, swords, spears, shields, chariots, various ornaments, cooking and practical household equipment and musical instruments. They very likely invented the wheel which was used by potters to shape clay. They also used the wheel to move larger objects, and they put the wheel to use on their chariots. They wove fine cloth, and made glass out of sand. Archeologists have dug up glazed stoneware more than 4,000 years old.

There are indications that the Sumerians and their successors, the Babylonians, knew a lot more about astronomy than did the people who came after them. Men who have studied the early civilization of these people were surprised to discover that the Babylonians knew certain facts about the planets. They say there is strong evidence that these people knew about four of the satellites of Jupiter and seven of the satellites of Saturn. We do not know if they had telescopes, but they could hardly have known about these satellites without a magnifying glass of some kind.

At its height of glory, the Sumerian society was wealthy, powerful and complex. But their greatest work was their huge temples, called ziggurats, which were adorned with rectangular columns and colonnades. The front of the temples were enriched with mosaics in geometric pattern of red, black and white. These ziggurats were several stories high and covered an area of about 500,000 square feet. This would cover an area about 600 feet wide and 800 feet long, which is as large as three city blocks or about as large as the area of the United States Capitol. It was an amazing piece of architecture, as beautiful, well built and large as one of the largest government buildings in Washington, D.C.

Certainly it is totally illogical, unreasonable, and non-historical to believe that these people could spring up out of apeland and into the Old, Middle and New Stone Ages, and then, without leaving any written history, could within a few hundred years create marvelous inventions and build immense buildings, without developing a written language before 3000 to 4000 B.C. as the evolutionists teach our children in their history books. Certainly these people could not develop suddenly in a few hundred years without developing writing, mathematics, sciences, and inventions tens of thousands of years before that, if the evolutionary assumed hundreds of thousands and millions of years would be true. There would have been some evidence of these people going back 10,000, 20,000, 30,000 and 50,000 years. So why are the Leakeys and other anthropological fossil hunters digging around Africa and other parts of the world looking for fossils of people who are assumed to have lived millions of years ago? What they are finding are fossils of apes and other creatures and of men who had scattered into all parts of the earth as hunters and food gatherers and were covered with the muddy sediments of Noah's flood.

History books usually refer to four prominent civilizations that arose about 3000 to 4000 years before Christ in four different parts of the mild temperate zones of the earth. These four great regions of civilization were in the river valleys where food and shelter were easily obtained: the Nile River valley of Egypt, the valley of the Tigris and Euphrates rivers in Mesopotamia, the Indus River valley in N.W. India (to the east of Mesopotamia), and the valley of the Yellow River in northern China. Although there are other comfortable river regions that could be referred to, one more prominent one in the early history of the world is the Jordan River in Palestine.

3.   JERICHO IN THE JORDAN RIVER VALLEY

I will refer to this region of civilization next because it is considered one of the world's earliest. It is the ancient civilization centered around Jericho near the Jordan River, about 15 miles northeast of Jerusalem. The origin of these people has been set at about 5800 to 6800 B.C. But as Rene Noorbergen in his *Secrets of Lost Races* (1977) states: "[These dates] become rather nebulous when exposed to scientific critique, for as yet there is no foolproof dating method." He says it is best to compare the date of the origin of Jericho with the dates of the rest of the other great ancient cultures of the world, the Sumerians and Egyptians.

While the Sumerians and Egyptians grew up along the banks of great rivers, Jericho in the Jordan valley region developed near an oasis which had an abundant supply of water from a gushing spring that gave forth a thousand gallons of water per minute. Near this oasis as well as in the Jordan valley nearby the early settlers could grow crops of wheat, barley, lentils, figs and other foods and fruits, as well as have domesticated cattle, sheep and goats. Here they built a city of eight acres with some 2,500 or 3,000 people. To defend themselves from warlike intruders, a large series of walls of stone and at least one massive tower were built. The tower was at least 30 feet in diameter and 20 feet high and perhaps higher. These are the walls that could have fallen to Joshua's trumpets about 1250 B.C. The homes had large rooms with doors. The walls were made of mud bricks. The floors were covered with a fine layer of highly burnished plaster.

4.   THE PEOPLE OF THE INDUS VALLEY IN INDIA

Another remarkable ancient civilization going back to about 3000 B.C. was in the Indus valley which lies in northwest India, east of Mesopotamia. This civilization has been called the Dravidian. They had one common language and could write their language but no one so far can decipher what they wrote. No doubt it was one of the new languages after the Confusion of Tongues at the Tower of Babel. This civilization was not known to exist until 1920 when by accident two of their numerous long buried cities were uncovered: Harappa and Mohenjo-Daro. The culture of this civilzation called "Harrapan" reached from the Arabian Sea to the Himalayas and from eastern Iran to the Ganges River valley. It was one of the largest early civilizations. The largest of their cities uncovered so far was Mohenjo-Daro. It had wide streets with rectangular blocks. The homes were one and two stories high with courtyards and bathrooms. They had a well-planned drainage system similiar to that of many modern cities of today. They had a sanitation system, and their sewers were lined with baked brick, with manholes for service entrances. They made use of copper, bronze, gold and silver, and made beautiful toys for their children. Their artistic work would be prized by any culture. They had bathrooms, household tools made of bronze and copper, pottery and jewelry. There is evidence that these people carried on trade with the Sumerians to the west.

But as suddenly as these people seemed to have appeared on this earth, their culture seems to have disappeared. It seems that Aryan people from the west and northwest took over. The Aryans are ancestors of present day Hindus. The Dravidians moved southward where they still may be found in India, while the Aryans, not accustomed to the confinement of cities, preferred the open spaces. Here again we have another case of where a civilization instead of evolving degenerated into decay and has become lost.

5.   CHINA

In the east there no doubt were in those early 3,000 to 4,000 years before Christ roving bands of hunters and food gatherers with their own language. They wandered onward to Southeast Asia and then northward until they came to China, where, in the Yangtze, Yellow and other river valleys, they founded another nation, living as an advanced civilization with their own language. The Chinese have set 2250 to 2850 B.C. as the beginning of their history. The first of the 3 rulers are referred to as the Age of the Three Sovereigns and then the next 5 as the Age of the Five Rulers. Impossibly long reigns have been attributed to these rulers. But the "impossible" ages are not so impossible in light of the ages of the people given in the Bible before and shortly after the Flood. This will be considered further on. Historians ask where did these people come from? Although the Chinese language largely remains as it was a few thousand years ago, these early Chinese developed a highly complex ideographic system of writing. It is hard to learn because it consists of thousands of characters.

They developed movable type and gun powder long before Europeans did. Where did they get it from? historians ask. They became skillful in the casting of bronze implements and vessels. They have produced beautiful silks from silkworms, and also porcelain, jade and architecture. The Japanese and Koreans learned much from Chinese culture.

6.   EASTER ISLAND

Out in the Pacific Ocean lies Easter Island which produced another amazing early civilization that has baffled anthropologists and students of mankind for years. More than 100 stone giant-heads weighing up to 50 tons are scattered on this barren volcanic island. No one has yet determined who quarried the stones, carved them, moved them five miles and set them up. Originally these enormous stone statues were set on stone platforms and on their heads had been placed huge red stone topknots, which had been transported from a distant quarry. The few hundred natives know nothing about the history of these statues. To quarry, transport and set up these stones would be a rather difficult task even with the machinery available today. These people could also have been some of our earliest ancestors.

7.   ASIA MINOR

Moving back to the Mideast, we find another ancient advanced civilization north of Palestine in Asia Minor. Two sites have been excavated to some extent: Catal Huyaek and Ebla. Catal Huyaek is believed to have begun existence before Jericho in Palestine. Located in eastern Asia Minor at the base of the Taurus Mountains, it is believed that they flourished between 5400 to 6200 B.C. From a volcano nearby it obtained obsidian, a dark hard glossy volcanic rock, from which were made various artifacts, knives, mirrors, spearheads, and tools for working in leather, bones and wood. They painted entire walls with scenes of animals and outdoor life. Besides painters and sculptors they had potters, who made household utensils, and stonesmiths. They also made fine tools, utensils like axes and hammers, and weapons like daggers and spearheads. There were weavers who made fine yarn, basket makers, metal workers and wood workers.

The other civilization in the region, Ebla, was in the northern part of Syria. Under the charge of the University of Rome, excavations of this mound, or tell, were started in 1964. Ebla was the head of a thriving empire about 2400 B.C. at the same time Egypt and Sumer were in their glory. Ebla with its commerce, arts and advancement carried its influence to other lands. Ebla is mentioned in some of the writings of the Egyptians and Babylonians. At Ebla a royal palace and large temple were uncovered. Cuneiform, or wedge shaped, writing similiar to that of the Sumerians was found. Excavators found over 14,000 inscribed tablets, but the writing in cuneiform was not Sumerian or any other similiar language. It was another different language, no doubt due to the Tower of Babel confusion of tongues which happened a few hundred years before. Later 100 clay dictionaries were found that gave the Sumerian meaning for about 3,000 words of the Eblaites.

For a few hundred years between 3000 and 2000 B.C. Ebla was one of the great powers of the Near East. It carried on commerce with other lands. Its metal workers and weavers running into thousands of workers, were widely known and their craftsmen exported beautiful wooden furniture often overlaid with gold. That they had contact with other regions is evident from some of their tablets in which Sodom and Gomorrah of the Bible are mentioned.

8.   THE ISLAND OF CRETE

West of Asia Minor lie the Island of Crete and Greece, where more highly advanced early civilizations are found between 3000 and 2000 B.C. On the island of Crete a high civilization was evident about 3000 B.C. It was called the Minoan culture, after its great king Minos. They built beautiful cities, such as Knossos. Here a palace, built about 2200 B.C., was uncovered, which spread over about four acres, and was five stories high. It had beautiful corridors, halls, throne room, living room, treasure rooms, and many other rooms. Most amazing were the bathrooms with running water, flushing toilets, and drainage systems which were superior to anything in Europe until the nineteenth century. The pipes could be flushed, and there were man-holes for inspection and repair. Their drainage pipes look modern.

Frescoes on the palace walls picture the brilliant life of the lords and ladies of that culture. The frescoes show dancing women, leaping dolphins and beautiful landscapes. Their artists and craftsmen made masterpieces of great beauty: delicate carvings on stone and gems, jewelry of gold and pottery as thin as eggshells covered with delicate designs. There are pictures of gayly adorned dames and lords wearing their hair in long curls, standing in lively groups, dancing, sitting and talking. There are pictures of women wearing veils and of peasants in joyous harvest festivals carrying sheaves of grain in their arms.

Clay tablets covered with writing were found, which show that these Cretans had developed a system of writing in syllables. But so far no one has deciphered their writings. A Roman historian, who wrote a short time before the birth of Christ, mentioned that in his day the Cretans claimed that their ancestors had invented the alphabet and that the Phoenicians only made it better known in their sailings.

Each home had its own loom, so each home no doubt made its own cloth. The women's dress was elaborate, with careful fitting, fine sewing and beautiful embroidery. They had numerous kinds of kitchen utensils with perforated skimmers and strainers and many other devices that appear strangely modern in shape. They were good sailors and traders and spread their goods, arts and civilization throughout the entire eastern part of the Mediterranean. But like many other ancient civilizations, it faded away about 1500 B.C. Someone wrote: "Their origins are unclear, their language unknown, their fate is obscure." But those who know and believe their Bibles have a simple and certain answer to all this.

9.   ANCIENT GREEKS

About 3000 B.C. the Minoan civilization was carried north to Greece where it centered in Mycenae near Corinth and became known as the Mycenaean or Greek civilization. The Greeks developed an alphabet and their words form the basis for many of the words used in technical English today. Without a knowledge of Greek many of our words in English are foreign words to the average American. A news commentator mentioned recently that English is becoming the universal language of the world, just as Latin and Greek were a number of centuries ago. But because many of our English words, especially in the technical field, have a Greek and Latin background, they are not well understood by the average person without consulting a dictionary. The evolutionists love to use these words of Greek and Latin derivation because they appear to give their assumptions a learned, technical and scientific backing.

10.   EUROPE PROPER

In Europe proper, advanced civilizations are not found in the 3000 to 1000 B.C. era. Although there are evidences of settlements in Russia and other parts of Europe, these areas were not developed early because good hunting and food gathering could easily be found by roving bands of people in the woods and grasslands of the north. No doubt these people moved about as the Indians did in North America before the coming of the Europeans. The evolutionists love to dwell on the Neanderthal and Cro-Magnon peoples who are assumed to have evolved in the course of hundreds of thousands and millions of years and lived in caves and poorly constructed shelters. Rather, these people because they roamed about, lived in small groups and inter-married. They degenerated in the course of time and lost many of the abilities and know-how of their ancestors. Many of them degenerated like the natives on the southern tip of South America did, so that Charles Darwin wondered whether they were even human beings. Otherwise, the

Neanderthal and Cro-Magnon people are considered to be physically the equal of people of today. In fact, according to *Mysteries From Forgotton Worlds,* by Charles Berlitz, "The original Cro-Magnon man, in the opinion of most anthropologists, had a brain capacity superior to modern man." These people were very evidently more of the post Tower of Babel people who roamed around Europe.

Most of Europe, and especially the northern part in the early years of mankind, appears to have been inhabited mostly by tribes who lived without cities, money, governments and writing. Their life was taken up in hunting, fishing, gathering food, and in simple farming of grain, vegetables and cattle. Their crafts were pottery making and working in bronze. In some places weaving, leather working, ceramics and embroidery were taking place.

The evolutionists love to dwell on the caves that people lived in while evolving from apes. But caves and rock shelters were used by advanced people only a very small part of the time. Most of the time they lived in the open, or near the entrance of caves as our American Indians did in the southwestern part of Colorado and other southwestern states. Otherwise, they had movable shelters such as tents when they roamed around like legendary Robin Hood in England and the American Indian.

In some of these caves are found paintings of bison, reindeer and horses. In a cave near Lussac, France, is a sketch of a young lady wearing modern-type clothing with a hat and carrying a purse. Really looks out of line with people who are assumed to be primitive! In describing the abilities of the so-called Old Stone Age art, pre-historian writer Robert Silverberg states:

> The cave paintings are upsetting to those who prefer to think of Quaternary man as little more than an ape. Not only do they indicate great craftsmanship, but they point to a whole constellation of conclusions: That primitive man had an organized society with continuity, religion and art. It was also dismaying to learn that the earliest inhabitants of Western Europe ... had scaled heights of artistic achievement that would not be reached again until late in the Christian era. That explodes the theory that man's rise from barbarism had been steady and always upward.

11.   ENGLAND

In England and in Brittany of northern France we find more unbelievable feats of so-called primitive man, which confound the evolutionists. There are the megaliths, or in ordinary English the huge

or great stones of England and France. *Mysteries of the Ancient World*
by *National Geographic* (1979) claims that the oldest of these stones
dates from about 4500 B.C., and the most recent from about 3,000 years
later. Four thousand and five hundred years B.C. is possible if they were
set up by people before the Flood and if that area was not covered by
the sediment of Noah's Flood. These stones range from individual
stones, called menhirs, to complex collections of huge stones such as
the ones in Stonehenge. The greatest number of menhirs in one place
are near Carnac in Brittany of France. More than 3,000 stones are lined
up in straight lines, eleven and twelve abreast and cover a distance of
about two and one-half miles. One stone, the Grand Menhir, weighed
380 tons and was about 69 feet high before it was broken into five pieces
by lightning. Here again we ask: Could any primitive man have
transported and erected such huge stones without any engineering
abilities? These are amazing feats of our so-called primitive(?)
forefathers that we marvel at today.

12.   AFRICA

Although Africa did not have any advanced civilization after the
Flood except in Egypt, there always were roving bands of Africans who
moved throughout the continent fishing, hunting and gathering fruits
and other foods. Because of the enormous Sahara desert few people
migrated south and formed civilizations. The bones of apes and other
animals, and of some human beings that the Leakeys and other
evolutionary anthropologists are finding, are no doubt the fossils of
animals and people caught and covered up in the horrendous,
frightening, muddy, turbulent flood of Noah's day. These fossils became
exposed in time, especially in the Rift valley of eastern Africa, where,
like in the Colorado River valley, sides of the walls of flood sedimentation
became exposed. It is only in the last 1,000 years or so, due to the
activities of Europeans, that Africa is becoming advanced in agriculture
and industry.

13.   THE AMERICAS

From all indications, mankind migrated from Europe and Asia to
the Americas by two routes sometime after the Tower of Babel. The
most evident route was the few miles across the Bering Sea, which
Eskimos today can cross with little difficulty. From there men and
women could have migrated south to the warmer climates of the United
States and Central America in not too many years. They roamed onward
through South America and established cultures along the way. Remains
of campsites more than 10,000 years old, according to some, have been

found at the southern tip of South America. They could have peopled these continents with remarkable speed. No evidence of ape-fossils is apparent.

Since the people after the Flood were highly advanced, as is evident in Egypt, Sumer and elsewhere, they could easily have made boats such as the Minoans and Phoenicians built to cross the Atlantic centuries before Columbus. If not by sails, then at least by riding the currents of the Atlantic Ocean, they could travel from Western Europe fairly easily on the route of the North Atlantic current, and with prevailing winds they could reach the northeast coast of South America. Going through the islands of the West Indies, they may have reached the regions of the Caribbean Sea, with landings in the Gulf States, Central America and northern South America. This would explain how a cache of Roman coins was found in Venezuela, and how hundreds of ancient Phoenician writings were found in Brazil. On October 31, 1986, human bones were found by workers quarrying gravel near Lower Red Lake in northern Minnesota. A state archeologist said they were bones of Indians buried 4,000 years ago. People could easily have been in North America shortly after the Tower of Babel, as well as before the Flood.

14.   THE UNITED STATES

As for the United States, the first to discover America was not Columbus in 1492 or Leif Ericson about A.D. 1000. Crossing from Europe to America, the first to come could have been some of those same people who set up those large stones in France and Great Britain and other European lands. On a prehistoric site called Mystery Hill in North Salem, New Hampshire, is a 200 foot hill, and on top of it are 22 large stones aligned somewhat like those stones in Britain and France. Similiar huge stone arrangements have been found in Central America. Some of these stones are carved and appear to be older than the Aztec, Mayan and Toltec civilizations of Mexico and Central America. Such huge stones have been found also in Peru.

15.   MEXICO

In the valley of Tehuacan of Mexico, thousands of animal bones, artifacts, bones of seventy humans and remains of many plants, especially of early corn, have been found dating back, according to some, between 3400 and 5200 B.C. The Mexicans of those days had a kind of picture writing. A few of their books or writings have survived, but little has been accomplished in decoding their picture writing. Evidence of civilizations in other parts of Mexico, southwestern United States and

Central and South America are three prominent ones: Aztec of Mexico, the Mayan in the jungles of Guatemala and the Yucatan peninsula, and the Incan of Andean Peru. The achievements of these civilizations compare with those of Egypt and Sumer.

The Mayans built a temple in Tikal, Guatemala which was the highest building in the Americas until the first skyscrapers were built in New York. Lost among the trees and covered by them for centuries, this steep towering temple was lost for centuries until rediscovered. It rose to a height of over 200 feet. The temples of these people were adorned with wall paintings and sculpture. They developed a system of writing the language they spoke, but so far no one has been able to decipher it. Although their mathematical works are understood, their complex system of writing was in the form of picture writing. Their books were written on sheets of paper that they pounded from bark. After the Spaniards conquered these people in 1562 the archbishop of Yucatan had their books destroyed as the works of the devil. Among these people, as well as among the Indians of the United States, there is widespread belief and tradition that their forefathers came by sea from the East "by floating on huge canoes for weeks." This conforms with the belief that island-hopping took place between Europe, the Azores and the Caribbean islands.

Although all these people in the Americas raised vegetables of various kinds, one of their most stable crops was corn which they developed into more productive varieties as time went on. These people also created a calendar that was more accurate than that used in Europe at the time. They also were versed in knowledge of the moon, planets, and stars.

16.   THE INCAS OF PERU

The most amazing of the native American civilizations was that of the Incas in the Andes of Peru. These people built a great empire with big cities, irrigation works and highways, amazing structures, and artistic works of all kinds. But the claim is made that the greatest art work was done by people who preceded the Incas.

In Peru and Bolivia, temples, forts and palaces were built before the days of the Incas with stones weighing 50 to 300 tons. Some of these stones are rectangular, others have ten to twenty angled planes and each fits exactly with the next stone. The blocks fit perfectly together and so closely that the thinnest gauge of a machinist could not be inserted between them, and all these blocks were laid without cement. The question is how were these blocks of stone cut, moved up mountains and then fitted perfectly together? These stones no doubt were placed in the wall for fitting, then taken out again and again for a perfect fit. And all these stones dovetail and interlock, so that the whole system seems an impossible operation.

At Oilantaitambo, Peru, is one of the pre-Inca fortresses. The blocks of stone weighing over 150 tons are made of very hard andesite that was quarried at a mountain seven miles distant. Somehow at an altitude of 10,000 feet these blocks were quarried, lowered down the mountain side, brought over a canyon with walls 1,000 feet straight up, and there were raised up another mountainside and fitted together for the fortress. Some people believe that this is a human impossibility. But evidently these people had a technology and way of doing things that we know nothing about. But we shall hear of the wisdom, knowledge and abilities of Adam and Eve and their descendants further on.

In the Andes region are more such fortresses and complexes that simply baffle us today. There are paved roads, roads over mountains, tunnels through mountains, citadels, underground chambers, storage cisterns, etc. Although these people had everything necessary for transportation, they seem to have lacked one very essential thing, namely, the wheel for carts, wagons or chariots. Yet although no wheels for transportation have been found, THE WHEEL was there, for wheeled toys have been found among Mexican toys for children. Certainly, if these people erected all those seemingly impossible buildings and put wheels on toys for their children, they could also have put wheels on advanced transportation systems. I am sure that when one studies the activities and results of the Flood that wheels and many other artifacts of technology will be found under thousands of feet of sedimentation. On April 10, 1967, the newspapers reported the finding of a human bone embedded in a vein of silver, and also the finding of arrowhead made of copper four inches long 400 feet below the ground in the Rocky Point Mine in Colorado. Many other objects like this, and fossils, have been found many hundreds and thousands of feet below the surface of the earth.

Going back to the pre-Inca days of Peru, showing how advanced and sophisticated these people were, objects have been found that are made out of platinum. This shows an advanced stage of technology, for 1,750 degrees centigrade is needed to melt platinum. These people needed advanced knowledge in making metals requiring such great heat.

Two hundred and fifty miles south of Lima lies the Nazca Valley of Peru. The entire valley is covered with huge figures: spiders, birds, monkeys, turtles, snakes, fish, even a whale and an immense figure of a human being. There are geometrical figures of triangles, rectangles, and short lines that resemble roads. There are strips that look like airfields. These lines and figures are barely recognizable from the ground unless one is standing directly in line with them. Move a few feet away, and the lines fade into the rest of the desert floor. Although these lines are not readily seen from the ground they are clearly visible from airplanes. In fact, they can be seen from Skylab orbiting 270 miles above the earth.

On a towering cliff near Paracas, Peru, an 800 foot long carving called the Candelabra of the Andes can be seen from a distance out in the Pacific Ocean. When Spanish conquerors first saw it they thought it was a sign from heaven of the Trinity. The most amazing picture of all was found on a piece of pottery at Nazca, which showed the faces of five girls: one in yellow, one in white, one in black, one brown and one red. This seems to indicate these early people had knowledge of the different races of people around the earth. All this archeology and architecture around Peru sound like a tale of evolution, but at least these are facts that are scientifically true.

Although the Incas in Peru and other South American cultures were very advanced in architecture, art, and also in agriculture, they had no system of writing or putting in words the language they spoke. The closest the Incas came to recording their thoughts was the use of quipu, which was a series of strings of different lengths, colors and thicknesses, in which knots had been tied. These strings and knots with all their various combinations were used to record information of various kinds. Relaying spoken words through them seems a probability.

17.   SOUTHERN TIP OF SOUTH AMERICA

Continuing down to the southern tip of South America and forward thousands of years to the present day we come to a race of people that Charles Darwin came into contact with when he was sailing around the world. These people whom Darwin considered next to savages, were a good example of the cultural descent of man to degeneration. Their degeneration should have disproven the idea of evolution that later developed in his mind as he sailed around the world. This idea of evolution later developed among evolutionists into the so-called theory that man descended from apelike creatures. The cultural descent of these people and of many other primitive and savage people do not prove the evolution but the degeneration of man, in spite of all the progress man has made in recent decades in increasing the speed of things. In spite of all the progress made in the medical field, man still dies as he always had.

III. COMPARING THE ASSUMPTIONS OF EVOLUTION WITH THE FACTS OF ARCHEOLOGY

So far I have presented the assumptions of the evolutionary belief or creed in regard to the origins of man. Then in contrast I gave the evidences and facts appearing in the records and histories of mankind and in the remains of their advanced civilizations as revealed by archeology.

When one compares the evolution of man from animal apedom with the historical fact of civilizations suddenly appearing all at once all over the world; and when one compares anthropology (the study of the origin of man according to the evolutionary belief) with archeology which shows highly civilized people appearing suddenly and simultaneously all over the world, there just is no correlation. The facts of archeology disprove the guesses and assumptions of the evolutionists.

If the Leakeys and other evolutionists, instead of looking for fossils of people who migrated and roamed about the rural areas of Africa before the Flood, would turn their study of the early origins of mankind (anthropology) to the study of archeology, they would find our forebears whom they are searching for. By studying the life and culture of early ancient peoples, by excavations of cities, relics, artifacts, etc., in Egypt, Sumer, Babylonia, the Indus valley, Central America and Peru, they would find that our ancestors came not from apelike creatures, but from highly intelligent and advanced people who built pyramids, towers reaching to the heavens, and other structures and buildings that we marvel at today.

Archeology conforms to what the Bible tells us in the first eleven chapters of Genesis, and archeology confirms the origin of man as reported in the earliest history given in the Bible. Although neither evolution nor creation can be proven scientifically by actual observations, tests or proven experiments, the Bible however is reasonable and logical and verified by archeology and other histories. The history given in the Bible is confirmed by archeology.

All I have written has been so beautifully expressed by Professor A. M. Rehwinkel in his book *The Flood*. I must quote it in this context. On page 42:

The Bible has proved itself to be a reliable and an accurate record of the most ancient historical events. In fact, for many large areas of ancient history the Bible is the only record we have.

Archeology, excavations, and honest historical research have proven the Bible to be an absolutely reliable source book. And yet, when writing these textbooks, modern historians disregard this source material entirely and treat it as though it were non-existent. But this is unscientific, unscholarly, and nothing less than intellectual dishonesty. That branches of the human race have lived in caves, no one will doubt; that large sections of the human family degenerated to the level of savagery cannot be questioned; but to conclude from this that the entire human race has sprung from a race of cave dwellers or has evolved from a race of savages or of beings even lower than a savage, is drawing an unwarranted conclusion.

HOW WELL STATED!

IV. THE EARLIEST HISTORY OF MANKIND ACCORDING TO THE BIBLE

1. THE FIRST CHAPTERS OF GENESIS

After the background I gave on the evolutionary belief, and after a study of archeology, it is important that we next consider what happened in history on the basis of the first chapters of the Bible. The origin of the earth, sun, moon, planets, stars, quasars and the universe, and what is claimed in regard to the Big Bang and black hole theories, will all be skipped until further on.

ADAM AND EVE

Starting with the creation of Adam and Eve in the Garden of Eden, we find people who actually were the forefathers of people like the Egyptians and Sumerians. Before God created man, He created and prepared this earth as a habitation for him. This earth as it was created by God was absolutely perfect in every imaginable way and was beautiful, restful and pleasant beyond imagination. It was as Genesis 1:31 states: "And God saw everything He had made, and behold *it was very good."* What God pronounced good, was good beyond description. It was complete and perfect to the smallest details and beautiful beyond comprehension. There were no weeds, thistles, or thorns or anything to disturb the happiness of man. It was almost heaven on earth. The earth brought forth everything that was needful for the desires, pleasures, comforts and wants of man. There was sufficient food for man and animals and there was no struggle for existence between men and between animals. There were no deserts, cold, uncomfortable regions; no sickness, no death. The most pleasing, comfortable and pleasant islands of the South Seas today would not compare with the entire earth of that time. The Bible in Genesis 2:8-15, describes the Garden of Eden as being an extraordinarily beautiful, restful and pleasant home for Adam and Eve — so that even without clothes they could be perfectly comfortable. With all its gold and precious stones it must have been most beautifully adorned.

The persons of the Triune God, in creating man, went into consultation as we would say and into thoughtful deliberation and declared: "Let us make man in our image after our likeness: and let them have dominion over the fish of the sea, and over the fowl of the air, and over the cattle, and over all the earth, and over every creeping thing that creepeth upon the earth." Gen. 1:26 Going into consultation, it was as if the Triune God wished to put His greatest wisdom and highest skill into His final creation.

Man was to be a creation different from all that had been made. He was God's representative on earth, clothed with authority to rule as the visible head and monarch on this earth. Flesh and spirit, heaven and earth were to be put together in mankind and therefore man was to be allied both to this earth and to heaven. As God is a person, a being, so was man to be; as God was righteous and holy, so was man to be. As God is Lord over heaven and earth, so man was destined to be lord over all the earth. He was not God but man, not Creator but a creature, but he was to be an earthly image of the Creator, a being made in the likeness of God. With his body he belonged on earth, from which his body was to be formed, and with his spirit or soul he belonged to God in heaven, for God was to breathe into his nostrils the breath of life from God. Thus man was to be the connecting link between heaven and earth, between God and the world, with the spirit of God Himself within him.

To create this glorious creature, God did something altogether different and unique. He did not simply issue the command and have man come into being all complete, but He formed him in a peculiar way. God took a lump of clay from the dust of the earth, and out of it the Divine Creator produced a wonderful form, different from all the others. Erect it stood, its face turned forward and upward. For the time being, the form was lifeless, but God breathed His life-breath into it, and now life, like a current, swept through the entire body. With its eyes it beheld God with a look of gratitude. And now this beautiful form began to move; there was heavenly light in its eyes, peace and serenity surrounded it everywhere, its high forehead screened great thoughts and its hands deftly were engaged in the things at hand. There was in this being not the wild, unreasoning impulse of animal desires, but the calm deliberate movement of a thinker who weighs his actions before he performs them. Lordly and majestically he stood amid all the other creatures. He was known at once to be the master of all his eyes surveyed. With this being God held serious conversation; soulless animals were brought before him and instinctively he knew their qualities and, endowed with the gift of speech and language, he gave to each of these a name. Adam evidently was the most knowledgeable man in the field of biology covering botany (plants), zoology (animals) and their subdivisions that there ever was.

If he had been a student in one of our best universities, Adam would have finished with flying colors and the highest possible honors, passing with a 100 in all subjects. With the brilliant, faultless mind God gave him in botany he evidently knew not only the tree of the knowledge of good and evil of which he was not to eat, but also all the other trees and plants of the earth that God surrounded him with. Then in the field of zoology he knew all the beasts and cattle of the field and the fowls of the air and named them in his language as God caused them to come before him. Although the fish of the sea are not mentioned, he, no doubt, knew them also. And, no doubt, he also knew the minerals of the earth and how to put them to use. Adam and Eve's grandchildren worked in brass and iron, as Genesis 4:22 states: "Tubal-cain [was] an instructor of every artificer in brass and iron."

Adam, *the man* of all times, did not need to study books to know and name all creatures, plants, elements and minerals God had created. He instinctively knew more than all the scientists of the present age. Adam, as he came forth from the creation of God, knew more than any man that ever lived on earth, he was the wisest man, he was *the scientist* of scientists. But the greatest wisdom he had was that he did not have to guess about his origin, he knew he had not come forth from an apelike creature but from the hands of Him who created him and all things visible and invisible. Without any doubt he knew the origin and makeup of everything in the universe. He had more than the equivalent of a doctor's degree in every field. Only one doctor's degree he did not need - the Doctor of Medicine, because there were no sickness or ailments of any kind and therefore he knew nothing about all this. Adam made known his will in speech and he expressed his thoughts. There was also in this being something no other creature has: a never-dying soul.

However, lonely and alone this being stood in the midst of a vast domain, the most stately man that ever lived. He had no companion, no one to share his joy and fortune. Therefore, once more the voice of the Almighty Creator spoke: "It is not good that man should be alone; I will make him a helper/comparable to him." Gen. 2:18. Sleep was brought upon Adam, and while he reposed, God removed a rib from his side and fashioned it into a woman. She was brought to Adam who at once recognized in her his own flesh and blood. Eve, as she came forth from the hands of God, was the *Miss and Mrs. Universe* of all times, the most beautiful, intelligent, adept, graceful, loving, perfect queenly-looking *woman of all times.* The most outstanding people today, compared to Adam and Eve, would appear deformed and degenerated, for in Adam and Eve there were no defects of any kind. In mutual wonder and joint adoration these two most beautiful, wise and royal people this earth has ever seen, who were united in marriage by God Himself, stood in devout worship before their Creator and with fabulous knowledge and skill began to rule this earth which God had given them as a dowry.

Adam and Eve as they came forth from the creative act of God were evidently the equivalent of people some 20 years old today, but were actually only zero years old. They were mature human beings, just as the universe was a mature universe at the time of creation. Without sin, Adam and Eve were without ailments, disease and decay. They had the potential of living forever on this earth without any sign of decay or growing aged. These two most marvelous people were our true foreparents, our ancestors.

However, the most marvelous feature of the creation of Adam and Eve was not merely that their bodies were specially created and that they were given rational minds and the ability to formulate their thoughts and express them in speech and writing. When the persons in the Trinity gathered in consultation to create these glorious first human beings, the crowning point of their decision was this: "Let us make man *in our image after our likeness,* and let them have dominion. . . . over all the earth." Gen. 1:26 [Emphasis/Added]

Of what does the image of God consist, which truly sets man aside from the animals and makes him the most glorious of all God's earthly creatures? From other portions of the Bible we learn that the image of God consists especially of two characteristics: a blissful knowledge of God and perfect righteousness and holiness. Man was given a knowledge not only of the things of this earth but also of God Himself. Man as he was originally created knew who and what God is. He knew and understood not only the works of God in nature but also God's will in spiritual things. He knew perfectly what God wanted him to do and not to do. It was not necessary for him to study the Commandments to determine the will of God. And man had the ability then to live in accordance with that will. Furthermore, man knew God as one who loved him and blessed him. To think of God was to think only of a happy, blessed, peaceful relationship. Indeed, the knowledge Adam and Eve had of God was to them a source of sweetest blessing and sublime bliss.

As stated above, Scripture tells us that the image of God consisted also of perfect holiness and righteousness. Man as he was originally created was righteous and lived in accord with the will of God. He was good and without sin, he was *perfect,* except that man could disobey God. Man therefore was holy in the sense in which God is holy, who hates that which is evil and loves that which is good. Adam and Eve therefore had a good conscience and had no reason to fear God or try to avoid Him.

The image of God distinguishes man from every other creature. There is a vast difference between apes and other animals and man. Part of the image of God was that man was to have dominion over fish, fowls, cattle, all other animals and over all the earth. Man was created to be different from all other creatures on earth. Man also was destined to live forever. As he was created, man would never die.

But sad to say all this changed when mankind through Adam and Eve disobeyed and turned away from God and rebelled against Him by listening to the enticements of Satan and eating of the tree of knowledge of good and evil, of which God had asked them not to eat. God told Adam and Eve, "The day that thou eatest thereof thou shalt surely die." Gen. 2:17

However, Adam and Eve did not die physically immediately, although one of the first deaths was a murder: one of their sons killed another son. What a discouraging and dreadful moment that must have been! Yet Adam and others of his descendents did not die for almost 1,000 years, living to 900 and more years. They lived as though they might never die.

2.   THE EARTH BETWEEN THE FALL OF MAN AND THE FLOOD

Before continuing with mankind it is well to consider what was happening to this earth upon which they were living. The earth no longer was the completely pleasant place it originally was, because of a curse resting upon it. Genesis 3:17-19 states: "cursed is the ground for thy sake; in sorrow shalt thou eat of it all the days of thy life; thorns also and thistles shall it bring forth to thee; . . . In the sweat of thy face shalt thou eat bread." The Apostle Paul states in Romans 8:22, "the whole creation groaneth and travaileth in pain." And yet even though sin and death had entered the world, it was still a world far superior to what we are living in today. Luther said it was "a veritable paradise compared to the world that followed."

The earth, between the time of creation and the Flood, must have remained a beautiful, delightful place. A daily mist watered the earth. There were no violent storms with lighting, thunder, hailstones, tornadoes. That some people today cringe in fright in the midst of severe thunderstorms and lighting is because people, even unbelieving atheists, know that God still rules and controls all things. The land of this earth then was no doubt low and rolling so people could easily move about anywhere on earth. The soil was rich, deep and fruitful as becomes evident when we consider the coal beds that are claimed to have been formed by dense vegetation which was compressed together at the time of the Flood.

Professor William Winston of the University of Cambridge, England, wrote in his book *A New Theory of Earth* (1696):

"The antediluvian earth was much more fruitful than at present; and the *multitude of the vegetable production much greater*. The ground was tender, soft and full of juices. The antediluvian air had no large, gross masses of vapor or clouds hanging for long seasons in the air. It had no great drops of rain descending in multitudes together, which we call showers, but the ground was watered by gentle mists and vapours ascending in the day and descending in great measure again in the succeeding night. The world was then free from violent winds, storms and agitations with all their effects on the earth and seas."

And as the earth still remained a superior place after the curse of God was placed upon it, so also did those first people remain superior to all people since then.

3.   THE MANY CENTURIES BETWEEN CREATION AND THE FLOOD

Before considering these people and their civilization, it is well to first consider the length of time between the creation of Adam and Eve and the Flood, and then to the days of Abraham. In the margin of many of our English Bibles are dates stating when certain events occurred. These dates were calculated by an Irish archbishop, James Ussher, or Usher, and were printed in the margin of the King James version in 1701. Ussher placed the creation of the world at 4004 B.C. and someone after him even stated the hour of the day in which it occurred. The evolutionists simply love to ridicule such a definite figure. But all this is not so out of place as are the ridiculous dates and ideas of the evolutionists who place the origin of the universe 15,000,000,000 and earth 4,500,000,000 years ago and declare the universe was formed by a Big Bang in three minutes. This will be considered further on.

Ussher computed his figures by a very complicated addition and subtraction of dates from the different chronologies (a study of time periods), given in the Old Testament. Ussher's calculation of 4004 B.C. is based on the Hebrew text of the Old Testament as given by the Masoretes. The Greek Septuagint translation of the Hebrew Old Testament, the Samaritan Pentateuch and Josephus give different ages to the patriarchs from Adam to Abraham at the birth of the oldest sons, and these increase the length of time for this period of the Old Testament history. The Septuagint lengthens it by 1,466 years, Josephus by 1,201, and the Samaritan Pentateuch by 301 years. These different figures do not change the date of creation by more than 1,500 years.

Another factor that must be taken into account is the use of the word *begat* in the Old Testament chronologies. In the dates for the Old Testament patriarchs given in Genesis 5 and Genesis 11, Ussher takes the word begat in the literal sense. While this seems to be the natural thing to do, other parts of the Bible indicate that begat is also used in the wider sense, denoting mere ancestry even of great great-grandchildren. Such is the case in Matthew 1:8 where it is stated, "and Joram begat Ozias." However, from the Old Testament I Chronicles 3:11-12 we know that Joram was the great-great-grandfather of Ozias, with the names of Ahaziah, Joash and Amaziah being omitted in Matthew 1:8. Joram was the father of Ahaziah; Ahaziah was the father of Joash; Joash was the father of Amaziah; and it was Amaziah who was really the father of Ozias, who has also been called Uzziah and Azariah.

A similiar case is given in Genesis 46:18, where it is stated that Zilpah bore sixteen souls unto Jacob, while the text shows that her grandchildren and great grandchildren are counted among the sixteen. The purpose of the genealogies of the Old and New Testaments was mainly to give a history of the Messianic Promise, to show the descent from Adam and Eve to the *promised Seed* of the woman, to Jesus the Savior of the world.

In spite of all these variations, the time of the creation of the world can hardly be extended more than a few hundred to a couple of thousand years beyond Ussher's 4004 B.C. Some extend the date of creation even to 8000 B.C. All this only makes more possible and plausible the claims of some archeologists and historians that a high state of civilization already existed in Egypt and Sumer as long as 3,500 to even 4,000 years before Christ. Professor Arndt in his book, *Bible Difficulties*, written in 1932, p. 51 strongly urged a couple of times:

> . . . to be sober and humble in announcing the results of our chronological calculations, bearing in mind that in the Scriptures God in His wisdom has withheld from us such information as would make a complete and absolutely certain chronology for the Bible times possible.

So I will not burden you with pages of Old Testament chronology.

4.   THE VERY LONG LIFE OF THE FIRST PEOPLE

However, in regard to the Old Testament patriarchs, several things should be mentioned. One is in regard to their longevity or extremely long life, living 900 and more years, or about 10 to 12 times as long as people live today. As a result of this, many generations could have been living together at the same time, so that Adam could tell the account of creation and the fall of man to seven or eight generations down the line. He could have told Methuselah and Lamech, nine or ten generations down, and they could have told Shem the son of Noah, and Shem could have told Abraham. In this way the account of creation passed through only two people from Adam to Abraham, covering 2,100 years according to Ussher's chronology, or about one-third of the world's existence.

Moreover, one must not think that these highly intelligent people had no written records. *The records and history that may have existed* at that time were most likely destroyed in that extremely violent, turbulent, muddy destructive Flood in Noah's days.

Another matter to bear in mind is the traditions of the Egyptians and Babylonians. Each had ten pre-flood (antediluvian) kings similiar to the ten patriarchs of the Old Testament Bible. All this gives credence to the Bible account of people who lived as heads of families or rulers in the days prior to the Flood, even though the length of life given in both the Egyptian and Babylonian records was extremely highly exaggerated. The *Reader's Digest* (September 1977, p. 130), refers to an English archeologist, Sir Leonard Woolley, who in 1922 began to dig in Mesopotamia.

> Even before Woolley had begun his dig, scholars possessed the so-called Sumerian king-lists, a skeletal history of royalty. "It starts with kings who reigned before the Flood" noted Woolley, "and the reign of eight add up to the total of 241,000 years! The chronology is evidently absurd."

The Sumerians after the Flood obviously had some idea of a civilization living before them in the days before the Flood.

Another matter in regard to the long life of the Old Testament people is *why they could have lived so long* and why the life of people after the Flood was shortened more and more as time went on. Shortly after the Flood people lived about one-half as long, about 450 years. By the time of Abraham it was down to 175 years. Evidently one cause for this involved the protective water canopy that was placed around the earth. Genesis 1:6-7 states:

God said, Let there be a firmament in the midst of the waters and let it divide the waters from the waters. And God made the firmament, and divided the waters which were under the firmament from the waters which were above the firmament; and it was so.

Scientists believe that this water canopy could have provided protection against long-range radiation from the sun. This canopy in turn could have resulted in preserving the protective ozone layer which scientists fear the earth is losing, with holes in the ozone layer over the South Pole. Therefore it is believed that if the harmful radiation were kept from the earth in pre-Flood times by the water canopy and by a greater ozone canopy, better health, longer life span, and perhaps greater size of pre-Flood creatures could be expected. The entire earth as it was originally created was such that men would live forever without sickness, disease and death. No doubt greater radiation amounts plus other factors with which God cursed the earth have resulted in gradual deterioration of mankind and decreasing length of life.

5. NO PREHISTORY IN THE BIBLE

One more thing should be mentioned in regard to the people whose names are listed in Genesis and also mentioned by name again in the New Testament books of Matthew and Luke. The history given in the Bible is not based on guesses and theories but on the actual names of people, and when they lived, how long they lived, and what they did during the time the evolutionists like to refer to as prehistory. There is an awful lot of real history given to us in the Christmas story of Matthew and Luke, which is most of the time passed over rather readily as something dull, dry, uninteresting and boring. Luke in Chapter 3, beginning with the 23rd verse states: "Jesus . . . [was] the son of Joseph, which was the son of Heli, which was the son of Matthat," etc., for about 60 generations, and then finally toward the end of the chapter continues with "which was the son of Shem." Then going back to Genesis 10:6-11, we are given the relatives of Shem, descendants of his brother Ham, of whom we are told that one of Ham's sons was Cush, and Cush had a son named Nimrod, who was therefore a great nephew of Shem. Regarding this Nimrod, Genesis 10:8-11 states: "Nimrod began to be a mighty one in the earth . . . And the beginning of his kingdom was Babel and Erech, and Accad, and Calneh, in the land of Shinar." Babel is also referred to as Babylon. Babylon, or Sumer, is where the history books of the world begin. This is the beginning of their actual history. But the

Bible continues with the great-uncle of Nimrod: Shem, the son of Noah. Luke 3:36 continues with what otherwise is called prehistory by stating:

> Shem which was the son of Noah, which was the son of Lamech, which was the son of Methuselah, which was the son of Enoch, which was the son of Jared, which was the son of Mahalelel, which was the son of Cainan, which was the son of Enos, which was the son of Seth, which was the son of Adam, which was the son [or created one] of God.

And the forefathers of Noah lived mostly over 900 years. This is the history which the evolutionists ignore and despise, and which the history books that they control lack. *But what better so-called pre-historic history or true history can we and our children have* than that which is given us in the book of Genesis. If the evolutionists would only consider the first eleven chapters of Genesis in the same spirit that real scientists do in the search for the truth in the research laboratory, they would see that the Bible account of creation is the only sensible and reasonable explanation for the origin of all things.

The time has come to take the gloves off in fighting for our rights and the rights of our children in their education — not by getting the Bible into the community schools of the land but by taking out the religious and anti-religious beliefs and creeds of the evolutionists. I will refer to this when I treat the separation not merely of Church and State, but in the words of the First Amendment: the separation of Religion (including the religion and anti-religion of the evolutionists) and the State, which states: "Congress shall make no law respecting *an establishment of religion.*" There will be more on this subject further on.

6.   MANY CENTURIES ARE COVERED IN THE FIRST FOUR CHAPTERS OF GENESIS

Continuing with the very first people on this earth, with Adam and Eve and their children and grandchildren and great-grandchildren and onward, one may get the impression in reading those first chapters of the Bible, Genesis chapters 2, 3 and 4, that the events recorded there happened in a very short space of time. The main purpose of the history given there was to show how, after man rebelled and sinned against his Creator God, God provided a rescue, a salvation from the curse man had fallen into, and showed the descent through which the Rescuer, the Savior, was to come. Evidently a considerable lapse of time took place. After God placed Adam and Eve in the home He had prepared for them in the Garden of Eden, they quite certainly did not rebel against God and immediately defy His authority by eating of the forbidden tree of the knowledge of good and evil. The fact that they knew of the river that flowed through the Garden which divided into four other rivers, each with a name given them (Pison, Gihon, Hiddekel and Euphrates), indicates that they dwelt there long enough to explore the wide region, that could have extended over a large region of the Middle East, for them and their descendants to dwell in. That gold and silver and precious stones were found in the land of Havilah pre-supposes that this region had been explored, and therefore quite some time had elapsed. So the time between the creation of Adam and Eve and their mistrust of God and rebellion against Him and their fall away from God into the hands of Satan could have taken much longer time than many suppose. But the Fall must have been sometime before the conception of their first child, who was begotten in Adam and Eve's sinful likeness.

Also, the story of Cain and Abel recorded in chapter four required a considerable length of time. Both of these brothers had grown to manhood together, very likely with a large number of brothers and sisters. No doubt Adam and Eve, in obedience to God's command: Genesis 1:28, "Be fruitful and multiply and replenish [fill] the earth," had very many children not only early in life but as the years went on. Very likely child bearing in those early centuries of fertile humanity extended far beyond the 50 years of today. Both Cain and Abel had progressed beyond the easy hunting and food gathering that was readily available. Cain and Abel with their families were already into animal raising, and into raising fruits, vegetables and grains for their families before the sad event of the first human death mentioned: Cain killing his brother Abel. In fact, Genesis 4:3 states: "In *the process of time* it came to pass that Cain brought of the fruit of the ground an offering unto the Lord." [Emphasis Added]

Although all mankind rebelled against God, sinned and fell away from God when our first foreparents disobeyed God's simple command, and thereby became estranged and separated from God, another estrangement and separation took place after Cain killed his brother Abel. Cain and his descendants became more and more separated not only from God but also from their other brothers, sisters, nephews, nieces, etc. The curse of becoming a fugitive from murder and a vagabond was placed upon him. Complaining to the Lord that this punishment was greater than he could bear, God assured him of protection by placing a mark on him. Then in the rest of chapter four the first and most prominent of Cain's descendants are mentioned and also the work and crafts they became involved in. Already the son of

Cain, named Enoch, had numerous descendants, so that a city was built by him and named after him. Then Genesis 4:18 continues, "And unto Enoch was born Irad; and Irad begat Mehujael: and Mehujael begat Methusael: and Methusael begat Lamech."

Concerning this fifth generation from Adam, or of this great-great-great-grandson on Cain's side of the family (if no generations were missing because of the way the word BEGAT has been used in Old Testament chronology), there is evidence of great progress made in *material* things of this earth. God had commanded mankind to have dominion over all the earth. Lamech had two wives, who bore him three outstanding sons as well as daughters. Son Jabal and his descendants (and there most likely were many of them) dwelt in tents as they tended their animals. Jubal and his descendants were active in music, playing harps, organs and very likely other musical instruments. Tubal-cain and his descendants were busy making metal objects out of brass and iron and also were working with copper and tin. This is the earliest indication of metal crafts being developed on the earth. The life and minds of the descendants of Cain were directed more and more toward the things of this world and their enjoyments. Even the names given to their women show this, for Adah means "the ornamental one," Zillah "the sweet-sounding one," and the daughter Naamah "the lovely one."

Genesis, in chapter five, continues with the descendants of the most prominent and important son of Adam and Eve—Seth and his descendants from whom the Seed of the woman, the Savior, was to come, as promised after the Fall in the Garden of Eden. After giving the generations of Adam through his son Seth, we come in the eighth generation after Adam to another Lamech. This Lamech is the father of Noah. But because of the long lives of those early generations and because of one generation overlapping a number of other long-living generations, some 1650 and more years had passed between Adam and Noah, if some generations had not been omitted, because of the broad use of the word begat.

By this time, as far as God was concerned, two different races or classes of people had become very prominently evident: "the sons of God" or believers in a savior from sin and the "daughters [and sons] of men" or unbelievers. Genesis 6:1-2 states after referring to Lamech and his son Noah and Noah's three sons, Shem, Ham and Japheth:

> And it came to pass when men began to multiply on the face
> of the earth, and daughters were born unto them, That the sons

of God saw the daughters of men that they were fair: and they took them wives of all which they chose.

Accordingly, in the course of the centuries since the creation of man, the descendants of Cain and the descendants of Seth developed into two fundamentally different lines of people. The Cainites were called by God the children of men and the Sethites or at least most or some of them the children of God. The Cainites were worldly and wicked like their forefathers. They long ago had forsaken God, defied Him, very likely even denied His existence, as the evolutionists do today, and they lived according to the thinking of their rebellious minds. In these people we very likely already had the first evolutionary HUMANISTS, the worshippers of man's abilities, the proud HOMO SAPIENS, SAPIENS, as the evolutionists like to refer to man of today.

In the course of time this defiance, rebellion and corruption spread to the families of the sons of God, to the believers, as it does even today. It shows itself not only in denying the existence of God but also in laxity of morals. In approximately 16 centuries or so the number of human beings evidently increased to millions of people, as we shall see further on, and men belonging to the descendants of Seth permitted worldly, fleshly considerations to influence them in the choice of their wives. No doubt also the female descendants of Seth were lured to the male descendants of Cain. The children of God were influenced by their ungodly neighbors and became like them. The daughters of men made the enjoyment of all that the world has to offer the goal of their lives, and their beauty became a snare to the sons of God. The result of this intermarriage was that the children of God became ungodly, God-defiant, and worldly like the children of men: hero worshippers, man worshippers and finally evolutionary humanists.

Out of all this flowed a general moral decay and corruption resulting in evil spreading like wildfire, finally destroying all that was godly in this world. With AIDS spreading like wildfire throughout the world today and men crying to the government to find a cure for the killing disease that they have brought upon themselves and others much or most of it through sex perversion, one wonders if we are not living in days such as shortly before the Flood when Noah and his family were the only believers left. Fortunately, there are today still considerably more than eight Godly people left.

In regard to the descendants of Adam turning so ungodly and God-defiant as they did, there may have been a number of factors in addition to the strong inclination of mankind to ignore and disobey God and His will. No doubt the land of that time was extremely productive with a greatly better climate than after the Flood. With the land watered by gentle mists, with lovely springtime-like weather and with soil being extremely fertile, so that man and animals could easily find all the food that was necessary, it was an easy life.

Another factor was *the length of life*, 900 years and more, that men were given to live. Mankind had a wealth then that is not granted today. With the large amount of time that those descendants of Adam and Eve possessed, they could easily abandon their concern about their Creator, or even forget that there was a Creator, to whom they were responsible. Most of these people, not seeing death for centuries and centuries, could have believed that they would live forever. The people could easily have become outwardly more anti-establishment as far as God was concerned, anti-God, God-denying, God-defying, and became *corrupt* and *filled with violence* and *wicked* and *every imagination of the thoughts of their hearts was only evil continually.*

7.   VERY LARGE FAMILIES — MILLIONS OF PEOPLE

In regard to the population from Adam to the Flood, the families, in obedience to God's command to fill the earth, and because wide-open spaces were available, no doubt were very large consisting of at least 10 to 50 children, and perhaps more. Genesis chapter five states, after each of the partriarchs, that he "begat" sons and daughters, indicating that there were very many of them. Long after the Flood, we are told in Judges 8:10, that Gideon had 70 sons. Ibzan, Judges 12:9, had 30 sons and 30 daughters; Abdan had 40 sons. When the children of Israel were in Egypt, we are told "the Israelites grew and multiplied exceedingly." Even in recent years 10 to 15 children in a family were common. One negro woman in Ohio, in 1946, gave birth to a 27th child. There are numerous cases where there were 20 or more children.

Another factor that led to large families before the Flood was that people lived 900 and more years, and produced children long past the age of procreation today. Noah was 500 years old when he begat Shem, Ham and Japheth. Because the earth was very productive and because there was much land for human development of this earth, families were large in order to fill the earth as God commanded. In addition, because climatic conditions were much more ideal then, and because the soil was virgin rich, food was very plentiful and easily obtainable.

Because of all this and because people lived hundreds of years, there could easily have been a tremendous explosion in population growth.

Computing the population a number of different ways, it has been estimated that by the time of the Flood there could have been 1 to 10 billion people living. With 1,600 and more years covering the span of time from Adam to the Flood, there could have been as many people living as there are today.

8.   HIGHLY ADVANCED AND HIGHLY TECHNICALLY-INCLINED PEOPLE

What type of civilization did these people have? Adam and Eve, before they fell into sin were the most perfect, flawless people of all time, created in the image of God and endowed with the gift of speech and a most wonderfully keen intellect, with a knowledge of all creatures and plants and minerals of this earth. Adam and Eve were endowed with the ability to rule over all things on this earth and have dominion over all things. With this ability and endowment they could create a highly advanced civilization as rulers, lords and masters of all things that God had made for them. Adam no doubt immediately began making tools and implements that would serve their welfare. It did not take him eons, millions of years, before he began making use of fire, as the evolutionists claim it took their prehistoric people to do. And no doubt it did not take Adam and Eve long before they put their thoughts and speech into writing and began counting and calculating. Adam's son, Cain, was already building a city in the second generation, according to Genesis 4:17. It was not long before Adam's descendants and maybe Adam himself were working with minerals, mining them, smelting and purifying them and creating out of the minerals all kinds of implements, tools, weapons and string and organ types of musical instruments.

These people could easily have developed a civilization and built buildings and structures that were far superior to what the early Egyptians and Sumerians built. Long before what evolutionists call prehistory, Adam and Eve and their descendants were making tools, inventions and metal products. It is amazing that while evolutionists write about the great antiquity of man going back millions of years they do not consider the possibility of people being equal or superior in mental capacities and abilities to ourselves who lived in what they call prehistoric times. If we today could dig below thousands and thousands of feet of sediments that were laid over the earth at the time of that turbulent, violent, muddy Flood with its wild storms (the like of which this earth has never seen since, and with totally disastrous earth upheaval), we could be mightily surprised at the advanced civilizations that undoubtedly existed then. People can hardly believe that Noah and his sons (maybe with hired contractors of that time) could have built such a large ark with all its compartments and three floors. The construction and engineering abilities, with a considerable knowledge of mathematics and use of tools and advanced art of building that Noah and his sons had, no doubt were carried over into the post-Flood years very readily. And that is why the architecture and civilization that was found in early Egypt and Sumer were just a natural carry-over from pre-Flood technology and architecture.

Egypt, Sumer and other suddenly-arising, amazing civilizations would not have been possible if they had not had a carry-over from Noah and his descendants in a pre-Flood civilization. Pyramids, sculpture, statues, sphinxes made of hardest granite; the ability to write, highly organized government and skills and techniques of all kinds would not have been possible if a civilization that had been destroyed in a world-wide destructive flood had not preceded Egyptian and Sumerian civilizations.

From all this it is quite evident that the people before the Flood had not only increased into millions of people and become great masses of people covering the earth, but had reached high stages of culture and civilization. These were the Golden Years in the history of mankind, just the opposite of what history books start out with — half ape, half man, ignorant, backward primitives and savages. Evolutionary history books used in schools like to picture man as more backward and helpless than the lowest degenerated savages of today. (See the quotation from W. West in the third paragraph of this book.)

With the ability to write, especially since there was only one language before the flood, records and history were handed down not only by word of mouth but also by actual written records. Since everything that man had ever produced or built before the Flood was destroyed or buried in hundreds and thousands of feet of mud which was turned into stone in many cases, all these records were lost also. Yet pre-Flood records were not totally lost, for Noah and his sons could pass on to the next generation not only their technical and architectural know-how from a previous civilization, but also the list of the patriarchs who lived before the Flood, their ages and their children. So today, although the Bible does not give a detailed history of the pre-Flood years, we do have the names and some facts regarding some of the most important people who became forefathers of the Seed of a woman, the Savior, promised in the Garden of Eden.

9.   "OOPARTS": OUT-OF-PLACE-ARTIFACTS

Besides the Bible, another source of what the pre-Flood civilization was able to accomplish is seen in the study of "OOPARTS." This no doubt sounds like something strange, but "ooparts" are *Out-Of-Place-Artifacts.*" These ooparts are artifacts or objects that archeologists have found while digging into ancient civilizations and that appear to be out-of-place for the backward civilizations some think these people must have had. Some of the archeologists, according to *Secrets of Lost Races* by Rene Noorbergen (1977), p. 2, think:

> In many cases, the technical sophistication of the ooparts extends far beyond the inventive capabilities of the ancient peoples among whose remains they were discovered . . . Is it possible that these ooparts bear testimony to the existence of a super-civilization of human origin and development at some distant point in the history of mankind? Sounds far out, doesn't it? Yet what are the chances of its being so? Is it conceivable that there may have been a period in human history when there was (a) civilization(s) that was (were) comparable or possibly more advanced than our own twentieth century society?

On page four he continues thoughts similiar to what I stated a few paragraphs back.

> The convulsions of nature [he is referring to the Flood] not only buried the antediluvian people but also utterly destroyed their technological achievements, for this tremendous upheaval was certainly enough to obliterate any form of machinery or construction.

Another outstanding, and, I must say, *scientific* statement that he made among many others is given on page 21:

> To reconstruct the events, that happened before a flood destroyed all of mankind, cannot be done without combining archaeology, geology, conventional history and Biblical history.

How accurate is this man's judgment here! I did not see this statement until I got this far in writing, but seeing what I have written regarding the illogicalities of evolution in the field of archeology, the Egyptians and other advanced peoples given in conventional secular history and just now in Biblical history, I must consider one more subject: geology. This will be done when analyzing the Flood of Noah's days.

Some of the ooparts mentioned are a human bone and copper arrowhead four inches long found in a silver vein 400 feet below the ground in Gulman, Colorado in 1967. Another oopart is a metallic vase dynamited out of solid rock 15 feet below the surface in 1851 in Dorchester, Massachusetts. The sides of the vase were beautifully decorated with silver. In 1891, in Morrissonville, Illinois, a gold chain of fine workmanship was found in a lump of coal which had broken in two. Many other such ooparts have been found. Possibilities of know-how in batteries and electricity in those days are mentioned. All of this is possible if we want to give God credit for having created a human being far superior to any that exists today.

On page 205, Noorbergen sums it all up:

The major assumption of orthodox historians — that our civilization is the result of gradual development from primitive beginnings — can now seriously be challenged. Ooparts, Biblical history, archaeology, geology, paleontology, and ordinary level-headed thinking have guided us in that direction. The weight of evidence is growing daily — evidence that our early ancestors created a society that surpassed ours in all aspects of development.

10.   IMMENSE CREATURES

One more thing must be mentioned regarding those pre-Flood or post-Adam people, and that is their size of body. First let us consider the size of the animals of those early centuries of the earth. My classmate, Hilbert R. Siegler, a research administrator, stated in his excellent book, *Evolution or Degeneration — Which?*, p. 22,

There is also considerable evidence to support the belief that the originally created plants and animals were not only superior because of their hereditary potential but also from a morphological standpoint. In fact, vertebrates of the past may have excelled in size, intelligence, and in capability to meet the exigencies of their situation.

Everyone is acquainted with the huge dinosaurs. Great beds of dinosaur fossils bones are found in various parts of the world. They have been found all over the Midwest, in the Black Hills, the Rocky Mountain region and in the Gobi Desert. In the Dinosaur National Monument, in Colorado and Utah, bones of over 300 dinosaurs of many kinds were found.

In the Red Deer Valley of Alberta, Canada, 26 different varieties of thousands of dinosaurs were discovered. Some were over 80 to 150 feet in length, and some giant dinosaurs must have weighed 40 tons. Huge mammoths were found frozen in Siberia and Alaska. Some bears have been discovered that make the Alaskan Kodiak bear look like a dwarf. Birds of that time stood 10 feet high, two feet higher than the largest ostrich. Some birds had wing-spans of 25 to 30 feet and laid two gallon-size eggs, eleven inches in diameter. Turtles were discovered that were 12 feet long. Ostrich fossils are as big as those of giraffes. Bat fossils have wing spans of 15 feet and are as large as a sheep. All in all fossil bones of huge animals have been found in sedimentary rock and stone beds throughout the world.

So one would naturally expect mankind originally being much larger also. The Chinese have tales of "men twice as tall as us," who once lived in a delightful earth but lost it by not living "by the laws of nature." Genesis 6:4 says of the people who lived just before the Flood,

> There were giants in the earth in those days; and also after that, when the sons of God came in unto the daughters of men, and they bare children to them, the same became mighty men which were of old, men of renown.

They were very likely as large as, or larger than those the children of Israel encountered in Palestine when they returned from Egypt. Numbers 13:33 speaks of the people living in Palestine being giants, and the children of Israel as small as grasshoppers in their sight. We are all familiar with the story of David and the giant Goliath. People in the days before the Flood were mighty men who were strong and heroic and men of *renown*, stately appearing people, and some were looked upon as heroes and as the nobility of that time. These people certainly did not look like they came from apes. They were highly adept, skillful, developed, and highly capable in many fields.

Lest someone might think that this is a "myth" of the Bible, I will refer you to an evolutionary book, *Man, Time and Fossils*, by Ruth Moore (1953). On p. 249 she refers to a huge jaw and teeth that were found in Java and sent, 1941, to Dr. T. Weidenreich of the American Museum of Natural History. He and others believed it was the "jaw of a giant". He called it *meganthropus paleojavanicus* which in plain English means "giant man of ancient Java." He came up with a new idea that man's ancestors were actually giants, but this is merely another evolutionary idea.

Ruth Moore writes in her book, p.p. 250-251

> Weidenreich could not resist playing with the idea of how large these early giants might have been. By comparing the teeth and bones with those of living animals and from careful anatomical

measurements he decided that the Java giant was much larger than any living gorilla, and the Chinese giant was one and a half times larger still. That would have made him twice as large as a male gorilla! [The Biblical words come inevitably to mind: "There were giants in the earth in those days." (Genesis 6:4). She continues quoting Weidenreich]: "I believe that all these forms have to be ranged in the human line and that the human line leads to giants; the farther back it is traced. In other words giants may be directly ancestral to man."

Petrified fossils of a giant were found not only in Java and China but also in South Africa and were reported to Dr. Tracy Weidenreich by Robert Broom, a world-renowned anthropologist. Evolutionists, contrary to their own theories, report similiar findings today. In the November 1985 *National Geographic* a remarkable statement is made on p. 629:

At 5 feet 4 inches tall, the boy from Turkana was surprisingly large compared with modern boys his age; he could well have grown to six feet. Suitably clothed and with a cap to obscure his low forehead and beetle brow, he would probably go unnoticed in a crowd today. This find combines with previous discoveries of *homo erectus* to contradict a long held idea that humans have grown larger over the millennia. Our ancestors on the African savanna may have been much taller than we ever imagined. Indeed, we may have reached our present general size more than a million and a half years ago, with some populations in poorer environments becoming smaller fairly recently.

With brilliant, gigantic human beings living in those earliest centuries, some think that their large size would explain how some of those immense buildings and stones could have been set up in Egypt, Sumer, France, England, Easter Island and elsewhere. But one can be certain that these people did not use only their huge brawny muscles, but also that they used their brilliant minds and that they used them to the fullest extent.

In reading all this I have often wondered how Hollywood all these years could have missed the boat so badly as it did. Not only Hollywood, but also the *National Geographic, Time, Readers Digest,* the news media, television and book writers have missed one of the greatest stories of all time outside of the creation of this earth, the earth-destroying Flood, and the story of Jesus, the Christ, the Savior of mankind. What better story could there be for Hollywood than the story of the intelligent, highly skilled and advanced people in the early centuries of this earth?

V.   THE PRE-FLOOD HISTORY, GEOGRAPHY AND CLIMATE OF THIS EARTH

Before considering the *horrifying flood* of Noah's days, it is important that we know what the conditions were on earth before the Flood. An important element before the Flood, which played a major role in the history of the people of those approximately 16 centuries or more was the geography and the climate of those many centuries.

1.   THE EARTH'S SURFACE BEFORE THE FLOOD

What was the earth's surface like between the creation of the earth and that devastating, destructive Flood that changed the entire crust of the earth? Although nothing definite is stated in the Bible, general hints are given in those first chapters of Genesis. At the end of the sixth day of Creation, Genesis 1:31 states, "And God saw everything that He had made, and, behold, it was very good." The mere fact that everything was *"very good"* indicates that mankind could freely roam all over this earth without any major obstacles such as mountains and deserts. All land could have been connected, since much of the water we have today could have been in the canopy of water vapor above the earth. God's command to "be fruitful, and multiply and replenish the earth" indicates that God did not place any physical barriers on the surface of the earth to hinder the spread of mankind throughout the earth. When God caused the dry land to appear on the third day, it is very likely that He created gently rolling land that could easily be traveled without major obstacles. Although Genesis 7:19-20 states in regard to the Flood waters that "all the high hills were covered . . . and the mountains were covered," the hills and mountains were very likely much lower in elevation than they are now, after the "fountains of the great deep were broken up." With the land of the earth easily traversed to all corners of the earth, people could easily populate the entire earth in a very short time, so that the descendants of Adam and Eve could have been in all parts of the earth within a century. And since much of the water that is now in the oceans and seas was in the canopy above the earth, as we shall see shortly, the land most likely covered a much larger part of the earth than it does today, making travel around the earth easy.

2.   THE CLIMATE BEFORE THE FLOOD

Another factor relating to those first 16 centuries that made people highly mobile, active and industrious, was the climate of the time. Fossils found in all parts of the earth indicate that before the Flood there was a uniformly mild climate throughout the entire earth, even in both the north and south polar regions. There were no weather extremes and violent storms as we have today. As Professor Alfred Rehwinkel put it in "The Flood" p. 7; quoting Alfred Wallace.

> The climate was a mantle of springlike loveliness which seems to have prevailed continuously over the globe. Just how the world could have thus been warmed all over may be a matter of conjecture; that it was so warmed effectively and continuously is a matter of fact.

That it is a fact is evident from fossils and frozen animals found in Siberia fully preserved when they were suddenly frozen to death. The fossils are of animals and plants that today we find only in warm climates. There seems to have been only one warm climate, with no different climate zones such as there are on earth today. Before the Flood there very likely were no desert zones and arctic zones, and there were no high mountains like the Rocky and Himalaya Mountains to form climatic or physical barriers. The land was low and rolling. There very likely were no jungles and no open seas between large land masses such as exist today between North America and Siberia and between England and Europe. For this reason, mankind and animals of all kinds were distributed all over the earth, and the various kinds of animals that entered into the Ark with Noah were living in the area where the Ark was being built. Most likely it was not necessary for some of the animals to migrate thousands of miles to get to the Ark, as would be necessary today.

3.   THE CANOPY OF WATER VAPOR ABOVE THE EARTH

The reason the climate was so beautiful, pleasing and pleasant all over the earth was no doubt due to the water vapor that existed all around the earth. To give warm temperature to all the earth, the earth could have traveled around the sun without the present 23 ½ degree tilt. For this reason the sun would have shone on all the earth evenly, also in the north and south polar regions. Even the evolutionists believe that there were at one time warm, tropical climates in the polar regions.

One thing regarding the creation story that puzzled me from boyhood on was the second day of creation, of which we are told in Genesis 1:6-7:

> Then God said, Let there be a firmament in the midst of the waters, and let it divide the waters from the waters. Thus God made the firmament, and divided the waters which were under

the firmament from the waters which were above the firmament. And it was so.

The problem is where is all that water above, if God separated the waters this way. Certainly when God divided the waters the second day, He must have placed more than the approximately two inches of water that is above the earth today. Evidently very large quantities of water must have been placed above the earth as a blanket of water vapor to form a pleasant climate shield and to protect the entire earth from the rays of the sun. The high water content above the earth acted as a sort of water canopy surrounding the earth, and this water canopy absorbed much of the heat and direct rays of the sun. The heat of the sun was diffused equally over all the earth, so that pleasant climate prevailed even at the North and South Poles. This made it possible for sub-tropical plants like ferns to grow there.

The book *The Genesis Flood,* by John Whitcomb and Henry Morris, states, p. 256:

> In the present atmosphere, the stratosphere is quite cold. However, above the stratosphere, the temperature becomes quite warm, well above even the boiling point of water, so that it would be possible to sustain a tremendous amount of invisible water vapor in the region above the stratosphere, if it somehow were placed there. These high temperatures in the upper atmosphere remain high both day and night, so that there would be no possibility of vapor condensation at night. [The book stated earlier, p. 240.] It is known, however, that the region above 80 miles is very hot, over 100° F and possibly rising to 3000° F, and is in fact called the thermosphere for this reason. High temperature, of course, is the chief requisite for retaining a large quantity of water vapor.

Much of this was learned through the International Geophysical Year and the satellite program.

Therefore when God separated the waters, He placed vast amounts of water *above* the firmament in the far outer reaches of the atmosphere. The firmament was used to separate the vast amount of waters in the canopy above from the vast amount of water in the oceans.

4. THE GREENHOUSE EFFECT OF THE PRE-FLOOD WATER CANOPY

No doubt the pre-Flood water canopy caused luxuriant vegetation over the entire earth from pole to pole. Animals and mankind developed better also. Within only a couple of hundred miles of the South Pole there is evidence of luxuriant plant and forest growth that thrived there, and within 800 miles of the North Pole, subtropical forests and large fossil leaves of palm trees have been found. In the frozen ground of the New Siberian island a large fruit tree with green leaves and ripe fruit has been found.

The reason this pre-Flood vapor canopy is referred to as having a greenhouse effect is that it acts like in a greenhouse where the heat is trapped by the glass windows, so the temperature in the greenhouse rises. The vapor not only kept the temperature pleasantly warm but also caused a uniform temperature from pole to pole. For this reason, remains of plants and animals have been found in polar regions that ordinarily are found only in the warmer climates of the earth today. Also in the desert regions of Africa and the United States there are evidences that these regions once had luxuriant growth and that the regions were once moist and well-watered with trees that grew fast and large.

John Barker in his booklet *Creation* 1993, states p. 32:

> Because of the insulating effect of the canopy there would be comparatively little temperature difference between artics & tropics, summer and winter, and day and night; conditions would be almost universally 'tropical'. Since the global temperature differences cause the winds and weather there would be no strong winds or rain storms, rather there would be a calm, humid atmosphere permitting abundant continuous growth of lush vegetation. In keeping with the abundant vegetation there would probably have been more carbon dioxide in the atmosphere; this would have emphasised the greenhouse effect still further.

5.   THE PROTECTIVE GREENHOUSE EFFECT ON MANKIND AND ANIMALS

As mentioned previously mankind and animals lived longer and were healthier and grew larger in those first centuries under that protective canopy. The rays from the sun that bring on decay, deterioration and harm to the body and that cause aging and death in living creatures were intercepted by the canopy, and as a result men and animals lived to greater ages, up to almost 1,000 years for much of mankind before the Flood. The fact that pre-Flood people lived 900 and more years is found not only in the Old Testament history of the patriarchs but also in the records and literature of many other nations. However, only in Genesis is the record carefully preserved.

Today only a thin atmospheric blanket protects us from the deadly rays of the sun and from harmful extremes of heat and cold. Only a thin amount of water vapor moderates our climate. The vapor also may have helped preserve the protective ozone layer around the outer reaches of the earth. Scientists today fear that our earth is losing it rapidly, especially over the Antarctic.

6.   THE ARROGANCE OF THE PRE-FLOOD PEOPLE

That people before the Flood and after it were highly advanced is evident from excavations that the University of Pennsylvania and the British Museum undertook in 1922 at the ancient site of Ur in Chaldea. Under the charge of Leonard Woolley they found the remains of a number of civilizations and cities built upon the ruins of preceding ones. Far below the first city they found deep pits which contained the tombs of great kings and queens. They found ornaments of gold and sky-blue lapis lazuli and remains of other fine art. Mr. Woolley wrote in his book, *Ur of Chaldees*,

> There was found the famous gold dagger of Ur, a wonderful weapon whose blade was of gold, its hilt of lapis lazuli decorated with gold studs.

Further on Woolley writes:

> The contents of the tomb illustrated a very highly developed state of society of an urban type, a society in which the architect was familiar with all the basic principles of construction known to us today.

From all this it is evident that the people before the Flood had attained a highly developed stage of culture, skill, and civilization. They had reached a great development. It could easily have been the Golden Age in the history of mankind. Most certainly it was the exact opposite of what history books teach our children — man started as half ape and half man, ignorant, backwards, a savage who took millions of years to learn how to use the fires that lightnings started. What poor logic to think like that!

With this background concerning conditions prevailing in the centuries between the creation of the world and the earth-shattering Flood, we can imagine the clearly evident arrogance; the pride; the self-importance; the overbearing, haughty, braggadocio spirit; and the man-worshipping, God-denying and God-defying spirit that very likely became more evident among mankind. Because they lived in a veritable paradise compared to what we are living in today, (in a world beautiful and pleasant beyond our present imagination, with people highly endowed with all kinds of mental abilities, talents and know-how, a superior people in things of this world, enterprising and cultured, adept in all kinds of skills of the human body, living for centuries without any fear of death because centuries of life most likely still stood ahead of them) one can easily imagine the arrogance and defiance that mankind assumed over against their Creator whom they totally ignored and defied. People could travel all over the earth with the greatest of ease. Pleasant weather constantly made the South Sea island weather of today look violent in comparison. Very little if any shelter was necessary. The most pleasing food was super-abundant, "everything was going our way," so why be concerned about anything or anybody else and, above all, about God and eternity. No wonder Lamech in a braggadocio spirit could boast to his two wives, Adah and Zillah: Gen. 4:23F "Hear my voice, ye wives of Lamech, hearken unto my speech . . . If Cain [his great, great grandfather] shall be avenged sevenfold, truly Lamech seventy and sevenfold."

With 1600 or more years of such arrogance and wickedness of men over against each other and of rebellion against God the point was reached where almost all mankind worshipped only themselves the history given to us in Genesis 6:1-6 states:

> And it came to pass, when men began to multiply on The face of the earth, and daughters were born unto them, that the sons of God saw the daughters of men that they were fair; and they took them wives of all which they chose. And the LORD said, My spirit shall not always strive with man, for that he also is flesh; yet his days shall be an hundred and twenty years. There were giants in the earth in those days; and also after that, when the sons of God came in unto the daughters of men, and they bare children to them, the same became mighty men which were of old, men of renown. And God saw that the wickedness of man was great in the earth and that every imagination of the thoughts of his heart was only evil continually. And it repented the LORD that he had made man on the earth, and it grieved him at his heart.

Gen. 6, 11-13 re-emphasizes:

> The earth also was *corrupt before God* and the earth was *filled with violence* . . . all flesh had *corrupted* his way upon the earth . . . I will destroy them *with the earth. [Emphasis Added]*

God emphasizes a number of times that the people were *corrupt, filled with violence, wickedness, corrupted.* Although God referred to them as *giants in the earth, mighty men which were of old, men of renown,* yet they were totally unconcerned about God and His will.

Evidently they ignored and denied God entirely. They did not even have idols that might direct them to thoughts of any kind of god. Woolley writes:

> In no single grave has there been any figure of a god, any symbol or ornament that strikes one as being of a religious nature.

They evidently worshipped themselves as many humanists do today because of their wisdom and abilities and strength. "I am *the greatest — homo sapiens sapiens — super wise guys.*" They were great in the things of this world, but earthly and materialistic in their attitudes. They were concerned only about the things of this world.

Because the wickedness of man was so great, God determined to destroy all the pleasant things He had made for mankind. Genesis 6:7-8 states:

> The Lord said, "I will destroy man whom I have created from the face of the earth, both man and beast, creeping thing and birds of the air, for I am sorry that I have made them". But Noah found grace in the eyes of the Lord. NKJV

VI.   THE FLOOD

1.   NOAH'S ARK

After the first rebellion against God took place in the Garden of Eden (through the rebellion of Adam and Eve by disobeying the will of God), God still gave mankind hopes of being restored back to God through the promise of a Savior. God promised Adam and Eve that a "Seed," a descendant of theirs, would bruise the head of Satan, destroying the power of Satan over mankind and restoring mankind back to God. To keep that promise to Adam and Eve, God saved Noah and his family in that worldwide Flood. God gave Noah instructions how to build an ark in which the seed of mankind and the Seed (the Savior) would be saved.

Much has been written about that ark. A few notes are in place in regard to questions people may have. One is about the size of the ark. It was about 450 feet long, 75 feet wide, and 45 feet high with three floors of deck space. This was large enough to hold 569 railroad stock cars. It was estimated that two of every species of land animals could have been placed easily in less than half of the ark's space.

The number of species of animals in the ark depends on how one regards the term *species*. A species is usually a group of animals that can interbreed freely and produce fertile offspring. From a single pair of canids can be born all types and varieties of dogs, wolves, jackals, and coyotes. Over 200 different varieties of canids have come from a few wild dogs. Endless varieties of pigeons have been developed from the rock pigeon. The same is true of the cat family, such as leopards, tigers, lions and the common cat. Yet the different *kinds* of animals have never crossed over or merged into each other. This fact has caused Robert Clark to conclude in his book, *Darwin: Before and After,*

> Every theory of evolution has failed in the light of this modern discovery, and not merely failed, but failed so dismally that it seems almost impossible to go on believing in evolution.

The same is true of the different races of mankind. All have come from Noah, and yet what a difference in color, eyes, size and general appearance! What caused the change, when and how it came about is a mystery, although the Bible gives some hints of what brought it about.

That all the different *kinds* or even varieties of animals within the kinds could readily be available to enter the ark was no doubt due to the more or less level make-up of the land surface at the time and mild climate that prevailed all over the earth. Very likely all of the created kinds of land animals were living in that part of the earth where the ark was built, as well as in all other parts of the earth at that time. If some animals needed higher elevations or desert-like or jungle-like surroundings to survive, this also could have existed all over the world in different areas of the earth.

In regard to building that huge ark, which was nearly as large as many ocean liners today, mankind at that time was as highly advanced as we are today, so building the ark was no problem. Compared to the marvelous feats of building the pyramids shortly after the Flood, the building of the ark could have been a small construction job in comparison. The mechanical ingenuity and the executive ability shown in construction of the pyramids no doubt were learned and handed down through descendants of their forefather, Noah.

Although Noah and his three sons had 120 years in which to gather the material for the ark and build it, this does not mean that they constructed it entirely without hired help. They could have hired carpenters, shipbuilders and other workmen from among their ungodly neighbors, just as we hire outsiders, who do not believe in what individual churches profess, to build churches.

The destructive forces of the Flood came from two sources. Genesis 7:11-12 states:

the same day were *all the fountains of the great deep broken up,* and *the windows of heaven* [or floodgates of heaven] *were opened.* And the rain was upon the earth forty days and forty nights. [Emphasis Added]

In thinking of the Flood, most people think only of the floodgates of heaven.

2. THE FLOODGATES OF HEAVEN

The first question that concerns us is: Where did all the water for forty days and nights of rain come from? Evidently it came from the canopy of water that was lifted up by God on the second day of creation. The waters above the firmament were very likely in a vapor form which protected the earth from the rays of the sun and made the earth a most pleasant place in which to live. It is possible that the water contained in that vapor-canopy of heaven was as great as all the waters upon the earth.

Very likely, when that protective vapor-canopy came cascading down upon the earth in those forty days and nights, the entire weather pattern of the earth was changed. Not only did thunder and lightning suddenly appear and the most violent hurricanes and tornadoes arise, but very likely they were the most violent that earth has ever seen. In addition, the lightning must have flashed without ceasing and the thunders must have rolled continuously. The water must have come down in blinding sheets of rain, almost like waterfalls when those floodgates of heaven were opened. Not only did the water come rushing down, but there must have been extremely steep changes in temperature at times as the cold air swept down upon the earth. If storms today are frightening and terrifying so that people cringe in protective shelters, what must the violence of those storms have been like!

Evolutionists try to explain where the water we have today came from. Preston Cloud in his book, *Cosmos, Earth, and Man*, p. 109 states:

> The initial atmosphere and hydrosphere are almost certainly the products of volcanic exhalation or sweating out of gaseous components from the materials that originally fell together to form the planet . . . a process referred to as outgasing.

Then he raises the question whether this outgasing could have occurred in a big burp, many burps or steady burps. He prefers the many burps; but the real question is what is the origin of all those gases that should have caused all the water? Again evolution explained nothing but merely made unscientific assumptions.

The *Minneapolis Tribune*, April 2, 1986, printed another explanation for all the water on this earth. It states:

> Scientists [rather evolutionists] from the University of Iowa have proposed a startling new theory of how water accumulates on the earth and other planets. They believe that small icy comets, never before detected, are hurtling into the earth's atmosphere at the rate of 20 comets a minute, releasing water in 100-ton quantities that over billions of years provided enough water to create the oceans.

If this were so, why aren't there waters and oceans on other planets and the moon? It is odd how evolutionists will concoct one theory after another, even if they are not rational and so long as they do not agree with the Bible. Again, from where did the icy comets come, that they assume are bringing water to the earth? Why aren't the moon and Mars receiving some of the water?

3.   THE FOUNTAINS OF THE GREAT DEEP

The second destructive source of the Flood was all the fountains of the great deep were broken up. Much more is involved in those fountains of the deep than is commonly imagined. The fountains of the deep involved the heaving up, shifting around and lifting up of the entire surface and crust of the earth. When the fountains of the deep were broken up, the whole earth very likely buckled up and continents moved and shifted around, as many geologists claim. What once were ocean and seas could have buckled up into mountains like the Rockies and the Himalayas. And what was once land could have been buried in five miles of deep ocean.

To get a rough picture of what might have happened at the time of the Flood we must consider that the crust of the earth was violently disturbed, the continents and mountains were lifted up and the lava, ash and deadly fumes of exploding volcanoes evident all over the earth today burst forth as happened in the Phillipines in recent years. There are evidences of numerous volcanoes even on the ocean floors and all over the earth. In the meanwhile immense worldwide earthquakes were shaking the earth. For 40 days rain cascaded down upon the earth from the water vapor that had been placed there by the Creator in the second day of creation. Also many wild hurricanes and tornadoes were messing up the climate when the weather systems changed with the appearance of jet streams and high and low pressure systems. Hurricane Andrew in 1992 in Florida would have appeared only as a breeze compared to the much wilder hurricanes and tornadoes that raged in unison all over the earth, the midwest floods of 1993 would have appeared like a mere brook compared to the flood water that covered the entire earth at the same time and the Los Angeles earthquake of 1994 would have appeared as a non-event when earthquakes were shaking the entire earth at the time of the Flood.

4.   WHAT THE POST-FLOOD GEOLOGY OF THIS EARTH TEACHES

So far we have considered what archeology, general world history and Bible history teach regarding the early history of the earth. But geology, a study of the structure of the earth's crust, teaches us very much also in regard to *changes* that took place. In this sense true geology is science based on facts. And as we study the features of the earth's surface changed since its origin, we will find that this changed crust of the earth harmonizes with what the Bible teaches and in that sense the Bible is based on facts. True geology and the Bible harmonize completely.

The Bible and the present geology of the earth do not clash, but the evolutionary theory of things taking place gradually on the surface of the earth uniformly over millions of years and the present geology of the earth do clash!

There are all kinds of geological features on the earth that show that vast, sudden and sharp changes have taken place on the earth since its beginning. One of these is the uplift of the mountains. Although the Bible says that the Flood waters rose to a height of 15 cubits above the highest mountains, this does not necessarily mean that they rose as high as the present height of the highest mountain. Since everything on this earth in the very beginning was "very good," there very likely were, as mentioned before, no high mountains and no desert regions to act as barriers for mankind but the land was more or less level with gentle rolling hills. That the Flood waters at one time covered the highest mountains that exist today is evident from the fossils of marine animals that are found in all mountain ranges of the earth, even the Rockies, Himalayas and the Alps.

There is geological evidence that these mountain ranges have been lifted up and that they buckled as they rose. A recent translation of the Bible, NASB, translates Psalm 104:5-9 as follows:

He established the earth upon its foundations, so that it will not totter forever and ever. Thou didst cover it with the deep as with a garment; The waters were standing above the mountains. At Thy rebuke they fled; At the sound of Thy thunder they hurried away. *The mountains rose; the valleys sank down. [Emph. Added]*

Not only did the mountains rise but evidently the continents shifted and split apart. Evolutionists believe that "the present is the key to the past," and that all changes on this earth took place uniformly, slowly and gradually, as they do today. Yet even evolutionists like Richard Leakey believe that vast, powerful changes of the earth took place in the past. In *People of the Lake*, page 1, he writes:

It is only a few million years since the [African] continent collided once again with Eurasia, a collision that was powered by the movement of vast plates that make up the surface of the earth and upon which the continents literally float like huge granite boats. At the time, the African landscape was very different from today . . .

The earth on which we live has three different fluids that affect the earth: the air (atmosphere), the water (hydrosphere), and the molten rock (magma) deep in the earth, upon which our earth's crust rests and floats. When the Bible says "the fountains of the deep were broken up" this most likely included not only the waters in the bosom of the earth but also land masses that were broken up, lifted and shifted, tilted, folded and faulted immensely as they were influenced by the fluid magma that God disturbed together with the air and the water. Since all the mountains of the earth have fossils near or on their tops, it is quite evident that they were lifted up during or after the Flood and buried billions of animals and plants and mankind in sedimentation. Not only mountain ranges, but also large plateaus in the western states of Colorado, Arizona and Utah, and Tibet in Asia, have been lifted up one to five miles with layers of sedimentation thousands of feet thick, with marine creatures in them. Even on ocean bottoms all kinds of mountain ranges, peaks and elevations are found. Evolutionists who believe that things have changed only slowly and gradually throughout billions of years, have a hard time trying to explain the mountains, their twists and folds, and the marine fossils found on them. Even remains of whales and other sea monsters, small and large, are found on mountain tops.

Richard Carrington in his book *The Story of Our Earth* wrote, p. 163:

> In the Old World, the Alpine and Himalayan mountain systems were upraised from the bed of the sea by the compression of the land masses on either side. It is awe-inspiring to contemplate the physical forces that caused these stupendous bodies of matter to be slowly lifted, and then ride over the neighboring shoreline in huge waves of twisted rock.

Did you notice the words *"slowly lifted"*? Although there are all kinds of evidence that violent physical forces were active, the evolutionists cannot let go of their belief that all things took place *slowly* and *uniformly* to defend their belief or creed that mankind slowly evolved from apes.

That high mountains are quite young is evident from the fact that human habitation has been found in the Himalayas and Andes above 16,000 feet, which are not now suitable for human occupation. Evidently these mountains must have been lifted up after humans had lived there. Evolutionists have a hard time explaining the upthrusting of the mountains and plateaus. Ruth Moore who has written a number of evolutionary books wrote *In The Earth We Live On:*

> The bewildering old question of what has elevated the mountains and the continents still has not been answered.

Two other evolutionists, Dutton and Batten, lamented:

A uniquely satisfactory theory of mountain building still eludes us.

But the Bible's compact statement "The same day were all the fountains of the great deep broken up," explains an awful lot of turmoil in just a few simple, factual words. And we must remember that this breaking up of the fountains of the great deep continued for five months for all this activity was not stopped until after some 150 days of violent turmoil in the sky, in the waters, and in the molten magma of the interior of the earth.

Evolutionists are simply dumbfounded at the origin of the mountains and high plateaus. Ruth Moore in her book, *The Earth We Live On,* wrote regarding geologist C. Dutton who worked with the U.S. Geological Survey, pages 242-3:

[He] knew well that the plateau [Grand Canyon region] on which he stood had not always had its lofty elevation. On the contrary, it had several times been at sea level and below, for most of that enormous mass of stone had been formed at the bottom of a shallow sea. That was unmistakable. The sedimentary rock and the fossils it contained, even the ripple marks with which it was often scored, proved the point beyond debate. In the course of time that once flat, even sea bottom, that smooth pavement of the sea, had been upraised . . . What had caused that immense elevation? What had raised a hundred thousand square miles of the earth's surface two miles and more above the sea? . . . With his eye fixed on the mountains, Dutton was, in essence, asking: What had produced them? How had they come to be?

As one travels throughout the U.S. parks and sees the explanation that the U.S. Interior Department gives for the origin of many of the geological features of the earth, and as one analyzes the fantastic and impossible explanations given, one wonders whether the evolutionists who seem to control that department plus many other public institutions, ever thought of looking at the simple, plausible, credible answers the Bible gives for all these geological features?

5.   VOLCANOES

Another destructive force that took place when the fountains of the deep were broken up was volcanic explosions and eruptions that took place all over the world in almost simultaneous unison. These volcanoes not only shook the foundations of the earth but they poured immense amounts of liquid magma upon the earth to give us the lava and fiery or igneous rocks that we have in Oregon and many other places on earth. The volcanoes belched forth dirt, mud, molten rock, steam, water, boulders and brimstone to add to the terrifying spectacle of God's righteous anger against mankind, which had denied Him and ignored His will. Some of these volcanos produced huge lava flows in various parts of the earth. The Deccan Plateau in India has volcanic rock and lava two miles deep and in the United States the Columbian Plateau volcanic material stretches over 200,000 square miles and averages 3,000 feet deep, and in one place is over three miles deep. The volcanic ash that exploded from volcanoes all over the world no doubt reached the highest parts of the atmosphere and helped disturb the storms still more.

Ruth Moore in *The Earth We Live On* wrote, p. 347:

By studying and mapping such lava flows and the more violent outpourings of hundreds of huge volcanoes that once dominated this northwestern section of the United States, the geologists hoped to gain additional understanding of these most spectacular of all the phenomena of nature. What caused the earth to shudder and shake and throw out molten rock and fire? What brought forth the overwhelming incondescent [red-hot] floods? Man had uneasily asked these questions for centuries.

On p. 353 she writes about the destruction of the island of Krakatao by the volcano on it in 1883:

The ill-fated island in the Sundra Strait between Java and Samatra was wiped from the surface of the sea in an explosion that sent a tidal wave racing around the world. But there must have been many hundreds of explosions of this order along the northwestern edges of the American continent, for the lavas that gushed up in their wake accumulated into the core of a mountain range more than six hundred and fifty miles long.

But being a faithful disciple of the evolutionists creed and ignoring the Bible, she states p. 354:

Millions of years later the Cascades began to stir again . . .

Because evolutionists regard the Bible account of the world-wide Flood as being unscientific, even though the sedimentary rocks and fossils prove it, they try to find other explanations even though these cannot be tested and proven scientifically. They stretch out what happened in the Flood over *millions and billions* of years in order to have enough time for life on earth somehow to evolve over millions of years.

In regard to the explosion on the island of Krakatao, it is thought to have been the loudest noise on record to this time. It has been estimated that it would take 100 of the most powerful hydrogen bombs set off at the same time to equal the noise of that explosion. It was heard 3,000 miles away, just four hours after the explosion occurred. Huge waves up to 100 feet were created in the ocean and rushed inland, along the low coastline of Java and Sumatra. Over 1,200 villages and cities were destroyed. The waves took the lives of nearly 40,000 people. The tidal wave carried a large ship inland a mile and half and left it stranded 30 feet above the sea level. Now going back to the Flood, what must this earth have been like when thousands of volcanos were exploding all over the earth, shaking and tearing apart the very foundation of the crust of the earth?

6.   EARTHQUAKES

Hand in hand with the terrifying volcanoes were the extremely violent earthquakes that no doubt makes the worst earthquakes of today appear almost as non-events. What havoc recent earthquakes have caused is seen in the greatest earthquake that has struck the United States. It centered in New Madrid, a small town about 100 miles south of St. Louis. The earthquake struck early in the morning of December 15, 1811, with a thunder-like noise and violent shock. Chimneys came crashing down, chairs and tables were shoved around, and buildings were rocked many hundreds of miles away. When the people ran out of their homes, the land was moving like waves on an ocean, and the people crawled instead of trying to walk. Black clouds of sulphurous vapors covered the area in complete darkness. When daylight broke, people could still see the land rolling like waves. Forests were torn down, and buildings were swallowed up by openings in the earth. Thousands of acres of forest land were swallowed up, hills disappeared and lakes were created in their place, one 70 miles long. In other places lakes were elevated and depleted of their water. The violence of that earthquake was felt in distant parts of North America. Bells rang in Virginia, chimneys fell in numerous eastern states, and Indians were terrified in the northern part of Canada. For a while the Mississippi River was lifted up and flowed backwards. A few hours later all the water that had gathered upstream came rushing back with a tremendous force and roar, destroying everything that lay in its way. Violent earthquakes as bad as the first occurred for several months. Wide fissures opened in the earth running in the same directions. People cut down tall trees so they would fall at right angles to the fissures. During shocks they clung to the trees to escape being buried alive when fissures opened below them. The last shock came ten years after the first one. When it was finally over, thousands of square miles of land had undergone great change. Much of it is still visible today. What must this earth have been like for a number of years after Noah's Flood?

To see the violence of some recent earthquakes, consider the disaster that hit Port Royal, Jamaica, June 7, 1692. Again the earth moved in waves and in many places the earth fissured open and then quickly closed. In some fissures people were swallowed, and in others they were crushed to death. Giant waves crashed ships into one another and tossed some on land beside houses that had not washed away. Over 2,000 people died in that disaster. In a very few minutes the city sank into the Caribbean Sea. There have been many other violent earthquakes in recent years as in California and China, where similiar immense destruction has struck the land, the people, and buildings. Above all, what a shamble and devastation that horrible earthquake in Armenia, U.S.S.R. created December 7, 1988. It aroused the sympathy of peoples all through the United States and the world. Yet all these earthquakes were only like minor events compared to when "All the fountains of the great deep were broken up" at one time all around the world during the Flood.

7.   TIDAL WAVES

Hand in hand with erupting and exploding volcanoes and destructive earthquakes came equally terrifying and destructive gigantic tidal waves. These killer waves, also called *tsunamis* in Japan, have risen as high as sixty feet above normal ocean waves, and in one instance 100 feet high. These huge killer waves are known to travel with terrifying speed. In one epic disaster in 1896, killer waves struck Japan, taking 27,000 lives. Repeatedly Japan has seen these tsunamis hit suddenly from the sea to smash, destroy, harm and kill. An earthquake in May of 1960 in Chile caused waves to speed 10,000 miles in 24 hours, or 400 miles an hour, doing severe damage in Japan and California, and from Alaska to New Zealand. The Krakatao volcano explosion caused killer waves as high as 125 feet to speed across the ocean in all directions. Even in Japan, Australia and India the killer wave made matchsticks of docks and boats. At Cape Horn it was still traveling 400 miles an hour. As a result, over 36,000 people were killed, 6,000 ships were smashed, and hundreds of villages in Indonesia were destroyed. In spite of facts like these, many people are still foolish and God-rebellious enough to believe that the Flood in Noah's day was only a local event.

Although tidal waves are usually referred to as waves created by tides, the term has been applied to unusually high, destructive waves sent inland by an earthquake, by underwater volcanic explosion, or by a very strong windstorm. Even windstorms have created waves that were 100 feet high. At Cherbourg, France, immense storm-driven waves cast stones weighing more than three tons over the wall of a breakwater built with large rocks and the waves moved 65-ton concrete blocks 60 feet.

The destructive power of flood waters is evident from what flood waters in recent years have done. They have moved blocks of granite weighing 350 tons more than a hundred yards. Boulders weighing 75 to 210 tons have been moved by flood waters only 15 to 20 feet deep. In the San Gabriel Mountains of Los Angeles 100,000 cubic yards of rock and soil were moved from each square mile of watershed in one brief flood. So we can well understand the immense amount of rock and soil that were stirred up by the Flood and moved and settled in sediment in all parts of the world as we shall see further on. It has been estimated scientifically that over 75 percent of the earth's surface is made up of sediment. In Colorado and Arizona sediments of earth and rock are at least as deep as the Grand Canyon, and in one place in India the sediments are about 12 miles deep. Although some of the basement rocks were lifted up when the dry land was formed during the third day of creation, yet these rocks, containing no fossils, were not like the repeated layers of sedimentary rock that were laid down during the Flood, when this entire earth was in one massive turmoil for 365 days or more.

In studying tidal waves, scientists have found them to be series of waves reaching down to the ocean floor and traveling fastest in the deepest waters. At depths of 24,000 feet a tidal wave can travel as fast as a jumbo jet, 600 miles an hour. In 900 feet the speed drops to 115 miles per hour. Over a shore line the speed may drop to 30 miles per hour, but because of the shallow waters the waves swell immensely in height. A wave that may have been only two feet high in the deep parts of the ocean may become a 100-foot-high-killer-wave as it comes inland at 30 miles per hour. The most deadly wave is usually not the first wave. When succeeding waves meet a wave that is going back out into the ocean, the two waves create a returning rushing wall of water much higher that will do immense damage.

8.   THE FLOOD AS A WHOLE

What vast devastation must have been created when all those forces of the earth worked together: rain gushing down from the canopy above the firmament, earthquakes shaking the earth, many volcanoes erupting and exploding at one time, continents shifting, mountains lifting up, tornadoes, hurricanes and wild windstorms raging, gigantic tidal waves with crosscurrents and whirlpools raising havoc. All this taking place at the same time, week after week, for 150 days with additional activity for another 200 days must have created tidal waves "perhaps several miles in perpendicular depth," as John Williams, a mineral surveyor, said. No wonder there are so many layers of sedimentary rocks of various kinds. Truly, the Flood was the greatest and most violent catastrophe in the history of the world, with total destruction of all forms of life and of the entire surface of the earth.

All this was clearly summarized by Professor Alfred Rehwinkel, LLD, on p. 329 of his book *The Flood:*

> It must be remembered that the Biblical Deluge was a world convulsion in which heaven and the whole earth were involved. It was God's intention and purpose to destroy that world which He had created for sinless man, and so all the latent forces of nature were unleashed to accomplish this greatest upheaval of all time. These great forces of nature — earthquakes, volcanoes, wind and water — formed a terrible alliance for a universal destruction. These forces, when combined, are capable of developing an agent for destruction and transportation so enormous that it is beyond human calculation. Even local floods caused by the rising of a single river or river system have at times changed the topography of a given area beyond all recognition. But such local floods, and even the greatest of them known in history, must be multiplied ten thousand times ten thousand to give a picture of that disaster which overtook the first world.

When one looks at the Minnesota River valley as one descends the valley at Mankato, Minnesota, and other river valleys like it, one can see that it must have taken much larger floods than Mankato experienced in recent years to cut out such a wide river valley two and more miles wide. The Mankato floods of recent years were only little rivulets compared to the flood waters necessary to gorge out such a wide valley. River valleys throughout the world are much too wide for ordinary floods to have cut out.

Not only have wide river valleys and canyons been cut out on the surface of the present land areas, but deep canyons have been found in the oceans far out on continental land shelves. Some of these below-water canyons are larger than the Grand Canyon of the Colorado. The great Bahama Canyon is twice the size of the Grand Canyon, 14,000

feet deep, 40 miles wide and 125 miles long. A canyon extends out from
the mouth of the Hudson River for about 300 miles. Along the eastern
coast of the United States, for about 400 miles, there are many canyons
extending out to the ocean drop-off. Submarine canyons like these are
found around almost all continents. Evidently these canyons were
gouged out toward the end of the Flood, when land masses were lifted
up, and ocean basins were lowered to receive all the extra water that
had showered upon the earth from the vapor canopy above which existed
before the Flood. As these waters rushed into the ocean, canyons were
cut in the soft sedimentation before the oceans were filled. Also,
geologists agree that large areas of the oceans have sunk. The head of
the Geology Department of Michigan University stated not long ago:

> Can we, as seekers after truth, shut our eyes any longer to the
> obvious fact that large areas of sea floor have sunk vertical distances
> measured in miles?

There is no question, looking at the present make-up of the earth's
surface, that it has been changed drastically. The geology of this earth
plainly shows that an ideal, beautiful, pleasant climate once prevailed
on this earth, including both the North and South Poles. The remains
of plants and animals that lie buried in those regions and in the lifted-
up mountains and in their buckled-up strata, and in the strata revealed
all over the earth, are clear evidences of the original condition of the
earth and of dynamic changes. It is as St. Peter states in II Peter 3:6,
"The world that *then was*" was clearly different so far as the climate and
structure of the earth's surface was concerned; it was changed
drastically, "being overflowed with water, *perished.*" And "The heaven
and the earth which are now" are totally different.

As a result of this, the Garden of Eden has perished, so its location
is unknown. It may have been in the regions of Palestine or Babylonia,
as some assume, but if it was, it very likely lies buried under hundreds
or even thousands of feet of Flood-sedimentation. Just as people, when
they moved from the Old World to the New gave the same names to
their new homes as they had in the Old, so the same thing may apply to
places like the Garden of Eden. Large logs of wood, hardened into stone
have been found in metallic mines and various kinds of animals and fish
are found in masses of stone. In the Badlands of South Dakota, the
strata are made up of a mixture of clay, shale, limestone and sandstone,
indicating that tidal movements created these strata, depending on
which direction the sediments came from. Fossil remains of dogs, cats,
crocodiles, deer, camels, horses, even rhinoceroses and numerous other
animals are found in the Badlands.

As a result of all the turbulence of the waters of the Flood, the fossil remains show that many creatures lie buried together in vast heaps. Ordinarily when fish die they float to the surface or sink to the bottom and are devoured by other fish. But in England, in an area that covers 10,000 square miles, millions of fish fossils have been found that show they died a sudden, very violent death. The remains show that they were "contorted, contracted, curved; the tail in many instances bent around the head, the spines stick out; the fins are spread to the full as in fish that die in convulsion," as geologist Hugh Miller stated. In one square yard of sandstone in England 1,000 fish fossils have been found.

The same is true of land animals. Their fossils also show sudden and violent death. They must have been covered quickly with layers of mud and other sedimentation or they would not have been preserved. A confirmed evolutionary geologist, Dunbar, stated:

> A carcass left exposed after death is almost sure to be torn apart or devoured by carnivores or other scavengers and if it escapes these larger enemies, bacteria insure the decay of all but the hard parts, and even they crumble to dust after a few years if exposed to the weather. If buried under moist sediment or standing water, however, weathering is prevented, decay is greatly reduced, and scavengers cannot disturb the remains. For these reasons burial soon after death is the most important condition favoring preservation.

Fossil graveyards are found all over the world, sometimes containing numerous dinosaurs or other animals, sometimes fish, and sometimes a mixture of many animals. Sometimes fossils of animals that ordinarily live only in warm climates are found in far northern areas. Fossils of animals that live in the depth of the oceans have been found in mountain tops. Bones of camels, wild boars, and rhinoceroses are found buried together. Elephants and other huge animals are buried by the millions in Siberia, Alaska, England and much of Europe. Hippopotami are buried by the thousands in Sicily. Geologists admit there must have been something very violent that took place to explain the way these animals died, were buried and were preserved.

What was true of the fish and land animals is also true of the people who lived before the Flood. If we could dig around in the depths of the earth's sedimentary rocks, we most likely would find the pre-Flood people and their advanced civilizations buried in those rocks.

9.   ENOUGH WATER TO FLOOD THE EARTH

The question is at times raised as to whether there was enough water to flood the earth. Seven-tenths of the earth's surface is water. The average depth of the ocean is twelve times as great as the average height of all the land surface. If all the depths of the ocean were leveled off and all the land leveled down to that same plane, all land surface would be covered with water a mile and a half deep. If sea beds can rise and the continents sink on the fluid fiery magma beneath the ground, there certainly was no problem in having enough water to flood the earth. Then with earthquakes and volcanoes and storms stirring up the whole mass of liquid and solids, there must have been a muddy mess that was unbelievable to imagine.

10.   READER'S DIGEST AND OTHERS NOW CONSIDER THE FLOOD A FACT

Although the news media, magazines, TV programs and others constantly blare out the assumptions and pronouncements of evolutionists as scientific facts, the *Reader's Digest* issue of September 1977, p. 129 headed one of its stories with this headline:

There is now compelling evidence to support the ancient accounts that once there was indeed a vast, universal Deluge.

Then came the actual heading: *Noah, the Flood, the Fact.* The *Reader's Digest* states:

Most scientists have agreed that it [the Flood] was based upon a local event — the overflow of a river, a mighty hurricane or typhoon — magnified in the retelling, gilded as a legend and finally concretized into the heroic stature of myth. Now, however, there is evidence that seems to indicate the Deluge might indeed have taken place. This startling conclusion comes, as we shall see, from the independent probing of two separate disciplines: geologists who have studied the shells of a tiny sea creature which lived when it happened 11,600 years ago, and archeologists who have deciphered what was written by the hand of man some 8,000 years ago.

Geologists and *archeologists!* I mentioned before, *archeology* (the study of the ancient people like the Egyptians and Sumerians and others and their civilizations' feats) and *geology* (the study of the changed structure of the earth since the Flood and the fossils found in it) as well as the Bible and pre-history *history* given in the Bible, plus plain common horse-sense, clearly give the facts regarding the first people on the earth. The *Reader's Digest* closes this story with:

> The Bible assigns no date for the Deluge. It says only that it took place. Now the shells of creatures long since dead, together with some of man's earliest written records on fragments of baked clay, offer compelling evidence that once there was indeed a vast, universal flood.

Even an evolutionist like Robert Silverberg, 1971, in *Clocks for the Ages*, pages 91-2, although writing as an evolutionist, gives a most beautiful super-description of the Flood. After referring to 1.5 million years ago, he writes:

> The previous epoch, the Pliocene, was a time of worldwide warmth; winters were mild everywhere, glaciers were unknown, the north and south polar regions were free of ice. Toward the end of the Pliocene a mighty stirring began in the earth's crust; a process of folding and heaving got under way, thrusting upward the ranges that would become the Alps, the Rockies, and the Himalayas. The climax of this upheaval was a quick and catastrophic fall in temperature that marked the end of the Pliocene and the start of the turbulent, frosty epoch we call the Pleistocene. [I will refer to the ice ages a little further on. He continues,] Though most changes in the geologic time-scale came about gradually, encompassing almost inconceivable spans, the shift from Pliocene to Pleistocene conditions seems to have taken place with astonishing speed: in 5,000 years or less.

But the evolutionists will not admit that the Flood is the explanation for all this sudden change.

Another evolutionist, Richard Carrington, in his book *The Story of Our Earth*, wrote on p. 155:

> Of the many kinds of animals inhabiting the Earth at that time, vast numbers were swept completely away. Not only individuals but whole races were destroyed, and extinction overtook the animals of land, sea and air with equal indifference. When the holocaust was over, the whole aspect of life on Earth had changed. Not a single representative of the dinosaurs, or of the mighty reptiles of the sea and air, remained alive.

And what explanation does he give for the sudden end of all these creatures? He says, p. 159:

> [G]eological events were probably the main cause of the great changes in the patterns of life . . . For instance, climatic changes

caused widespread modifications in plant life, so that the herbivorous dinosaurs were deprived of their food . . . Yet even when every external factor has been taken into account it is difficult to explain such widespread extinction of all the major forms of life. This has caused scientists to cast around for other theories, the most intriguing of which is the doctrine of racial old age.

Still others blame the extinction of many forms of animals on another planet or a comet getting close to the earth or hitting the earth. But "deprived of their food" and "racial old age" do not cause fossils to form. However it is hard for evolutionists to say that the Flood caused such widespread destruction and extinction, no matter how logical and reasonable it is.

The Flood is a geological fact that evolutionists cannot ignore. Evidence of the Flood is shown in many ways in the geological features of today's earth. It is shown:

1) In river valleys that are much too expansive to have been formed by present day floods.

2) In fossil graveyards present in the sedimentary rocks of the earth.

3) In stratum after stratum of sedimentry rock laid down by massive amounts of flood waters.

4) In large mountain ranges lifted up in recent times.

5) In the remains of marine fossils found on the tops of mountains.

6) In evidence of a drastic rise of the ocean level in recent times.

7) In evidence of a warm mild climate from pole to pole at a recent time.

8) In the massive amounts of different kinds of fossils buried together in one place.

9) In the sudden extinction of dinosaurs and other animals throughout the world.

10) In huge animals suddenly buried and frozen with tropical food in their mouths and stomachs, in Siberia and Alaska.

11) In the sudden rise of civilizations all over the world.

12) In many other evidences of a world-wide massive, destructive flood.

13) In the Flood account found among many nations and people.

11. THE FLOOD ACCOUNT FOUND AMONG MANY NATIONS

The stories of such a Flood which are found world-wide among many peoples, races, and nations are strong evidence of a world-wide flood. The *Reader's Digest*, in the September 1977 issue that I referred to previously, states in the opening paragraph:

> With variations, the Bible account of a great, universal flood is part of the mythology and legend of almost every culture on earth. Even people living far from the sea — the Hopi Indians in the American Southwest, the Incas high in the Peruvian Andes — have legends of a great flood washing over the land, covering the tops of mountains and wiping out virtually all life on earth.

Even though Flood stories prevail all over the earth the evolutionists deny such a Flood. On the other hand, if the Bible were the only place such a Flood is recorded and if stories of a flood were not prevalent among other people, the evolutionists could use that as evidence that there was no Flood. However, many of these Flood stories throughout the world are garbled and exaggerated in some of their details and lack the noble, factual simplicity of the Genesis account. Yet, in all these stories handed down from generation to generation, the essential facts of this devastating Flood are obvious. Most of these flood accounts say that a universal Flood wiped out all living creatures except some that were saved in a boat, and that a small remnant of mankind was saved.

Not only is the Flood account found among at least 200 people, tribes and nations, it is also referred to in many books of the Bible, in the Old Testament and New Testament. Jesus referred to it in Matthew 24:38 and Luke 17:26 when He referred to the Flood in connection with His own Second Coming, when there will be another destruction of this earth, this time by burning the elements of which the earth consists. The Apostles also, especially Peter, referred to it. (2 Peter Chapter 3).

VII.   THE POST-FLOOD RECORDS OF THE FLOOD

1.   ROCKS AND SEDIMENTATION

In connection with the Flood, mention must be made of the rocks and soil of which the surface of the earth is made, and what happened to them during the Flood. Today there are essentially three kinds of rocks: the igneous or fiery rocks, the sedimentary or stratified rocks, and the metamorphic rocks. The igneous rocks are the original primitive rock of the original creation. It is massive deep rock that is not stratified, and because it existed before plants and animals, there are no fossils found in it. But on top of this firm foundation there very likely was at the time of creation loose fertile soil that covered the entire earth to a great depth. It was soil like this, together with the mist that watered it, that made this earth so extremely productive from the days of the Garden of Eden to the time of the Flood.

Most of the stratified or sedimentary rock which now covers most of the outer surface of the earth is the rock that was laid as sediment in layers, or strata, by the action of the turbulent Flood waters. Some of the rocks with no fossils in them could have been created during creation. The original igneous rock evidently broke up into boulders when "the fountains of the great deep were broken up." The boulders were broken into large stones, then into pebbles, gravel, sand and clay by the turbulence of the Flood. This in turn was mixed with the loose fertile soil. All this mixture before it dried and hardened, was cemented together by clay and lime and other cementing substances. Most of these stratified rocks are now limestone, shale and sandstone. Because these rocks are made out of previously existing rock and soil, they are called secondary rock.

Then there is metamorphic rock. It is sedimentary rock that has been changed from one kind of rock into another through chemical action and pressure and heat; for example, rock changed from limestone into marble, shale into slate, and sandstone into quartzite.

2.   THE POST-FLOOD STRATA OF THIS EARTH

For 150 days great tidal waves and turbulences created by violent storms, earthquakes and explosive volcanoes rolled wildly back and forth mixing and remixing the broken up rocks, boulders, stones, gravel, sand and loose earth. These materials were mixed with lime, iron and other cementing substances. Whenever the rocking and rolling of this muddy mixture quieted down a bit another layer of sediment was laid on the bottom of the waters. In this way layer after layer of the soft, churned up materials were laid down in continuous strata, as sediments were brought in and deposited, first from one direction and then from another. In these strata are now found the fossils of all kinds of animals and human beings that were mixed in with the soft sediments.

The kinds of materials that made up the different strata, and the color and texture of the rocky strata, depended upon the location from which the materials were moved. The strata could consist of sandstone, clay, limestone, shale and other mixtures. Each lower layer would still be soft and level before the next layer was deposited on it. Extreme turbulence could have caused several feet of sediment to be deposited in a few hours, and since in some places the layers are thousands of feet thick, the build-up of sediment could have been very rapid.

Some evolutionary geologists say that it would take 100 to 400 million years for strata to build up on earth as it now exists. But they are going by what modern floods would accomplish over many, many intervening years. But the Flood in Noah's day was thousands of times as turbulent as any of the floods of today.

To understand how violent that Flood was, and how rapidly the layers of sediments were laid down, we must look at some of the many fossil trees and plants standing upright through successive layers of sedimentary rock. For this reason, these trees are called polystratea, or many-strata, trees. One such fossil tree in the Craiglieth quarry in England was 80 feet tall and stood at a 40 degree angle, standing among at least 10 layers of limestone. There were branches and roots on it. If the strata had been laid down over millions of years as the evolutionists claim, the top would have rotted away long before the next layer was laid down. Fossil trees standing in layers of rocky sediment have been found in Nova Scotia and Oregon; and throughout the world millions of trees lie buried beneath the surface of the earth among the rock strata. Most of them lie covered level with the face of the earth, few in an upright or in an angle position. Certainly one could expect in a violent flood that trees would be buried in all kinds of positions. Even very delicate plants like rushes and horsetail have been found intact and not broken among the sediments. These polystrate trees preach a sermon different from and more scientific than what the evolutionists preach in claiming the sedimentary strata of the earth were laid down slowly, gradually over millions of years instead of suddenly in a catastrophe like the Flood.

Thousands of fish with tails bent toward the head have been found in one quarry. This shows that they died suddenly and were quickly buried in the sediment that was turned into rock. Even fossilized worms have been found buried in the sediment. Likewise, thousands of dinosaurs have been found that were quickly drowned and buried in sediments. The same is true of many other very large animals, like the mammoths. In Siberia many of these were frozen almost instantly, with tropical vegetation still in their mouths and stomachs. Petrified forests have been found 100 miles from the South Pole.

Even today things like this are happening on a much smaller scale. On May 18, 1980, Mt. St. Helens in Washington exploded and erupted. Many trees were torn loose at the roots by the blast and washed into Spirit Lake. Hundred of trees have floated into shallow waters. Thousands have been found five years later fully submerged in an upright position buried in three feet of sedimentation around their base. Thousands of years from now some evolutionists could interpret these trees buried at different heights, as having grown there over thousands of years, and having been buried in slowly-deposited sediments over that space of time. But it all happened within a few months.

While some of the thick layers of sediment were still soft and pliant or easily bent, they were lifted up, before they had time to solidify into rocks, to great heights, forming mountains. Being still soft and easily bent, the layers did not split or break into pieces but were bent and twisted like pages in a thick, soft, papercovered book. Evolutionists have a hard time explaining how mountains like this could be lifted up slowly over thousands of years without the strata breaking into pieces.

3.   THE FOSSILS BURIED IN THE SEDIMENTARY STRATA OF ROCKS

Buried in the muddy sediments of the Flood that were changed into rocks are all kinds of fossils of animals and plants. The question is, How were all these fossils formed? The evolutionists like to explain the formation of these fossils of animals and human beings as being caused by layers of silt and volcanic ash covering these fossil bones over a shorter or longer period of time. The *National Geographic* (November 1985, p. 582), shows a picture of three hyenas ready to devour the body of a dead man and

> the . . . skull . . . tumbles downstream in a flash flood and is blanketed by successive layers of silt, pebbles, and the ash from an erupting volcano. Gradually water soluble mineral turn bone into stone.

On p. 585, referring to the partial skeleton and skull called Lucy, they state that the fossil was long hidden by layers of sediment and volcanic ash.

Evolutionist Richard Leakey in his book, *People of the Lake,* p. 6, states regarding fossils,

[T]he bones may be rapidly entombed in fine silt, . . . There are three circumstances around the lake where these essential processes occur: first, at the lake shore itself where gentle lapping waves throw a coat of silt over bones lying in the shallows; second, in the beds of streams tumbling down to the lake's edge; and third, between these extremes, at the point where the stream nears the lake water, thus forcing it to drop its silt.

But *gentle* lapping waves throwing silt over bones lying in *shallows,* and beds of streams tumbling down day after day will never preserve a fossil. Gradual covering with sediments could never have preserved those fossils. Above all this explanation for the origin of fossils given by the *National Geographic* and Richard Leakey could not even begin to explain the thousands and millions of fossils found all over the world. In many cases thousands of fossils are found heaped together in one place.

The *National Geographic* (November 1985, p. 589) states:

Faulting, uplift, and erosion have exposed hundreds of meters of lake and river sediments and a wealth of fossils at various depths, laid down over millions of years. And interlayered with these sediments are numerous beds of volcanic ash from many eruptions over those same millions of years.

Change the millions of years to a few years and you have an accurate description of the activities of the Flood of Noah's day, when the mud and sediments from the rushing, devastating waters of that Flood were laid down, and when the volcanic ash of many volcanos erupted while "the fountains of the great deep were broken up."

The *Reader's Digest* (June, 1976, p. 123) makes the same mistake in the article "Where Did The Animals Go?" They write of species of animals that became extinct as late as 11,000 years ago:

What happened to these animals? Why did they vanish? This is one of the great mysteries of American natural history, and scientists are engaged in heated debate trying to sort out the explanations . . . Enormous herds of animals were wiped out; whole populations of birds were extinguished . . . Why did they disappear?

One answer given is that bands of nomadic hunters from Asia, as they increased in population, eventually killed them. Another answer is that changes of climate in the Ice Ages killed them because of drought, exposure and starvation about 12,000 years ago. Others come up with still other unproven theories. Although they come very close to the account of the Flood, these evolutionists claiming to be scientists, just cannot admit that a devastating flood could have wiped out many of these species or kinds. After all, the bones of animals that have been killed by hunters or drought or exposure or starvation, are not preserved and fossilized. They definitely would not be found in huge masses of fossilized bones.

In the *Reader's Digest* (August 1981) there is the same false reasoning. The bones of huge animals, Diprotodon, are found near Lake Callabonna in northeastern Australia. The last of these animals also disappeared about 10,000 years ago, according to their estimates. Scientific expeditions in 1893 and 1953 found as many as 1,000 complete skeletons of these animals. The article states: p.p. 170 & 174

> Though we don't know how these huge beasts met their fate, here is what might have happened. [Then they concoct a story of how a drought hit that region, and as these animals walked laboriously from rich grasslands to the water in the lake that was drying up from the drought, they died, "not from injury but from frustration and exhaustion". Two of the animals] became two faint humps on the cracked dry bed of Lake Callabonna . . . The mud and the hot sun preserved them where they fell thousands of years ago.

In the hot sun those carcasses would have decayed and disappeared in a very short time. If the animals traveled from rich grasslands to that lake for water, they certainly would have found water holes somewhere nearer in that rich grassland. Who are they printing these fables for? Certainly not for most of the common people, who according to polls do not believe these evolutionary stories.

No! No! No! There is only one scientific explanation for those numerous fossils heaped together all over the world. An animal left exposed after death will usually be quickly eaten by other animals, or it will decay very quickly, and the bones will crumble to dust in a few years. We have an example of the buffalo in the early history of our midwestern states. There were millions of them, slaughtered ruthlessly, with the carcasses left on the ground. Today there is no evidence of them. To preserve a fossil the creature must be buried quickly, completely, deeply, compacted and shortly turned into stone. The most effective way of preserving the remains of a creature is burial in moist sediment, layer upon layer, as happened to those millions and millions of creatures at the time of the Flood. All that Richard Leakey and other fossil hunters in Africa are finding are the remains of animals, plants and humans that were covered with sediments at the time of the Flood.

4.   WHERE FOSSILS ARE FOUND

To repeat, fossils are found all over the world, even on high mountain tops. One place where fossils are especially prevalent is in the Rift Valley, which extends 5,000 miles, all the way from Syria down through the Jordan Valley, through the Red Sea area down through eastern Africa to the southern part of the continent. In the Rift Valley the earth's crust was wrenched most likely during the upheavals of the earth's crust at the time of the Flood. Toward the southern end of the Rift Valley lies Olduvai Gorge in Tanzania. Rifting or splitting of the earth's crust created a series of cliffs there over which swift rivers cascade, gouging down through accumulated layers of sedimentary rocks. This created the 25-mile-long Olduvai Gorge, a miniature Grand Canyon. Here many fossils of apes, of other animals, and of humans have become exposed. It is here that Louis and Mary Leakey and now their son, Richard, have found many fossils. Regarding all of this area, Richard Leakey wrote in his book *People of the Lake,* page 7,

> The deposits of an ancient, and now vanished, lake at Olduvai, in Tanzania, are three hundred feet thick; fortunately a recent seasonal river has sliced its way down through them, exposing in the twenty-five-mile-long gorge a vertical record of the past.

5.   ONLY A FEW HUMAN FOSSILS FOUND

Yet only a few fossils of mankind have been discovered. Fossil hunters have searched where many animal bones have been buried, but very few bones of humans have been found. It seems that it was God's deliberate purpose to destroy the pre-Flood world, to leave very few remains of those early people. He did the same with the Ark of the Covenant in the Old Testament and with Christ's cross in the New Testament. Richard Leakey himself remarked that all the remains of our first forefathers could be spread out on a couple of tables. Truly in destroying the pre-Flood earth and in reshaping and relandscaping it and burying the past civilization in thousands of feet of muddy sediments, God's intention was to destroy all remains of that highly civilized world. Those that are found resemble modern man.

6.   THE FORMER BEAUTIFUL, PLEASANT WORLD

Again, the whole earth, not just part of it, must have been a truly beautiful, pleasant world. Fossil ferns, palms, magnolias, cinnamons, breadfruits and other plants which grow only in India and China today and in other mid-earth climates, have been found in Alaska 160 miles north of the Arctic Circle. Fossils like this have also been found in Siberia, Greenland and Spitzbergen. Fossilized trees have been found in great numbers in northern lands where no trees grow today.

7.   FOSSILS FOUND IN UNUSUAL AREAS OF THE WORLD

Fossils of animals have been found in areas of the earth where such animals are not found or exist today. Alexander Catcott wrote, in 1761, *A Treatise on the Deluge:*

> Elephants, native of Asia and Africa buried in the midst of England; crocodiles, natives of the Nile, in the heart of Germany . . . entire skeletons of whales in the most inland regions of England; trees of vast dimensions, with their roots and their tops and some also with leaves and fruit, at the bottom of mines.

Benjamin Silliman, head of the Geology Department of Yale University wrote (1829) in his *Geological Lectures:*

> Respecting the Deluge, there can be but one opinion: geology fully confirms the Scriptural history of the event . . . Whales, sharks, and other fishes, crocodiles and amphibians, the mammoth and the extinct elephant, the rhinoceros, the hippopotamus, hyenas, tigers, deer, horses, the various species of the bovine family and a multitude more, are found buried in diluvium at a greater or less depth; and in most instances under circumstances indicating that they were buried by the same catastrophe which destroyed them; namely a sudden and violent deluge. [He continues,] A skeleton of a whale lay on top of the mountain Sanhorn on the coast of the northern sea. [This mountain] is three thousand feet high and there is no cause that could have conveyed the whale to that elevation except a deluge rising to that height.

In many cases what the evolutionists call the older fossils are found lying on the top of younger fossils.

VIII. THE ORIGIN OF THE MATERIALS OF THIS EARTH

1. COAL

Among the strata of the surface of the earth is coal. What is coal and from where did it come? Like all the sedimentary rock found in the earth in layers, so also coal is a rock, laid down in layers. In most cases it appears that coal came from masses of plants and trees that grew vigorously, abundantly and profusely before the Flood, even in the Arctic and Antarctic regions, where plants cannot grow today. From ferns, trees and other plants turned into coal, today it appears that much of the coal was formed from such plant life. The plant fossils found in the coal in both polar regions are the same as those found near the equator. There seems to have been only one climate prevailing from the poles to the equator. Billions of tons of coal have been discovered all over the world, in the United States, Nova Scotia, Russia, China, Australia, Europe and in North and South Pole regions.

It is estimated that it takes five to fourteen feet of rotted or compressed plants to produce one foot of coal. But there are some coal beds that are several hundred feet thick. If the thickness is only 300 feet and only five feet of plants are figured, it would have taken a deposit 1,500 feet thick to produce that much coal. Evolutionist Richard Carrington in his book, *The Story of Our Earth*, claims that coal was formed from peat, and in eastern Pennsylvania there are anthracite beds 40 feet thick. But how could enough peat be piled up to make hard coal 40 feet thick, yet be so far underground? While the earth has places where a number of layers of coal are sandwiched between layers of sandstone or limestone (which could easily have happened at the time of the Flood) it is however very possible that the Creator who created all other materials found in the earth also created much or most of the coal found today.

The coal that was formed by the Flood must have been formed very rapidly. In the coal beds, fossil trees have been found standing at an angle, and even upside down, and some trees up to 100 feet tall have been found going through several layers of coal. Coal seams have been found with boulders buried in the coal. This evidently was due to the violent turbulence of the Flood washing all kinds of different materials together at various times during the Flood. The boulders could have been transported in the roots of trees as they floated to their final resting place. One current of the Flood would drop a layer of non-organic sediments on one area of the earth, then another current would drop a layer of plant life on the same place to form alternating layers, and all this would have occurred in a very few days in violent turbulence. The evolutionary theory of uniformitarianism (that all things happened and developed very gradually over millions of years) is debunked by what the geology of the earth plainly teaches us.

In this connection, one theory of coal formation must be mentioned that might give the evolutionists a little hope for their theory of gradual development. This theory is that swamp forests and jungles grew for thousands of years in one spot, dying and accumulating plant debris, until the region slowly sank below the sea and became covered with thick layers of sediment. Later the region rose again, raised another forest and then slowly sank again. But the evolutionary geologist, William L. Stokes, does not agree with this theory. He stated in his book, *Essentials of Earth History*, p. 216.

> Even though all the biological, geographic, and climatic factors were favorable, coal still could not form unless the debris was submerged and buried in sediments.

He meant that this had to be done suddenly and quickly, because a slow covering would not do it, just as it does not do it today in the jungles. *There* plant life today dies, decays and rots into humus. Stokes also wrote, p. 216,

> Nor could the land have alternately risen and sunk, because a bed of coal to be preserved must remain *permanently* buried and, of course, could not survive exposure to erosion.

Above all, this theory of coal formation would not explain the coal found all over the world, especially in the polar regions.

Also the surface of the earth did not rise and fall sharply as evolutionists claim, except in the time of the Flood when "the fountains of the great deep were *broken* up." Except for the little movement the earth may make today in earthquakes or otherwise, the surface of the earth is as rigid and solid as a piece of steel. Outside of the probability that God created most of the coal directly, there is only one other possible way for coal beds to be formed. Great masses of plant life had to be torn up, floated together, deposited in one area and then rapidly covered with layers of muddy sediments to turn the mass of plant life into coal.

Theodore Handrich in his book *The Creation: Facts, Theories and Faith* has an interesting conclusion to his twenty pages in regard to "The Geology of Coal." p. 185:

After Christ had fed 5,000 men, He sent His disciples around to gather the fragments that had been dropped. We see this same character trait in God, the abhorrence of waste, in nature. We see it in coal and oil deposits. God salvaged something from a world that was destroyed because it had become corrupt. We wonder whether God will again salvage something of this physical earth when He creates the new heaven and the new earth.

2.   OIL — PETROLEUM

Hand in hand with the formation of coal goes the formation of oil and petroleum. The origin of oil has puzzled geologists ever since it was first discovered. The questions have been: Where did it come from, Why is it found so very deep in the earth (25,430 feet deep in one well in Texas) and How did it get there? *The World Book Encyclopedia* says, volume P, p. 297, "No one really knows how petroleum was formed." Dr. William Russel in his *Principles of Petroleum Geology* (1951), p. 163 states,

> Unfortunately, the results of the work on the origin of petroleum have in general been disappointingly vague and for the most part of practically no value in the search for oil.

Yet many geologists believe that oil is the converted remains of millions of trapped and buried marine animals. But the next question is: Where could so much marine or even vegetable life have existed in such immense amounts to supply the source of such enormous oil supplies throughout the world, even in the polar regions? What could have destroyed all these creatures? Why did they not decay immediately after dying as marine life usually does? What could have changed their bodies into petroleum?

If marine life supplied the material for the origin of oil, there appears to be only one answer, and that is, by the Flood. With the entire world (air, sea and land) in violent turmoil especially with worldwide earthquakes and volcanic eruptions in the sea and on land, immense masses of sea creatures could have been killed by the explosions and have been instantly buried under the resulting sedimentation. This puts the origin of at least some of the oil on the same basis as the origin of coal. We know that oil can be produced from garbage or corn or other vegetation. A ton of garbage has been converted into a barrel of oil in twenty minutes. So why claim only marine animals as the source of the oil?

However, other geologists question the theory of the organic origin of oil and gas. Because of its paraffin base, oil appears to them to be an inorganic compound. They believe there are no signs that living organisms had anything to do with its formation. To these geologists it seems impossible that marine life or plant life could have collected into pools totaling billions and billions of gallons.

3.   NATURAL GAS

The origin of gas is also a puzzle to geologists. *The World Book Encyclopedia* states, Volume G under "Gas" p. 53:

> The exact origin of natural gas is not known. But most geologists and chemists agree that it was created through chemical action on tiny plants and animals that lived, died and were buried ages ago. Billions upon billions of these little plants and animals lived on the shores of water that covered a large part of the earth's surface. They fed upon little except water and sunshine. Great numbers of these tiny living things sank and were washed into the ancient seas. In time they formed an ooze hundreds of feet deep called organic sediment. Explosions and upheavals on the surface of the young earth brought down layers of rock, which covered the ooze. Under heat and pressure the organic sediment fermented and decayed, forming gas and oil.

However, the weakness of this theory is that the ooze would have decayed and disappeared very quickly and long before it was put under any heat and pressure.

Other geologists maintain that the source of natural gas must have been deep within the earth, where fiery activity could create it inorganically. From this deep source, it could then creep up into the sedimentary rocks and hollows. The *Reader's Digest* in its April 1981 issue had an article:

> "Bonanza. America Strikes Gas". [Page 67 states:] Down to 15,000 feet, the heat and pressure created both oil and gas. But below this level the heat generally became so intense that the oil was broken down and converted into gas. The result is that the earth contains two very different zones of hydrocarbon fields: a relatively shallow one with both oil and gas; and a deep one that contains only gas [p. 68] . . . In 1978, near the border between Wyoming and Utah, using the new seismic techniques, drillers suddenly began to hit field after field of deep gas in a section of the Rockies that had always been known as a "well-digger's graveyard" [69]. . . In 1979 geologists from Cornell University and the [U.S. Geological Survey] looked beneath what had been

believed to be the East Coast's "basement rock," below which fossil fuels can't exist, and made one of the most important discoveries of this generation: a huge continental-collision area virtually identical to the one in the Rocky Mountains, [where gas could exist].

All this may agree with the opinion that another Cornell University professor has. The December 13, 1983, *Wall Street Journal* had an article entitled

"Astronomer believes oil and gas deposits are as old as the earth". Thomas Gold's idea suggests vast, but deep reserves . . . Scientists long have assumed that the world's oil and gas formed from decayed plants, dinosaurs and other biological matter. But Thomas Gold, a Cornell University astronomer, known for his moon research, lately has been challenging the accepted wisdom, and some people are beginning to take him seriously. As Mr. Gold would have it, most of the earth's methane, or natural gas, is abiogenic. That is, it is of nonbiological origin. It is derived, he says, from hydrocarbons that were present at the planet's creation and that became lodged 100 miles beneath the surface of primordial goo. Long before any brontosaurus lived, he adds, methane was slowly steaming up toward the surface, some of the gas converted to oil. But the theory is so radical that Mr. Gold is barely on speaking terms with the conventional geologists at major oil companies. Mr. Gold agrees that some natural gas was formed from decayed organic matter, but the majority, he says, is abiogenic.

This leads us to the real source of almost all the coal, oil and gas. Although it is very likely that some of the coal was formed during the Flood when the masses of trees and other vegetation were swept together in the Flood and buried and turned into coal; and although some of the oil was formed by either the fish or animals or plants being buried in heaps, the real source no doubt was God who created not only all the other minerals and buried them in the earth for the use of mankind but also much or most of the coal, oil and gas. If, as Mr. Gold claims, the natural gas comes from the depth of the earth from non-living matter, God evidently was the Creator of all this as He is the Creator of all things.

One thing more must be stated in regard to the origin of petroleum. There was petroleum before the Flood, for Noah caulked the ark with pitch or bitumen which is a product of petroleum. So not all petroleum came from buried dead fish, etc. Again, the answer is that God placed petroleum into the earth as he did many other minerals for the benefit of mankind, as He also placed the sun, moon and stars in the heavens for the benefit of man.

4.   ELEMENTS AND MINERALS

We come to the elements and minerals God created. From where did they come? What is their origin? The *World Book* in writing about either of the two, does not try to explain their origin. Gold, silver, iron, copper, tin, lead, nickel, sulfur, etc. are found on every continent. How all the different elements and minerals were formed no one really knows. R. S. Walker and W. J. Walker in their book *Origin and Nature of Ore Deposits* (1956) state, p. viii:

> There is so much difference of opinion among geologists regarding the mode of formation of ore deposits, that any attempt at setting forth conclusions regarding the subject is bound to conflict with other opinions.

The origin of minerals is even less understood than that of petroleum. Some believe that minerals originated from the flow of volcanic lava magma. But there is no evidence that any minerals are being formed in this manner today.

Another explanation is that at the time of the Flood not only were soil and rock dissolved or broken up into smaller pieces like sand, but also the minerals were somehow broken up, and when the flood sedimentation was laid down, the minerals also were laid down in seams and nuggets, so today they are found in the sedimentary rocks of the earth.

Iron is one of the most common minerals making up about five percent of the earth's crust. *The World Book Encyclopedia* states volume "I", p. 345 that some scientists believe that

> Great volcanoes spouted dust into the air and this fell into streams and rivers. The chemical-laden waters dissolved iron out of the rocks with which they came in contact. These iron-bearing waters flowed into the oceans. Here the iron slowly fell to the bottom. Heat and pressure formed these beds into rocks.

Then earthquakes and glaciers played in. But all this does not add up because in writing about "rocks," the *World Book* states:

> Ore deposits may be close to the earth's surface, or thousands of feet underground. In some regions deposits of iron and copper ores make up entire mountains.

Potash has a similar story. According to the *Reader's Digest* (May 1964), a rich deposit of potash was found near Esterhazy, Saskatchewan—enough to fertilize all the earth's arable land for 500 years. The bed of potash is 3,000 feet down and is mined like coal. Why was all this found in one place like this? How did it get there and also in beds in New Mexico, Germany, France, Spain, Poland and Russia? No answer is given.

Gold, silver and diamonds are found in all depths of the earth. Gold has been found as deep as 13,500 feet in Africa. Africa has mined a million tons of gold ore. All kinds of theories have been given for the formation of gold. The *World Book* states under "Gold",

> Scientists believe that gold is deposited from gases and liquids rising from beneath the earth's surface. These gases and liquids travel toward the surface through cracks and faults in the crust.

But the question is, Why then is gold not found in many more places of the earth? The *Reader's Digest* (July 1967), explains the gold in Africa with this:

> One theory is that long ago it was an inland sea, fed by roaring rivers which chewed gold-containing pebbles out of the surrounding mountains and deposited them along the shores [etc.]

But where did this original gold come from?

The simplest, most logical and common sense answer for the origin of many different minerals and elements is that God created them when He created all the other diverse things of this earth and placed them in veins and lumps and mountains when He dispersed all things at the time of the Flood. The most factual answer for gold and all other minerals is given in Genesis 2:11-12 where, in creating the Garden of Eden, we are told: "The whole land of Havilah, where there is gold; And the gold of that land is good: there is bdellium and the onyx stone." Psalm 104:24 declares: "O LORD, how manifold are thy works! In wisdom hast thou made them all: the earth is *full of thy riches.*" Nehemiah 9:6 adds, "Thou, even thou, art the LORD alone; thou hast made heaven, the heaven of heavens, with all their host, the earth, *and all things that are therein,* the seas and all that is therein. [Emphasis Added]

IX.   THE ICE AGE AND ITS PROBLEMS

1.   THE ICE AGE

Hand in hand with the Flood goes another quite evident matter: the ice age. The first question is, "Was there an ice age?" Byron Nelson in his book, *The Deluge Story in Stone*, p. 135, would not commit himself to that issue, except to state,

> While the present writer is in no wise concerned to establish the fact, he is of the opinion that *following the Deluge* there was a period when snows piled up in enormous thick masses in certain parts of the world, especially in the northern hemisphere . . . Whether such an ice age did follow the Flood in the places where ice seems to have covered the earth in great sheets, i.e., in northern North America and northern Europe (missing Alaska and northern Siberia, the latter the coldest spot on earth) we cannot say. We believe it did.

Theodore Handrich in *The Creation: Facts, Theories and Faith*, refers to scientists in England and Canada who advanced arguments against it on scientific grounds. George Price in *Flood Geology* (1946) wrote:

> However, a much better and more probable view is that this drift (glacial materials) was brought into its present position by some violent action of the ocean, though floating ice in large masses may have had something to do with the work.

John Whitcomb and Henry Morris in *The Genesis Flood* wrote, p. 247f:

> Perhaps the difficulty, however, was that the evidences for the supposed "ice age" have been misunderstood. The most characteristic indicators of ice action are believed to be tillites and striations, . . . [I]t is evident that these and other assumed indicators of glacial action may also be produced by many agencies other than ice . . . The Permian glacial deposits, so-called, have been found in Africa, South America, Australia and India . . . How such a great ice-sheet could be found in such a location seems impossible to conceive.

Alfred Rehwinkel in *The Flood* wrote two extremely well-written chapters on the Glacial Theory, substantiated with numerous convincing arguments against the supposed glacial material used to advocate the ice ages. Rehwinkel explains these materials, in his chapter on "The Flood the Most Reasonable Solution for the Glacial Theory Phenomena." He states, p. 309:

2.   WHEN DID THE ICE AGE TAKE PLACE?

Although the *Reader's Digest* at times prints articles from the
[evo]lutionary point of view, it did make statements in the October, 1969,
[iss]ue that give facts that fit in close to the time of the Flood. On page
[6]:

> During the last great advance of the Ice Age, which ended
> about 8,000 [?] years ago, ice sheets covered nearly 30 percent of
> the earth's land surface. [On p. 28:] In ice 10,000 to 14,000 years
> old [in the Antarctic], the Americans found layers of volcanic ash,
> possibly deposited during some world-wide cataclysm. At about
> 850 feet, they recorded ice that had fallen as pure snow at the time
> of Christ, and in the topmost layers they identified "dirty" ice
> containing thermonuclear fallout from our Atomic Age.

"Volcanic ash — world-wide cataclysm" sounds very much like the
account of the Flood.

Rehwinkel, as usual, summarizes everything very well in *The Flood*
p. 308:

> the Bible says nothing for or against an ice age as taught by
> modern geologists. The fact that the Flood was accompanied or
> followed by a sudden and radical change in temperature and that
> a severe and rigorous climate settled upon a certain region of the
> earth has been stated at greater length in a previous chapter. And
> that this cold period lasted for a long time in the regions affected
> is quite possible and even probable. It is also granted that huge
> masses of ice may have floated down from the polar regions before
> the diluvial waters had fully subsided and the continents had taken
> their present form. Nor is it denied that this floating ice may have
> been an effective agent of the Flood waters in changing the
> topography of the earth . . . However, that is something quite
> different from the accepted glacial theory.

3.   ONE OR FOUR PERIODS OF ICE AGE?

Many glacialists believe there were four or more ice ages. But
the 1920s some began to realize that all these ice ages were m[ere?]
different phases of one ice age. Quite a number of scientists be[lieve?]
believe that the glaciers merely shrank in size at intervals, that
the ice continued for some time, and that the glacial period [was?]
a nature simple to analyze. The four ice ages have been
mostly from gravel terraces in the Alps. Michael Oard, r[?]

[P]ractically all recognized geologists today
theory as a fact, but such acceptance itself is not
need it disturb us . . . the conclusions of the g
arrived at only by inferences and not by actual de.
may be well for us to inquire whether the prop
actually solve the problems in question or whether
problems even more difficult than those it claims to s
he raises a number of questions:] "What caused the ch
climate to bring about a world-wide glaciation?" [315]. .
never originate below an altitude of six thousand feet ev
Arctic region. [The ice of the ice age was supposed to have
south out of Canada, but on low, more or less level land;]
318] Ice, on a level surface, is a dead, immobile mass whic
be piled up to a considerable height, like so much rock or so
bales of hay, without causing the slightest movement . . . [p.
The pressure of thousands of feet of ice would be so enorm
and the friction of the molecules of ice so great that thousands
feet of ice would cause the bottom to melt at a rate more rapi
than it could accumulate on the top.

[Again p. 324] Glaciers move rocks downgrade, but moving rocks
upgrade is a different matter. The force that pushes glaciers on is
gravity but gravity moves only in one direction and that is
downward. There is no more inherent power in ice to move uphill
than there is in water to flow upgrade. [Then he wrote about a
gray boulder being lifted a mile high on Mt. Washington by a
glacier. He states p. 325] This is not science. This is faith, simple
faith, in a theory [regarding glaciers].

In the second chapter on glaciers he wrote, p. 319, of the immensely
destructive power of the Flood compared to the greatest floods of recent
history which must be multiplied ten thousand times ten thousand to
give a picture of that disaster which overtook the first world. Even in
these many times smaller floods of recent years houses, bridges, railroad
tracks and loaded freight cars were swept away with unbelievable force.
He states that the moraines, the so-called glacial drifts, the striated or
grooved rocks, the rounded boulders and the rocks moved from their
original areas can best be accounted for by the action of a flood such as
is described in the Bible. Again although a rock could hardly be lifted a
mile high, it could be carried by ice on that Flood, especially if that
mountain had not yet been raised up when "the fountains of the great
deep were broken up."

with the U.S. Weather Bureau, Montana, stated in an article on the ice age:

> The number of glaciations is still an open question. There are strong indications that there was only one ice age . . . as a consequence of the Genesis Flood.

The Genesis Flood by John Whitcomb and Henry Morris states, p.p. 295-6:

> [I]t is also true that it is equally difficult to account for the four stages on the basis of any of the other glacial theories that have been devised. The usual recourse is simply to attribute it all to fluctuations in solar radiation, but this is obviously entirely speculative . . . As a matter of fact, the reason that it is so difficult to account theoretically for the four glacial stages may be simply that they never existed. [p. 299] It is also possible that the ice sheets may have made numerous minor advances and retreats within a relatively short span of years.

4.   THE AREAS COVERED BY THE ICE

If the supposed glacial deposits would actually verify the extent of the assumed ice cap coverage, that cap would have covered 4,000,000 square miles of North America and 2,000,000 square miles of Europe and the western part of Siberia. The assumed ice mass was centered, not over the geographical north pole, where little sunshine falls, but approximately over the magnetic pole some 1,200 miles away. Because of this, northeastern Siberia, which is one of the coldest place on earth, was not covered. In North America, the ice is claimed to have covered all of Greenland, Canada, and the United States as far south as the Ohio and Missouri River, and the eastern part of Alaska. In Europe, the coverage is claimed to have been over Scandinavia and as far south as Berlin, Germany, the North and Baltic Seas, much of Great Britain, and the northwestern part of Siberia. Although the Antarctic is in essence a desert, because it gets less than two inches of snow a year, that too was deeply covered with thick ice and still is.

5.   EXPLANATIONS GIVEN FOR THICK ICE CAPS

The *Reader's Digest* (October 1969, p. 29) states: "What caused the last ice age? Scientists don't agree. All they are sure of is that several million years ago the earth began gradually to grow cold." Of course, the millions of years is part of the old evolution story. Then they give three theories: (1) the sun did not radiate enough heat at the time, (2) the cloud cover increased, (3) meteorite, volcanic or other dust helped lower the temperature. Another theory given is that the earth for some unknown reason at times changes its orbit, swinging out much further than usual from the sun, so the earth would at times receive less heat. According to Michael Oard, over 60 theories have been offered. Michael Oard is meteorologist in Montana.

A. C. Waters and A. Woodford, in *Principles of Geology*, p. 319, state:

Theory after theory have been suggested but all explain too little or too much. None can be considered satisfactory, at least in its present form.

Carrington states, in *The Story of Our Earth*, p. 177:

The most plausible suggestion is that these were due to variations in the amount of heat actually emitted by the sun, perhaps related to sun spot activity. Unfortunately, however, there is no proof that such variations have occurred.

The Genesis Flood, by H. Morris, states that no satisfactory glacial theory has yet been propounded, although numerous attempts have been made. However, as Norman Macbeth states in *Darwin Retried*, p. 113,

There is evidence that in the past there were changes of climate so violent and sudden as to merit the name *Klimasturz*, which can be translated as a plunge, tumble, crash or collapse of the climate.

This collapse of the climate could easily have taken place at the time of the Flood, as is very evident from the mammoths in Siberia, which I will refer to more fully further on, and which were overwhelmed by a sudden catastrophe, (Part 7 of this chapter). Theodore Handrich in *The Creation: Facts, Theories, and Faith*, p. 206, states that these mammoths:

had leaves and twigs in their stomachs, which do not grow in the regions where the carcasses have been found but in much warmer regions. Evidently, the region had a much warmer climate then than it now has, and this climate was changed very suddenly, as is indicated by the fact that the bodies of the mammoths were frozen solid before decomposition could set in . . . Whatever the immediate cause may have been, we know that the first cause was God.

Very likely the Flood, with the extreme cold that crashed suddenly upon the North and South Poles, and the presumed ice age, were one and the same catastrophe. While they were most likely simultaneous, they were different in the way they changed things on earth. The heavy rain that came down in sheets and buckets when the canopy collapsed could easily have frozen very suddenly as it hit the extremely cold temperature near the surface of the changed polar regions.

Another factor that could have created masses of ice is suggested by Sir Henry Howorth, president of the Archeological Institute of Great Britain. He thought that the supposed ice-sheet deposits could have been formed by a flood sweeping down from the north. His directions seem to be wrong. The massive floods in the south could have swept northward to the deep cold of the north. When the continents and mountains were raised up during the Flood, water could have poured over the frigid northlands in one great splash of water.

6.   EARTH'S AXIS TIPPED

Since God is the direct cause of all that took place in the Flood, and although the Bible account of the Flood does not give us all the details of everything that took place then, God could have performed other miracles to destroy the surface of the earth that then was, and also have created sudden intense cold, such as we have never heard of since. One of the unusual events could have been that the earth's axis was tipped, in order to create the present day unpredictable weather and also to create an intense cold in the polar regions since the time of the Flood. At that event much of the water in the polar regions could have frozen into solid ice.

For as long as we know, the earth's axis has not been perpendicular to the plane of its orbit around the sun, but has been inclined 23 $\frac{1}{2}$ degrees, and scientists have wondered when, why and how this strange arrangement came about. Prior to the Flood, the earth's axis of rotation was very likely perpendicular and a water vapor-canopy surrounded the earth. Because of this, the temperature could have been uniform all over the earth so that plant life and animals that today thrive only in warmer climates grew and lived in the polar regions, as is evident from the frozen animals and plants in Siberia. Today, however, it is different without that canopy over us. Without the canopy the temperature in the polar region drops rapidly below freezing. If the earth had no tilt and had a canopy over it, the temperature around the earth would be the same all year, without seasons. However, if the earth had both no tilt and no canopy, the polar regions would be continually very cold and the equator region hotter. If the tilt of the earth was much greater than the 23 $\frac{1}{2}$ degrees, the temperature extremes in winter would be much greater, and the heat in summer would be intolerable.

With this background one can easily imagine what could have happened in Siberia when those huge animals clad in fur died almost instantly with food remaining in their mouths, and in a very few minutes their bodies were frozen solid. With an earth tipped like that, the Flood waters as well as the canopy waters could have swept over them and the temperature could have dropped from 70 degrees above to 200 degrees below zero or colder almost instantly. Even in recent times temperatures in some mid-latitude areas have dropped 100 degrees in a very few minutes; but at the time of the Flood and above all if and when the earth was tipped 23 ½ degrees, the weather change could have been the most violent and extreme this earth has ever seen, as devastating as all the other catastrophic events and turmoils of the the Flood. The cold from outer space could have plunged in.

7.   FROZEN MAMMOTHS IN SIBERIA AND ALASKA

In connection with the Flood and ice ages belongs another topic: the frozen mammoths in Siberia and Alaska and the tropical vegetation of the polar regions. In Siberia and Alaska, mammoths, which were huge animals larger than present-day elephants, and many other animals, such as lions, horses, bears, bison, moose, wolves, rhinoceroses were found frozen suddenly and buried. The mammoths were 13 feet high and weighed 30 to 60 tons, with a hairy skin and long tusks weighing up to 200 pounds. The fossil fields of these animals have been worked for 200 years and the fossils are as vast as a coal field. The tusks have been used for centuries for ivory. The frozen carcasses have been found in an area covering thousands of miles of Alaska, northern Europe and Siberia.

It has been estimated that 5,000,000 or more of these animals perished suddenly in Siberia. Considering all the other animals, the number of animals that died in almost a flash must have been stupendous. The ivory tusks of these mammoths have been found in many places, some sticking out of the ground after recent flood waters in the area have washed away more ground. The ground in some places is almost entirely filled with the bones of these animals. Also hills are filled with them. In one mine 20,000 pairs of tusks were mined.

The flesh and bones of these animals had not been eaten by flesh eating animals of the time, but instead the flesh eating animals were buried with the other frozen animals. Death came so quickly that the luxuriant vegetation that they were feasting on in a tropical climate in the north at that time was not digested in their stomachs. Identifiable grasses, bluebells, buttercups, wild beans and other forage were found in their mouths and stomachs. The food they had available was so luxuriant that their flesh was marbled with fat. In some places like Greenland figs and magnolias had grown where only ice is found today.

Some of these mammoths have been found standing in an upright position as if they had sunk down where they were standing, surrounded and covered with muck and sedimentation. The carcasses of some of these animals have been thawed out to feed to sled dogs in Siberia and Alaska. Mammoth steaks have been featured on menus in restaurants in Fairbanks.

What could have killed and quick-frozen these huge animals and others with such suddenness before they could even swallow or lie down? An extremely intense cold must have swooped down upon them instantly like lightning; and this happened over thousands of square miles all over the north polar region. Sled dogs have been out in blizzard conditions for many hours and even for days in temperatures below minus 80 degrees without freezing. And blizzard winds are much more severe than quiet air. But here we had huge animals clothed in fur, and they froze to death before they could swallow. They must have been overtaken with an instant drop of temperature from 70 or more degrees above zero to 200 or more degrees below zero over thousands of square miles. It seems as if God wanted to leave a frozen memorial to condemn the foolish belief that everything has always happened slowly, gradually and uniformly on the earth. It is just more evidence of God's anger at the time of that Flood.

Although it is quite evident from the Flood why, how and when all these creatures suddenly perished, yet the evolutionists just cannot fit these frozen animals into their false theory of everything happening on the earth slowly, gradually and uniformly. Ivan Sanderson, in his "Riddle of the Frozen Giants," *Saturday Evening Post*, (January 16, 1960, p. 42), stated:

> The greatest riddle, however, is when, why and how did all these assorted creatures, and in such absolutely countless numbers, get killed, mashed up and frozen into this horrific indecency?

Another evolutionist, Charles Lyell, realized that these suddenly-perished animals went counter to the theory of uniformitarianism, so he tried to explain it by suggesting that they were caught swimming during a sudden cold snap. But that does not explain millions of them dying suddenly over thousands of square miles. Darwin also knew about these animals and admitted he could not find an answer for their sudden death in such vast numbers.

Robert Silverberg in his *Clocks for the Ages*, (1971) stated, p. 93:

This dramatic fall in temperature, the cause of which remains unknown, did not at once bring continent-wide sheets of ice. A period of thousands or even hundreds of thousands of years elapsed while the new climate of cold winters and cool summers was building up accumulations of snow.

But this theory does not explain the almost instantaneous death of millions of animals in Siberia and Alaska.

One evolutionist, however, did give an upright, common sense explanation. It was Sir Henry Howorth, president of the Archeological Institute of Great Britain, who wrote, in 1887, the book: *The Mammoths and the Flood*. He was a man who did not try to defend the Bible, but rather was very much hostile to it. By means of these mammoths he tried to prove:

In the first place that a very great cataclysm or catastrophe occurred, by which that animal, with its companions were overwhelmed over a very large part of the earth's surface. Secondly that this catastrophe involved a widespread flood of water which not only killed the animals, but also buried them under continuous beds of loam and gravel. Thirdly, that the same catastrophe was accompanied by a very great and sudden change of climate in Siberia, by which the animals which had previously lived in fairly temperate conditions were frozen in their flesh under the ground and have remained frozen ever since.

By providing all this, Sir Howorth did not try to prove that the Bible was true, as it actually is; but he definitely did prove loud and clear that the theory of uniformity that the evolutionists have made a part of their creed is *false*. Yes the mammoths and other suddenly-destroyed animals destroy the evolutionary theory that everything on earth has always occurred in a slow, gradual, uniform way. So here again geology, like archeology, destroys the theory of evolution.

In connection with these mammoths, one more creature should be mentioned. In the July, 1974, *Reader's Digest*, p. 121 are listed "Natures Seven Greatest Wonders." One of them is Baikal: Siberia's Giant Lake. It is a mile deep and has as much fresh water as all of our U.S. Great Lakes put together. In this lake are 40,000 seals. The *Reader's Digest* asks:

How did seals get there, 1,000 miles from salt water? One can only speculate that they must have been trapped when prehistoric Baikal was in some way connected with the Arctic Ocean.

However the turmoil and upheaval at the time of the Flood could easily explain also this.

8.   VARVES

In connection with the possible ice age, the varves on lake bottoms should be considered. "Varves" is a Swedish term for layers of sediments laid down on the bottom of glacial lakes. The source of the sediments is the sand, clay and gravel formed from the grinding action of the glaciers. Because it has an opaque, cloudy look, it has been nicknamed "glaciers milk." In the springtime the coarser grains of this sediment settled first. During the summer and fall and winter the rest settled to the bottom. Each varve has two sections, a dark one that settles in spring and a lighter one that settles later. On the basis of this information, the Swedish geologist, Baron de Geer and others have computed the ages of the glaciers and earth from the number of varves. On the basis of this method, the age of the glaciers had been figured as 8,000 to 15,000 years old.

But this method of reckoning ages and times was not as simple as all that. Even before de Geer and others finished their work, there was serious technical criticism of this method and of the over-simplifying of counting only one varve for each year. There could be days and weeks when the weather was warm or mild when not only the glaciers but also snow melted. Then a cold front could move in and there would be no thawing for days or even weeks. Then more thawing could follow. In this way a number of varves could be deposited at least in some summers. This could have been true especially right after the Flood and when the frozen ice covered the northlands. In that highly turbulent and unsettled weather after the Flood a number of layers of varves could have been laid down in quick succession, especially when the water may have still been in the process of "going and returning" from off the earth, as the word "continually" in Genesis 8:3 has also been translated. Other factors could also cause extra layers of sediments each year, such as flooding during the summer. In general, the varve method of reckoning time and ages has been questioned and rejected by numerous geologists.

X.   THE PERIOD AFTER THE FLOOD

1.   THE EARTH AFTER THE FLOOD

Taking into consideration all the turmoil that took place on this earth, during and shortly after the Flood, what was the earth like after the Flood? One thing is very certain. The world that emerged after the Flood waters receded bore little resemblance to the beautiful, pleasant, fruitful earth that had existed before. It was as II Peter 3:6 states, "The world *that then was*, being overflowed with water, *perished*." The immense amount of rain that poured down upon the earth in sheets from the canopy of moisture above, the wild destructive winds, tornadoes, cyclones and hurricanes, the temperature dropping 200 degrees or more almost instantly in the north, the fountains of the great deep being broken up, masses of land and mountains rising up, volcanoes and earthquakes shaking the whole earth, destructive tsunamis or tidal waves of enormous heights racing at high speeds over the waters of the earth, with all the fruitful soil of the earth intermixed with the dissolved and broken up rocks and other material—all this laid down layers of new sediments one and two or more miles deep. All this also created a totally new earth for the surviving inhabitants of this earth.

The rich virgin soil that existed before the Flood most likely was lost forever. When Noah and his sons and their wives came off the ark, they faced an entirely new world. Just as people from Europe, when they immigrated to new places in the United States, gave the names of old European localities to their new American cities, so Noah and his descendants no doubt gave old names that they had known from the pre-Flood world to the new places.

Most likely when God originally at creation separated the waters on earth and let dry land appear, the land area before the Flood was much greater than it is now. The gentle and more even surface of the earth before the Flood was changed after the Flood with higher elevations, great mountain-chains, and deeper ocean basins for the water fallen from the canopy. Much of the present sea bottom, especially the continental shelves around the continents, was once dry land.

The lush growth of bountiful, enjoyable fruits, nuts, berries and easy-to-obtain vegetables was all gone. The forests and the marvelous civilizations that had existed were no more. Rugged mountains and rushing rivers that were hard to cross faced people wherever they wanted to go. It seemed that they had been taken to another planet.

Not only was the earth different. The climate also had changed immensely. No longer did they have mild, pleasant spring-like weather with a protective canopy over them both to protect them and to pleasantly help water the earth. They had to face an entirely different atmosphere with heat and cold and violent, stormy weather. High and low pressure systems moved along by jet streams gave them constant changes in unknown weather conditions from one day to the next. With the protective canopy gone they could see their lives shortened, and also the lives of their children and descendants, and of the animals. Very likely, the plant life was also shortened.

What must have happened to all the water that once was in the canopy above, when God at creation "divided the waters which were under the firmament from the waters which were above the firmament"? Gensis 1:7 These waters were hardly lifted back into the heavens, for they are no longer there now. Very likely, when God lifted the land masses and formed the mountain ranges, He at the same time lowered some of the land to create larger basins for all the Flood waters.

All this agrees with Psalm 104:5-8: "Who laid the foundations of the earth, that it should not be removed for ever. Thou coverest it with the deep as with a garment: the waters stood above the mountains. At thy rebuke they fled; at the voice of thy thunder they hasted away." A more literal translation of verse 8 reads: "The mountains ascend, the valleys descend unto the place which Thou has founded for them." Truly, Noah and his descendants were living in a different world.

2.   THE PEOPLE AFTER THE FLOOD

What were the people like after the Flood? No doubt they were highly knowledgeable and were advanced technically. Rene Noorbergen, 1977, in his book, *Secrets of Lost Races*, thought that a few survivors like Noah and his family could hardly retain the technical knowledge that existed before the Flood. He wrote, p. 26,

> [W]e can be certain that it would have been impossible for this small group of [8] bewildered survivors to reproduce all of the aspects of the technological environment that were known to the antediluvian civilization. A technological society is dependent of course upon a large population for its maintenance . . . Consequently the degree of civilization that the surviving human family was able to reestablish in the post-Flood era was severely reduced . . .

However, this is not necessarily true, for Noah and his sons during all those years that they were building that large three-story ark, no doubt acquired additional technical skills in many different fields which they could readily teach their descendants. If they had hired contractors they no doubt learned many skills from them.

We are told that Noah lived 350 years after the Flood, and Genesis 10:1-4 already lists grandsons and great-grandsons of Noah. No doubt these and other descendants of the great-grandsons learned many of the technical skills that Noah and his sons carried over from the pre-Flood days. From these arose the highly skilled and advanced Egyptians, Sumerians and other nations. We already saw what an extremely advanced civilization the Egyptians had in order to build the pyramids and other architectural monuments. In fact, verses 8 to 10 of that same tenth chapter of Genesis mentions Ham, his son, Cush, and Cush's son, Nimrod, "the mighty hunter before the LORD And the beginning of his kingdom was Babel, . . . in the land of Shinar." Babel and Shinar and Nineveh take us to the advanced people of Sumer and Babylonia.

The names of some generations may have been omitted as happened in other cases in the genealogies of the Old Testament; but at least we can see that the technical knowledge that Noah and his sons had was transferred to the generations that followed after them. Abraham belonged to the tenth generation after the Flood. Because people were still living several centuries, and Noah himself lived 350 years following the Flood, several generations overlapped each other so the knowledge that Noah and his sons had could be transmitted to a number of generations onward by certain of the forefathers. These people also transmitted the story of the Flood to future generations although some of the future nations and tribes after the Tower of Babel transmitted garbled versions of the flood which were transmitted from parents to their descendants.

Not only did these people transmit the account of the Flood but they also transmitted a knowledge of the history before the Flood. Although the descendants of Abraham, the Hebrews, had the divinely inspired account of the history of mankind from the days of Adam and Eve, the Sumerians also had a somewhat garbled knowledge of those pre-Flood days. A few miles north of Abraham's home city of Ur in Babylonia, the Weld-Blundell Expedition discovered the Weld Prism, which contains a history written by a man named Nur-Ninsubur about 2,100 B.C. On this prism are listed the names of ten kings who lived before the Flood (no doubt referring to the ten pre-Flood patriarchs of the Bible). Regarding this man Nur-Ninsubur, Rene Noorbergen, in his book *Secrets of Lost Races* states, p. 26:

In his account he records the list of ten pre-Flood kings and ends his writing with the sad words, "and the Flood overthrew the land." The Sumerians and later the Babylonians and Assyrians further recognized the pre-Flood era as the source of superior literature. One Babylonian king recorded that "he loved to read the writings of the age before the Flood." Assurbanipal, who founded the great library of Nineveh, also referred to the great "inscription of the time before the Flood." It must be remembered that the reason the pre- and post-Flood civilizations advanced at a more rapid rate than our own today is that they were using their brains to their fullest capacity, whereas we, according to the physiologists, are using only one-sixth of ours.

If Noah and his sons, possibly with contractors, built that large ark, they and their descendants could build boats to cross the Atlantic, at least between Africa and South America. The Mayas in Guatemala spoke of the first men there possessing great knowledge.

While people before the Flood lived up to 950 years, the people after the Flood began to live much shorter lives, even though Noah still lived 350 years after the Flood. Very likely the canopy of water above the firmament helped filter out some of the harmful rays of the sun, which could be shortening today's length of life.

Another factor must be considered. This is in regard to the number of years women could bear children. It could have been many years or many decades more than the present age of about 50 years. For that reason there could have been billions of people before the Flood; and the numbers could also have increased into nations within a short time after the Flood. Genesis 10:32 states:

These are the families of the sons of Noah, after their generations, in their *nations*; and by these were the *nations* divided in the earth after the flood. [Emphasis Added]

3. THE TOWER OF BABEL

Immediately after Genesis 10:32 quoted above, comes the account of the Tower of Babel, Genesis 11:1-2:

And the whole earth was of one language, and of one speech. And it came to pass, as they journeyed from the east, that they found a plain in the land of Shinar and they dwelt there.

Shinar is the land that Nimrod, the great grandson of Noah, had built as a kingdom, Genesis 10:10. Historically, Shinar is connected with Babylon.

4.   THE LENGTH OF TIME BETWEEN THE FLOOD AND THE TOWER OF BABEL

Because the names of some of the patriarchs between the days of Noah and the Tower of Babel may be missing from the genealogies of Genesis 10 and 11, the length of time between the Flood and the Tower of Babel is uncertain. Most likely, the time span was from 150 to 350 years. On the basis of 2167 B.C. being the year for the birth of Abraham, it has been calculated that the Flood occurred about 2460 B.C. The Tower of Babel could have occurred 150 to 350 years after the Flood. But from other events recorded in the Bible, Babel and the Flood could have occurred some centuries earlier than that.

5.   THE PEOPLE AND THEIR SKILLS BETWEEN THE FLOOD AND THE TOWER OF BABEL

After the Flood people began to multiply again in obedience to God's command, "Be fruitful and multiply and replenish the earth." The skills and abilities (especially in construction) that were carried over from the pre-Flood people by Noah and his sons soon became evident in their building of cities and kingdoms. Not only could these people read and write; they had a knowledge of mathematics, construction, and engineering, as is evident from the Tower of Babel and their immense ziggurats or temples, built in the form of terraced pyramids.

These people wasted no time repopulating the earth and carrying on commerce and forming kingdoms. They evidently were much like the Germans who from about 1810 were granted land in the empty space of the Ukraine after the Russians drove out the Turks. By the third generation, in 1880, the area was so thickly populated that many young families took the first chance they had to move to America. The native Russians, watching these constructive Germans, said, "This is the way the Germans do it."

But only a few generations after the Flood the arrogance, rebellion, godlessness and God-defiance that prevailed in the days before the Flood became prevalent again especially when they planned to build a tower leading unto heaven. Perhaps they fashioned the tower like the ziggurats which the history books of our schools and libraries show in their histories of that time. They said, "Let us build us a city and a tower, whose top may reach unto heaven; and let us make us a name, lest we be scattered abroad upon the face of the whole earth" (Genesis 11:4). Very likely people were scattered throughout the world before the Flood. The purpose of building the tower was also to make "a name for themselves," to glorify and to deify man as men have done ever since the "children of men" in the days after Adam.

Instead of using the usual sun-dried bricks, they decided to make bricks that have been burned thoroughly, which would be able to better withstand the ravages of weather and time. And to hold the bricks together solidly they used slime or asphalt from the vicinity of Babylon.

However God, in His almighty power of creating speech, and also of changing the speech of people, disposed of all their arrogant plans. The saying is, Man proposes but God disposes. God confounded their language and confused their speech. This no doubt referred to families and tribes or nations, as they were called, which had descended from Shem, Ham and Japheth—and not to each individual person. Otherwise families could not have understood each other. Each family or tribe had its own tongue. Perhaps the miracle consisted of an inward process by which words connected with old associations of ideas were taken away from them, and each family or tribe was immediately given new and utterly different modes of expression. The confusion was so complete that the people could no longer understand one another, so that all working together was impossible. When they could no longer work together, they scattered by families, clans and tribes to all parts of the earth, and each group then began to develop its own distinct language, alphabet, writing, culture and civilization.

Today the arrogance of man (Homo sapiens, sapiens) is no different from what it was after creation, before the Flood, and before the Tower of Babel, and all through history. Anthony Feldman in his book *Space* (1980), p. 215, wrote about a star-devouring black hole:

If the theory is correct, the fate of the galaxy is sealed. It will only be a matter of time before the stars we now see in the night sky are consumed. Fortunately the time scale for such a catastrophe is very long—many billions of years—so before our own solar system is threatened, we may well have devised ways of escaping destruction perhaps by colonizing other galaxies out of a black hole reach.

See how "we" or "mankind" can get along without God. This was the attitude at the Tower of Babel and of the children of men.

6. EVOLUTIONISTS DO NOT KNOW THE ORIGIN OF LANGUAGES

Evolutionists cannot explain why people suddenly began speaking many different languages throughout the world. There are thousands of languages and dialects, and it is hard for a person today to learn another language. Evolutionists have tried to explain that man's speech has developed from the chatterings of apes and the cries, brays and grunts of other animals, and that it was only through a long process that the human race developed speech. But this is denied by men versed in languages. Noam Chomsky, a linguist, has stated that human language and animal cries and grunts are so different that they are not even comparable entities. Professor Max Mueller, a famous philologist, stated:

> There is one barrier which no one has yet ventured to touch, the barrier of language. Language is our Rubicon, and no brute will dare cross it . . . No process of natural selection will ever distill significant words out of the notes of birds and animals (from *Lessons on the Science of Language*, pp. 23, 240, 370.)

Another reason why language could not have risen from the jungle of animals is that the languages of primitive people are usually highly complex. The people on the southern point of South America, whom Darwin considered the lowest among human beings, and whose language was considered crude, had more than 30,000 words, or more than twice as many as Shakespeare used. The language of some tribes in Africa is more complex than the Greek. Ancient Greek and Latin are more complex than modern Greek and Latin. Evidently it took some time before the confused languages that arose at the Tower of Babel could be put into written words. No doubt they had to devise more different words to express their ideas and concepts.

7.   WRITING

After the language of mankind was confused at the Tower of Babel, and the different families and tribes began speaking their new languages, it took them, no doubt, some years to develop an alphabet and a system of writing for others to read.

But long before this, men had been writing down facts of history. Professor Bernard Ramm, in his book. *The Christian View of Science and Scripture*, states, p. 327, "In the fourth and fifth chapters of Genesis we have lists of names, ages of people, towns, agriculture, metallurgy, and music. This implies the ability to write, to count, to build, to farm, to smelt and to compose. Further, this was done by the immediate descendants of Adam."

If men could write before the Flood, they also could write after the Flood. During all that time, from the time of the Flood to the Tower of Babel, mankind had one language as Genesis 11:1 states, "And the whole earth was of one language and of one speech." Because language and writing very likely existed from the very creation of mankind, detailed genealogies of both the pre-Flood and the post-Flood patriarchs could be given to us with accuracy from the days of Adam onward to Noah and then from Noah onward. Such records could hardly have been kept without being written down, and a genealogical record was kept somewhere throughout the entire period. Very likely Noah took with him into the ark historical records of the patriarchs, which are summarized in Genesis. The reason there was no writing and no recorded history from before about 2500 to 3000 B.C. was that new languages arose after the Tower of Babel and old records were lost.

But then, as Zdenek Kupal, in *Man and His Universe* (1972), states writing began to appear all over the earth:

> The hieroglyphic signs of the ancient Egyptians, the cuneiform script used in the land of Sumer and Akkad, and the proto-Indian symbols (as yet undeciphered) found in Mohenjo-Daro of India were invented at about the same time and independently of each other.

Naturally, as the different families and tribes spread out over the earth they began to converse in the new languages with which God endowed each of them. Not too long thereafter they began to put their thoughts and speech into the writings they developed; and suddenly these began to appear all over the earth at about the same time. Writings have been found from about that time not only in Egypt, Sumer, Babylonia and India, but also in China, Japan, and among the Incas of Peru and the Mayas of Mexico's Yucatan Peninsula, and no doubt in Africa, Europe, Asia and other parts of the world.

8.   EVOLUTIONISTS LACK THE HISTORY BETWEEN CREATION AND ONE HUNDRED OR MORE YEARS AFTER THE TOWER OF BABEL

Beginning about 100 or more years after the Tower of Babel, the history books of the evolutionists begin with actual facts, dates, events, and names of people and not just guesses, assumptions and theories. They have no actual history of the time shortly after the Flood and surely not of the 1600 or more years before the Flood. They will never, by scientific methods or ordinary historical records, be able to trace the history of mankind with certainty beyond the times of the Tower of Babel, and surely not beyond the Flood. They know nothing of the Flood and of the names of people, tribes, and nations before the period of the confusion of tongues and scattering of the people. The only explanation, theory or guesses they can give is that over "assumed and presumed" millions of years mankind gradually developed until man finally started writing history.

Robert Wenke, in his book, *Patterns in Prehistory* (1980), p. 266, writes:

> For millions of years our ancestors had subsisted on the proceeds of hunting and gathering, yet within just a few thousand years between 10,000 and 3,500 years ago, domesticated plants and agricultural economies independently appeared in several different parts of the Old and New Worlds. What conditions elicited these parallel cultural responses, and why did these conditions exist only within this relatively short period of time?

If the evolutionists would not be so rebellious against God and His Bible and the history that is given there, and if they would not be so proud of themselves and man-worshiping, they would find the answer to their many unanswered questions.

The history that the Bible gives in regard to the origin of the universe and especially of mankind and civilization, is not based on guesses and theories, but on the actual names of people, and when they lived, how long they lived and what they did during the time the evolutionists like to call prehistory. No one has ever disproved the truth of this history, and no one has ever offered a factual history in place of it. Paul Welty, chairman, of the Asian Studies program — Northeastern Illinois State College in his book, *Man's Cultural Heritage — A World History* (1969), p. 6, makes the usual evolutionary attempt:

> About this time [3000 B.C.] man began to write and record his speculations, activities and laws, his experiments, his struggles and his hopes. He began what is properly called history. All of that almost immeasurable span of time before man wrote is called prehistory because no one recorded in writing what he had thought, done, felt and observed.

I must add: Except what the Bible tells us in going back another 1500 to 2000 years. Why not at least refer to this earlier historical record given in the Bible and why ignore it entirely? All known written records of mankind correspond with the several thousand years record given in the Bible, except that the Bible goes 1500 to 2000 years further back.

Paul Welty continues:

> We have the paintings of the Cro-Magnon man, and the fossils and products of other early man. We have learned much through

the marvelous detective work of our scholars who piece together a general picture from the few traces of themselves that our prehistoric ancestors left behind. Still, there are very few relics from the past, and our interpretations of them may be only partly true and even partly false. Without the written record, we do not know for sure.

WHAT A CONFESSION! But why do they not want to accept the history that the Bible gives of a few thousand years earlier, to the real beginning of things. There is a lot of real history given to us in the Christmas histories of Luke and Matthew, as well as in Genesis, which sometimes is passed over rather quickly or unread even by Christians. Luke, chapter 3, beginning with the 23rd verse says: "Jesus was . . . the son of Joseph, which was the son of Heli," etc. for about 60 generations, and then finally at the end of the chapter concludes with "which was the son of Shem, which was the son of Noah, Lamech, Methusealah, Enoch, Jared, Mahalalel, Cainan, Enos, which was the son of Seth, which was the son of Adam, which was the son [really, the created one] of God." *What better so-called pre-history history or true history can we and our children have!*

And oh! what a history or so-called prehistory do four great events of the early history of this earth and universe proclaim: The creation of the universe and of mankind, the Fall of man into rebellion against his Creator, the world-wide Flood and the confusion of tongues at the Tower of Babel. Looking at the immensity of the entire universe, at the clock-like precision of the solar system, at how the sun, the planets, and their moons drag each other along in perfect unison, and at the complexity of everything on the earth and especially of the human body, all this screams out loud and clear that there was an almighty *nonmaterial*, ever-existing Designer and Creator at the beginning of all things, who created out of nothing all the elements and the material things of this universe.

Further, the gradual degeneration and deterioration of all things on the earth proclaim that although the Designer and Creator originally created a complete and well-designed earth, something happened in the course of history to cause all things to decay and degenerate. This is evident from the second law of theromodyamics, which will be considered further on.

Then thousands of feet of sedimentation of the earth and the upheaval of mountain ranges proclaim as a historical fact that at one time in the history of the earth there were very violent floods and mountain upheavals and that this did not happen gradually, slowly and uniformly.

The sudden appearance of different civilizations all over the earth at about the same time, all speaking different languages, proclaims as a historical fact that mankind for some reason suddenly began to speak different languages and developed different cultures with different tribes, races and nations. There are today over 50 groups of different languages comprising about 6000 languages.

9.   THE FIRST CENTURIES AFTER THE TOWER OF BABEL — ALSO REGARDING CAVES AND THE NEANDERTHAL AND CRO-MAGNON PEOPLES

People after the Tower of Babel migrated to all parts of the world, and because they moved about in small groups, they scattered to places where food and shelter could easily be obtained, always moving onward and outward from Babel. Many very likely became mere hunters and food gatherers for some time. Although they most likely carried their own forms of shelter with them, they would at times live near the entrance of caves, until permanent housing could be devised out of the things at hand.

Caves have been used throughout history by mankind including some peoples of today, even when they are capable of making other shelters for themselves. In the Old Testament, Genesis 14:6, the Horites, whose name means cave-dwellers, lived in tents. The Edomites, Lot, David and Elijah also lived in caves briefly. There are people today in India, Veddahs, who live in caves, in the entrances close to light and air, in the rainy season and in grass huts otherwise.

Likewise even though those migrating people after the Tower of Babel knew about metals and fabrications from their forefathers, they used stones and flints wherever they could be found until metals could be discovered, and they gradually developed permanent settlements and communities. They learned to break flint in many different ways. How it was done is a mystery today. Knives were made from flint that were so sharp that they could butcher animals as fast as men today can with knives. From the animals that were killed, even savages would very soon learn how to make shelters out of the skins of animals.

Here I must mention the Neanderthal and Cro-Magnon peoples that the evolutionists delight in referring back to, in their attempt to find a transition from apes to men. Fossils of Neanderthal people were first found in a cave in the Neander Valley near Duesseldorf, Germany.

Since then, skeletons have been found in Belgium, France, and other parts of Europe. Although some of these skulls had sloping foreheads, they had brains as large as man today. An artist could picture these men as ape or statesman, and if they were dressed in a business suit, they could walk down Wall Street in New York and not be noticed. Actually, the brain of a Neanderthal man was larger than ours, so Neanderthal man proves nothing so far as evolution is concerned. They were just plain people, no different from people today, except they had larger brains.

Another set of fossils that are often referred to by the evolutionists are of some people who at times lived in caves like some of the Neanderthals. They are called Cro-Magnon, named after the small rock shelter of Cro-Magnon at the village of Les Eysies in France. Five skeletons were found: an old man, two young men, a woman and a child—all of whom could have belonged to one family. They were not ape-men, as some assumed, but they were tall, upright people with long legs and with brains as large as in people today. They and other similar fossils found in Europe were similar to people today. The brain size was from 1550 to 1650 cubic centimeters compared to an average of 1350 c.c. today. They were 14 to 22 percent larger—so why should they not be of recent origin instead of tens of thousands of years old. The fact that they lived in caves or occupied them at times proves nothing regarding their origin, as though they were the early advanced people out of ape-land.

Some of these cave people of the past painted on the walls of the caves remarkable pictures of animals like horses, deer, oxen, bison, mammoths and other animals, showing the animals in action.

Regarding these so-called primitive (?) people, *Life* magazine (1961), p. 169, states:

At Lasceaux in the main cave and several adjoining galleries, nearly 500 bulls, horses, antelopes and even a herd of reindeer swimming a river are painted with an artistry, power and accuracy of movement that have not been surpassed. The paintings there must be considered one of the world's great assemblages of art.

And then *Life* magazine continues with the old evolutionary creed:

By their art these men of the caves, the Cro-Magnons proved their possession of the highest capacities yet achieved in the long course of evolution.

Most likely these Cro-Magnons carried their abilities with them from the skills and knowledge they had at the time of the Flood.

Regarding this migrating of people, People of the World — A Study of World History (1984) by Allen Kownslar and Terry Smart states p. xxxviii:

Despite all the digging and searching done by archaeologists, we still do not have a full picture of prehistoric people. One reason for our limited knowledge is that prehistoric people lived and died out in the open. Exposed to weather, their bodies decayed, their bones were chewed by animals and bleached by the sun. Our information is limited for other reasons. Prehistoric people did not write their language. We have no written records to examine, to find out how they lived. We have to "read" their story in bones, tools and other remains of their lives. With this evidence, we can piece together parts of their story. But we have to make guesses about the rest.

Guesses and assumptions are the basis of all of the evolutionary story.

The *Reader's Digest* March, 1987, p. 167, states:

Today most anthropologists conclude that late Ice Age humans made a quantum leap forward from their uninventive predecessors . . . Much of what we know about these first fully modern humans — Homo sapiens sapiens — comes from the denizens of Ice Age Europe. Dubbed Cro-Magnon for the cave in France where their remains were first discovered.

The Cro-Magnon and Neanderthal people very likely were some of the people who were buried in the sediments laid down in caves and elsewhere at the time of the Flood. All that I have given so far is the pre-history that the school history books do not have, leaving the children in the dark, groping about, vainly looking for their ancestors among the apes. How un-scientific it is to ignore and actually despise all this information. True scientists do not proceed in this fashion. They use everything available to find the truly scientific answer.

Evolutionists and school-book historians record many of the same events that the Bible history gives from Genesis chapter 12 and onward. Genesis chapter 11, with the story of Terah and Abraham, merges perfectly into Genesis 12, so why shouldn't the first 11 chapters of Genesis be considered as the prehistory that school books and other history books should have? Why, except for rebellion against God, should these historians reject Genesis, chapters 1 through 11? Throughout the rest of the Bible these first 11 chapters are constantly referred to as historical facts and historical events.

On the other hand larger numbers of people soon after the Tower of Babel became tired of shifting around and wanted permanent settlements for their families. They gathered in the productive river valleys where the average annual temperature was a comfortable 70 degrees like in Egypt, Babylonia, Asia Minor, Palestine, Assyria, Persia, India, Southeast Asia, China and in the temperate parts of the Americas. With people available who possessed all kinds of technical skills, they quickly established homes and cities. Because Noah and his sons could build a huge ark, certainly their descendants after the Tower of Babel could build all kinds of advanced structures and even build boats to cross the Atlantic from Africa to the Americas and build civilizations in Peru, Mexico and the Unites States. See Chapter 2 regarding these people.

THE INTERLUDE

So far (in the *Prelude of the Song of Eternity*) it has been shown what happened in the course of human history from the creation of the earth to a few centuries after the Tower of Babel.

Now, in the Interlude, I shall cover first, the turmoil that the evolutionists have caused by promulgating through public institutions their unproven ideas of the origin of the universe, of the earth and of mankind, as though they were proven facts; and secondly, the positive hopes that mankind has in the written word of the eternal, almighty and all-wise *non-material* Creator and Designer of all things.

XI.   TEACHINGS, BELIEFS AND EFFORTS OF THE EVOLUTIONISTS

1.   WHAT EVOLUTIONISTS TEACH

According to the evolutionists, man descended from an apelike creature or from some form of an ape. Louis and Mary Leakey and their son Richard have been active in Africa for decades trying to find what they believe are the ancestors of mankind. Richard wrote in his book *People of the Lake,* pp. 24-26:

> As the dinosaurs slid into their monumental decline, a small tree-shrewlike creature snuffled its way out of the thickly covered forest floor and took to the trees, eventually to become the first of the primates. For the next thirty million years the primate order proliferated, producing scores of tree-living, insect-eating small nocturnal animals. . .Throughout this time new primate species were getting bigger. . .Many of them switched their activities from night to light: . . .Just when the prosimians seemed settled as a highly successful group of tree-dwellers, they gave issue to the monkeys, who promptly ousted their ancestors. . .Like the diminutive prosimians and the agile monkeys before them, the apes. . .thrived and proliferated, but the ones in which we are most interested are the so-called woodland apes, or dryopithecenes as they are known.

In most books written by evolutionists, terms derived from the Latin or Greek language are used, although English terms are available. Since this book is meant for the average person who is not acquainted with Latin and Greek terminology, I will use hereafter, wherever I can, the ordinary English terms. Two words often used by the evolutionists are "pithecus" which in Greek means "ape" and "anthropus" which in Greek means "man."

Regarding the apes Richard Leakey and his co-author, Roger Lewin, state p. 26:

> Here we will talk about just three apelike creatures that lived around fifteen million to ten million years ago: *Gigantopithecus*, *Sivapithecus*, and *Ramapithecus*. The last of these, *Ramapithecus*, a small creature (perhaps close to three feet tall), is currently favorite as the first true hominid [hominid means human-like]. *Sivapithecus* was bigger than *Ramapithecus*, but their cousin *Gigantopithecus* was probably enormous. .Now, if we are absolutely honest, we have to admit that we know nothing about *Ramapithecus*; we don't *know* what it looked like; we don't *know* what it did; and, naturally, we don't *know* how it did it. But with the aid of jaw and tooth fragments and one or two bits and pieces from arms and legs, all of which represents a couple of dozen individuals, we can make some guesses, more or less inspired. [Emph. his]

I would say that "guesses, more or less inspired" is an honest statement, especially when one reads of some evolutionists referring to evolution as a positive fact.

About twenty pages further on the two authors write:

> The hominids of two to three million years ago were of course the issue of the fifteen-million-year-old *Ramapithecus*. Because, for several reasons, the period between eight and about four million years ago is a fossil void, we can only guess what our ancestors were up to then. Nevertheless, the structure of human evolution is clear: we start off with an ancestor about fifteen million years ago; by three million years ago the hominid stock has proliferated to produce a number of related creatures, one of which is the *Homo* line that eventually becomes modern man; and during the further evolution of the *Homo* stock the rest of the hominids die out.

No proof is provided for all this claimed origin of mankind from Ramapithecus.

Richard Carrington, in his book *The Story of Our Earth*, states about the same things, p. 185:

> [F]ortunately most of the hysterical opposition to Darwinism has now abated, and what was once the 'theory' of evolution,

modified in detail but the same in essence, has passed into the body of scientific knowledge. Today it is no longer necessary, as it was even fifty years ago, to defend the simple fact that men, apes, and monkeys belong to the same great family.

The words "scientific knowledge" and "simple fact" used above are some of the bold attempts to make evolution an unquestionable fact. But no proofs are given.

2.   FACTS REGARDING APES, ETC.

There is no verifiable, scientific evidence that mankind has evolved from apes, but there is physical evidence that apes and mankind are different. When one compares the physical similarities between apes and mankind, he finds many dissimilarities and differences in the different kinds of apes and of mankind. While the gorilla may be shaped like man in some ways, it has a head that leans forward and hangs downward from the spine, the skull of the male has a high bony crest, shaped like the comb of a chicken and it has a chinless snout with powerful teeth that touches the breastbone. The gorilla has 13 pairs of ribs, while man has only 12. It has short, crooked legs and its arms serve as crutches and touch the ground as it knuckle-walks along. It does not walk like a human but is a knuckle walker. The gorilla's body is covered with thick hair. The chimpanzee also has 13 pairs of ribs, but has shorter arms. While the gibbon has 12 pairs of ribs, it has arms reaching down to the ankles. The orangutan and the baboon are also different in many respects and all the apes have thumbs instead of big toes, opposite the other four toes, so they all appear to have four hands.

The Pictorial Encyclopedia of the Evolution of Man (1975) by J. Jelinek, p. 18 tries to show how the apelike creature developed into man:

> The eyes moved forwards and closer together until their field of vision overlapped. But the development of the brain is the most notable feature. .[p. 45] one characteristic is the straightening up of the body, gaining an erect posture, so that changes occurred to the spine, the pelvis and the long bones of the limbs. Hands and feet are changed considerably. The structure of the sole of the foot changed, and developed a double arch. The facial skeleton became more flattened. The brain and brain-case grew larger.

An so on and on, and just like that it all happened over millions of years. Following that kind of reasoning, any other animal could also have changed into man in millions of years.

Although today evolutionists do not like to say that man descended from any living ape, they nevertheless contend that mankind evolved from some creature in the distant past which was like an ape in its physical and mental characteristics. But why split hairs about it? That creature would still be called an ape today. Apes and mankind *cannot be crossed,* man is not an ape, and despite some physical outward similarities that may exist between man and ape and all other creatures, there is not the least evidence or proof that mankind developed from an apelike creature, or from any other creature. An ape fossil could have features like a man and still be from an ape, and some human fossils could have apelike features and still be from a human being. Today, October 4, 1986, I saw a man who had a very backward-sloping forehead, and if someone would find his skull some day, he could be listed among the the apes of millions of years ago by the evolutionists — yet he appeared to be a very intelligent man.

APE-KIND VERSES MANKIND

Of all the different kinds or species of animals in the world, apes need special attention because evolutionists insist on making these animals a forefather of mankind, in spite of *the scientific fact* that one species has never and can never be changed into another species. They try to get around this problem by claiming mankind did not come directly from apes but that both apes and mankind evolved from an apelike creature. But finally what is the difference? If they both are varieties of the same species or kind then they should be able to produce common offspring. Man has never and can never be crossed with apes because *apes are another kind that can only be crossed with other apes.* Apes have always been apes and animals and will always be such, and humans have always been and will always be humans. There is no close connection between apes and man, except a bit in outward facial appearance. Otherwise an ape is still only another animal, even though *Homo sapiens sapiens,* evolutionists, insistently claim apes as their ancestors.

Although evolutionists claim that apes and mankind have a common ancestor, the Word of the Creator of all still reads in I Corinthians 15:39:

All flesh is not the same flesh: but there is one kind of flesh of men, another flesh of beasts.

This Scripture *F A C T* is supported by laboratory tests which clearly show differences between ape flesh and human flesh. There are differences in blood, differences in bodily make-up, differences in skulls and a different mode of walking on all four extremities, both legs and arms. Above all there are vast mental and speech differences. An ape may be led like any other animal to do certain things after long and repeated training; but it cannot be brought by means of education to think, reason, compute, analyze and speak with humans. Although apes have lived side by side with mankind for hundreds of generations since the very beginning of creation, apes still are only apes. Above all, among all the fossils, no fossil evidence of a common ancestor for man and the ape has ever been found.

3.   EVOLUTIONIST VERSUS EVOLUTIONISTS

Because evolutionists can find so few fossils to give their ideas of evolution any support, John Pfeiffer, himself an evolutionist, stated in his book *The Emergence of Man*, p. 12: "It seems that every time a man finds a human bone he goes crazy on the spot."

Because of the weak and false ground evolution is standing on, a number of evolutionists have softened their position on it. Ruth Moore, in her book *Man, Time and Fossils*, 1953, states p. 3:

And now in the middle of this century another time has come when new findings are upsetting older theories and opening the way for another rapid surge forward. It is still too early for the final verdict, though even now it is clear that the current and traditional theory of how and when man evolved must be changed. Some long-held and respected beliefs will have to be revised and the textbooks rewritten, for much of what has been said and some of the supposed facts are now found to be incorrect. Darwin's theory of evolution is being modified — though in the end strengthened and reaffirmed. Darwin was wrong, but right.

Although Darwin was wrong, they just cannot let go of him.

On p. 8 Ruth Moore continues:

Even in its earliest stages this new dating — dating with carbon-14 or radiocarbon — also indicated that man is younger than science had ever dared to think. As man's time was compressed a new dilemma was created. Could man have evolved in the shorter time set by the new dating? Could the tremendous differences between primitive man and modern man have been achieved in a shorter time?

A similar confession was made in Ronald Schiller's "New Findings on the Origin of Man" in the *Reader's Digest* (August 1973, p. 89-90):

The descent of man is no longer regarded as a chain with some links missing but rather as a tangled vine whose tendrils loop back and forth as species interbred to create new varieties, most of which died out. . .It may be that we did not evolve from any of the previously known human types, but descended in a direct line of our own.

The last nine words are quite a confession. The statement "as species interbred to create new varieties, most of which died out" is not an evolutionary statement but a truly scientific one based on actual facts, if he is referring to varieties within species. As I shall point out later on: *kinds* of animals stay *kinds,* i.e., dogs stay dogs, and do not change into cats or horses, or apes into men, but species of dogs can be bred into varieties of dogs by selective breeding. If left alone, as Schiller states, varieties die out and revert to the original basic species.

As far as men advancing is concerned, they have in many cases degenerated, if left to themselves in small groups. Many groups of people have advanced very little and even degenerated from their early history, as *Life* magazine in its *Epic of Man,* (1961) points out. It lists present isolated groups of people like the primitive aborigines of Australia, the caribou Eskimos of Canada, the Berbers in Morroco, the Newars of Nepal. Many of these people have what is called a "Stone Age" culture. If this is true today, certainly there must have been similiar people living a few thousand years ago in the time after the days of the Tower of Babel dispersion. Some of these people today, though they appear to be backward, have a highly complex language and are intelligent and friendly.

Charles Darwin also had quite an eye-opener in his trip to the southern tip of South America. When he saw some natives of Tierra del Fuego he said:

I would not have believed how wide was the difference between savage and civilized man.

He found it hard to think of them as fellow human beings. When Darwin's ship the Beagle came there and a party went to shore, these natives did not even have an animal skin for protection, and one woman nursing a newly born child, stood looking at the ship while sleet fell and thawed on her naked bosom and the skin of her naked baby. These natives slept on the cold damp ground like animals. One would think that these backward people would have turned Darwin's mind in the right direction by thinking of the degeneration of man instead of the evolution of man.

After the evolutionists got their South African ape moved onward and upward, they finally came to their upright man, *Homo erectus,* or erect man. The first fossil of this type that they mention in the *National Geographic* (November 1985) is Java man (1893) with the Greek name, *Pithecanthropus erectus* [ape-man who walked erect] and then Peking man of China (1920) termed *Sinanthropus pekinensis*.

4.   HOAXES AND FRAUDS OF EVOLUTIONISTS

Regarding Java Man, *Life* magazine, p. 130, states in summary: A young Dutch doctor, Eugene Dubois, thought he would be the one to find bones of ancient man. He reasoned that either Africa or Malaya would be the place because ape-creatures were still living there today. He accepted an appointment with the Royal Dutch army in Sumatra. When he heard that skulls were to be found in nearby Java he went there. Fossils of all kinds of animals could be found there. In September 1891, he found a molar tooth, a month later he found the top part of a skull about three feet away, and a year later, in August 1892, a thigh bone about 50 feet away. *Life* magazine makes this statement:

> As a skilled anatomist Dubois could tell what it was: An essentially human thigh bone, belonging to a being that walked upright. The implications were staggering. Dubois had to make certain. He studied and measured the apelike skull and the humanlike leg bone, for a momentous decision was forming in his mind. Not until 1894 was he ready to make a public statement of it. Then he announced to the world that the low skull and the human leg bone had belonged to the same creature. Nothing could have been more startling, an apelike head and the upright posture of a man. Deliberately and almost provocatively, Dubois named this creature he had materialized from the past *Pithecanthropus erectus*.

In 1895 Dubois showed these fossils at the International Congress of Zoology at Leyden. Ten of these zoologists believed the fossils were bones of apes, seven thought they were human and seven that they were missing links between apes and men. So less than one-third of the prominent zoologists considered them of evolutionary value. Thirty years later Dr. Dubois admitted that he had found two truly human skulls near where he found his Java man and in the same strata level. Finally before his death, he stated that his Java man was only a giant gibbon. This is one of many frauds concocted by evolutionists to bolster their preconceived notions of evolution.

Did you notice how *Life* magazine built up Dubois' knowledge, scientific ability, and expertise using the words "skilled anatomist," "implications were staggering," "studied and measured the apelike skull," "momentous decision," two years to "make a public statement," "startling," "deliberately," and "almost provocatively." Quite a build up for something that proved to be false, if not a fake and fraud.

Another famous fossil skull was found near Piltdown, England, called the Piltdown man or *Eoanthropus dawsonii* or in plain English, "The Dawn man of Dawson," which was claimed to be 250,000 to 300,000 years old. The fossils, consisting of four incomplete skull fragments, a tooth and a jawbone were found in a gravel pit over a three year period from 1908 to 1911 by an English lawyer, Charles Dawson, hence the name of the fossil. Dawson was one of many evolutionists who had been searching frantically many years for the missing link between apes and men. Although some men acquainted with fossils doubted the immense age and claim of the fossil as a link, because the skull appeared to be human and the jaw from an ape, this fossil was proclaimed in school books to our children for 40 years to be evidence for evolution. However in 1953, Dr. Kenneth Oakley and two professors at Oxford University showed that this jaw bone was from a modern chimpanzee and that it had been stained and touched up. They also showed that the teeth had been filed and artificially stained with iron salts to make them appear ancient human teeth to match the human skull. The skull was only about 800 years old or less. For 40 years this fraud was hailed by the evolutionists as a link between apes and men.

Another hoax or fraud was a meteorite-fragment found in southwestern France in 1864. It was claimed to contain evidence of life from outer space. Not for almost 100 years was it given a close examination. A French microbiologist found that it had been changed by adding bits of glue, gravel, coal, seeds and tissues. It seems the hoax was to discredit Louis Pasteur who a few weeks before had delivered a strong "defense of divine creation as the only possible source of life."

Refusing to believe God's account of the origin of man, many people fall for such a planned hoax and fall prey to such lies and frauds. This reminds us of what is proclaimed in II Thessalonians 2:11:

> [F]or this cause God shall send them a strong delusion that they should believe a lie: That they all might be damned who believed not the truth, but had pleasure in unrighteousness.

Another famous fossil hoax that must be mentioned is Nebraska Man, based on a single tooth found in a river bed in 1922 by Harold Cook on his ranch near Agate, Nebraska. This Nebraska Man was graced with the highly scientific name of *Hesperopithecus haroldcookii*. Hesperia in Greek means Westernland and since Nebraska is in the west and the Greek *pithecus* means ape, what better high-sounding scientific name could be imposed upon this so-called ape-man? Evolutionists must chuckle and giggle in their story-time hours as they devise Greek and Latin names for supposed predecessors of mankind. The worst is that some of these supposed predecessors turn out to be hoaxes and frauds.

This tooth was declared by evolutionists of the American Museum of Natural History to be proof that an ape-man or forerunner of mankind lived millions of years ago in America. In 1925 the American Museum again reaffirmed its position that the tooth was a near-human type, and declared that no tooth had ever been subjected to such severe scientific cross-examination, and added that "every suggestion raised by scientific skeptics was weighed and found wanting." Henry Osborn, one of the most eminent students of ancient fossils (paleontologist) of that day, and Professor William Gregory continued to declare with the voice of experts that this tooth belonged to a creature midway between the apes and man. Leading evolutionists throughout the world proclaimed the creature to be man-ape or ape-man. Professor Gregory was one of the highest ranking men in the field of evolution that dealt with the age of man and his supposed evolution from apes. He was the Curator of Comparative Anatomy in the American Museum of Natural History and Curator of Fishes. He was also professor of vertebrate paleontology at Columbia University. Dr. Osborn, in a momentous address at the American Philosophical Society of Philadelphia on April 28, 1927, placed this *Hesperopithecus* earlier than all the other near human fossils found to date. Drawings were made of males and females from this specimen, all based on just one tooth. The cry of evolutionists seems to be "Give us a tooth," and they will supply all the rest from imagination with plaster of paris or with drawings.

In the Scopes "Monkey Trial" in Dayton, Tennessee in 1925, this *Hesperopithecus haroldcookii* was frequently thrown up to William Jennings Bryan in the course of the evolutionary controversy because that molar was found in his state of Nebraska. The so-called experts, such as Professor H. Newman of the University of Chicago, ridiculed him and laughed him to scorn during the trial because they claimed the proof was not contestable. That tooth became a weapon in the hands of the evolutionists during that court-trial-of-the-century, and that was to affect greater evolutionary teachings and beliefs in the decades to come. Very likely, because William Jennings Bryan (three times presidential candidate 1896, 1900, 1908) could not disprove the supposed antiquity of that tooth he gave answers to Attorney Clarence Darrow questioning him in the trial regarding the age of the earth, which he would never have made otherwise. When Darrow lured him into answering how long the days were in the six days of creation, he replied: periods of time, covering a period of millions of years. People in the court room gasped in unbelief and shock that Bryan would make such a statement. Could this contradiction of his cherished Bible have affected his health the next few days and caused his sudden death a few days after the trial? If Bryan had only known the facts given in the next paragraph! He was a crushed man after that statement. The Scopes "Monkey Trial" and its viciousness will be referred to more fully later in this book (Chapter XXIV, Part 14C).

Scientific truth finally prevailed! Only a few months after Dr. Osborn in 1927 made his famous address before the American Philosophical Society of Phildelphia and two years after the Scopes trial a number of other teeth were discovered. Finally it was admitted by the eminent Professor Gregory that the tooth came from the jaw of *a wild pig.*

For your amusement I will quote what the *Omaha World-Herald* printed February 24, 1928:

Hesperopithecus, alias, the Million-dollar Tooth, has taken another tumble, and, oh, what a bump it got! Instead of being the sole surviving remnant of a noble Nebraska Neanderthal, it turns out to be a grinder from the prehistoric jaw of one of his pigs. Instead of being worth a million, it is worth, judging from the price of pork on the hoof today, perhaps all of 30 cents.

Professor Gregory had declared it to be worth a million dollars.

For a warning against believing all that the so-called experts and what the news media proclaim, I will quote another paragraph from the *Omaha World-Herald:*

It isn't so much the loss of this tooth's fame which we mourn as it is the loss of our faith in the infallibility of science. If there is so little difference between a pig's tooth and a man's that the one may be mistaken for the other for eight years, aren't there infinite chances for error in the identification of the fossilized fragments out of which such an amazingly strange prehistoric fauna has been recreated for us?

Shouldn't this latter paragraph from that Omaha paper be a warning to all the news media to be careful about printing as actual facts all that the evolutionists are still declaring about things being millions of years old and other evolutionary guesses, assumptions and presumptions?

5.   RECENT EFFORTS OF EVOLUTIONISTS

The first man of recent years to "Search for Our Ancestors" among the fossils in Africa was Dr. Raymond Dart, professor of anatomy at South Africa's University of Witwatersrand at Johannesburg. In 1924 a skull was delivered to him from a limestone quarry near Taung near Johannesburg. It became known world-wide as Taung's Child or Dart's "baby," and it was proclaimed in headlines around the world as the missing link. Although several English authorities were skeptical and expressed disagreement saying that it was only "the distorted skull of a chimpanzee," yet *Life* magazine in 1961 printed a lengthy report defending Dart's claim and that of his friend, Dr. Robert Broom, a Scottish physician who scouted for fossils all over the earth and finally in Africa.

In the November 1985 issue of the *National Geographic,* a feature story was printed entitled "The Search for Our Ancestors." On the front cover of that issue they showed a three dimensional picture of the Taung child's skull which was presumed to be 1,000,000 to 2,000,000 years old. They claim on p. 578:

> The child died at the age of five or six, and the bones ended up in a cave. Accumulating debris gave the skull protection against the usual destruction by animals, insects, and soil acids. Gradually waterborne carbonates percolating into the cave replaced the organic portions of the bones, turning them into stony fossils.

But, accumulating debris does not preserve bone. Millions of buffaloes died or were killed ruthlessly in our western plains 100 years ago, but no bones were preserved within a few years by accumulating debris of violent western winds. Evidently the skull of this child was preserved not by "gradually water born carbonates percolating into the cave" but by the massive, devasting flood of Noah's day, which quickly buried millions of skulls and skeletons of men and animals under many layers of sand, rock, mud and lime which preserved those bones until dug up by miners, excavations and road builders, or were exposed to view by windstorms, heavy rains and local floods.

Another fossil about which much ado has been made world-wide is *Zinjanthropus boisei,* found by Dr. Louis Leakey, an anthropologist, and his wife Mary. *Zinj* is Arabic for East Africa and *anthropus* is Greek for man and *boisei* honored Charles Boise who helped finance the search for early man. In the January 1964 issue of *Reader's Digest* on p. 157 it is stated:

For three decades they had spent half their working lives on hands and knees exploring East Africa's fossil-rich prehistoric lake beds for traces of the genesis of man, searching in the land which more than 100 years before, naturalist Charles Darwin had guessed to be the birthplace of the human race.

And this was done in hot blistering sun to prove evolution.

On July 17, 1959, while her husband was sick, Mary went out searching alone and found this *Zinjanthropus* or East Africa skull. The skull was dated by the University of California's new potassium-argon dating process to be 1,750,000 years old. Later tests indicated that this might be 500,000 too great. (I will refer to the rock-dating methods and their supposed reliability further on.) Dr. Leakey, while "still dizzy from drugs," took "one glance at those colossal gray teeth" and he was "certain that they predated Peking man by several hundred thousand years." He did not even use and need any rock-strata-dating methods, which evolutionists usually use to back up their wild dating claims. We know how wrong many so-called experts in other fields are today. In the financial world many people have lost hundreds of thousands of dollars because of the bad guessing and advice given by so-called experts in the financial world.

But what old "Zinj" or old "East African" was, whether ape or man, seemed uncertain in the Leakey family. Son Richard Leakey stated he no longer believed this creature to be an ancestor of man. Dr. Carleton Coon, University of Pennsylvania, an anthropologist and supporter of Leakey, said, "Twenty years have passed since these events. The scientific world is still divided between Leakey's supporters. . .and those who through honest skepticism or conflicting theories do not believe in the apparent age of these remains." Professor Lord Zuckerman of the Department of Anatomy, University of Birmingham, England and Dr. Oxnard, professor of anthropology, University of Southern California, have declared that Zinj and Dr. Johanson's "Lucy" were not links between apes and man.

However, the Leakeys have gained financial support. The *Reader's Digest* (January 1964, p. 163) states:

Since the Leakey's discovered Zinj, Olduvai Gorge has become world renowned. The National Geographic Society in the United States is backing the the Leakeys financially, and with the help of trained assistants they can now explore more of the drama-packed terrain in one year than all the previous years put together.

In that November 1985 *National Geographic,* referred to earlier, is
another evolutionary story, p. 625 entitled "Homo Erectus Unearthed,"
by Richard Leakey and Alan Walker. In it they tell of a 12-year-old boy
who lived 1,600,000 years ago, as they presume. They say this boy
"disappeared beneath layers of lake sediment and river borne ash from
distant volcanoes." But that would hardly preserve his body any more
than it would today. He evidently was quickly covered by muddy
sediments and ash as very likely happened in the turmoil of the Flood
of Noah's day. The gradual covering of bodies does not preserve them.

One of the wildest attempts to prove that man evolved from apes is
given in that November 1985 issue of the *National Geographic* in its
feature story, "The Search for Our Ancestors" by Kenneth Weaver,
senior assistant editor. Page 563 states:

> from 24 to 5 million years ago, an array of early ape species
> spread throughout the Old World. Sometime during the last half
> of the epoch the ancestral line of pongid (ape) and hominid (man
> and his ancestors) split.

Page 564 continues:

> Suddenly a primate that stands, walks, and runs on two legs is
> discovered in a three-million-year-old stratum — with a skeleton
> so strikingly like our own.

Then a series of pictures is shown: first of five reconstructed
skeletons, then nine reconstructed skulls, and finally nine paintings of
fully fleshed humanlike beings reconstructed by artist Jay Matternes, in
which he tries to give the impression that this is the way mankind evolved
from apelike creatures to human beings of today. All these
reconstructions are from a few bones that could be either from apes or
from human beings.

In regard to the nine paintings of male creatures, it is stated that the
artist focused mainly on the skull which they claim was the main area
of change. Then in the next sentence they mention that vast differences
like this exist even today in different human beings, stating, p. 574:

> All populations today. . .exhibit an immense range of physical
> variability, both within groups and from group to group; compare
> the Eskimo with the Brazilian Indian, the Pygmy with the Masai.
> Earlier hominid species undoubtedly also existed in variable forms
> as a result of their adaptations to local environments.

So all these reconstructions of skeletons and skulls mean nothing.
Another man could turn what they call an ape into a man because many

people today, including very intelligent ones, have skulls like what they show. In fact there is very little difference, if any, between what they call the first apelike man and the first manlike man. And their best fabrication, or story telling, is that as apelike men and inferior men advanced in time, they died out. They stated p. 575, "These two forms" (Australopithecus 'Southern Ape' robustus and boisei) "disappear from the fossil record, apparently as evolutionary dead ends." [Again, p. 577:] "But by 30,000 years ago they" (Homo sapiens Neanderthals) "had died out or been assimilated by anatomically modern humans." Actually there are humans today who look like what they call Neanderthals of 30,000 years ago.

On p. 579, the *National Geographic* raises

Two obvious questions: Who were the ancestors before 4 million years ago? And what was it that induced the first hominids to forsake an arboreal existence and become terrestrial?

The answer given is:

Some 33 million years ago. . .a small fruit-eating animals called *Aegyptopithecus [Egyptian Ape]* climbed through the trees of a tropical forest in northern Africa.

Don't be surprised at the 29 million years difference between 33 million and 4 million because the evolutionists throw around the millions of years as if they didn't amount to much. This fad of millions of years of the evolutionists started about 100 years ago, when they tried to make evolution appear plausible. Another problem they have is, what was before that Egyptian ape, although they claim that over millions of years that ape evolved also. But true scientists do not draw such conclusions without actual facts.

A good example of how evolutionists, like Richard Leakey and Donald Johanson (who found Lucy), think and reason and ignore very clear evidence of the Flood in Noah's day is given in Richard Leakey's book, *People of the Lake* (1978). Referring to the fossils of 34 adults and 10 infants who all died at the same time and same place, the book states, p. 73:

Apparently, close to 3.5 million years ago, a group of these individuals perished in some sudden catastrophe. Very probably they were closely related to each other, forming a kind of proto-family group, a social pattern we might expect to see many times in human history. If so, what sudden catastrophe overtook them? Initially, it looked as if they may have been drowned by a flash flood in a stream bed, perhaps while they slept. But the geological

nature of the deposits now rule this out. Were they victims of a
particular virulent disease? Had they chanced upon a luxurious
abundance of poisonous berries or mushrooms and made the fatal
error of eating them? Perhaps they were asphyxiated by noxious
gases from the sudden blasts of a volcano? We will almost certainly
never know. Johanson says that I'm sure that as I get older and the
years go by my interpretation will get more and more dramatic.

I would not question that last statement. Evolutionists love the dramatic.

Flash floods do not preserve fossils nor does death from poisonous
berries or noxious gases. However, Noah's flood would. But evolutionists
will not consider the evidence of this geological fact, even though this
is the logical and reasonable explanation.

6.   HOMO SAPIENS, SAPIENS — SUPER WISE MAN

Finally, after showing the development of man from a small monkey,
ape, or chimpanzee into Australopithecus or Southern Ape, East African
man, Java man, Peking man, fake Piltdown man, erect man, handy man,
Nebraska-pig-tooth man, Neanderthal man and Cro-Magnon man, the
evolutionists arrive at man of today: Homo sapiens or Wise Man. The
National Geographic of 1985 got rid of Neanderthal man by declaring
on p. 577: "[B]y 30,000 years ago they had died out or been assimilated
by anatomically modern humans." *Life* nature library (1964), p. 168,
has Neanderthal man disappear 40,000 to 50,000 years ago. It states:

The green valleys of the beautiful Dordogne region of France
are walled in by gentle limestone cliffs, which at many points are
honeycombed with caves, many of them the long time homes of
Neanderthal man. Sometime after he disappeared from these
caves, modern Homo sapiens moved in.

Just like that all this happened! But where did Homo sapiens come
from?

Richard Carrington, another disciple of the evolution belief, in his
book *The Story of Our Earth* (1956), p. 210 states that Homo sapiens

may have been directly descended from their Neanderthal
predecessors, but their anatomy makes this extremely unlikely.
Another view is that they had been present in Europe from much
earlier times, and had developed along parallel lines to the
Neanderthalers from a forebear of the same type as Piltdown man.
[But Piltdown was proven to be a fraud in 1953!] But if this were
so, it is odd that no record has survived of the early years of their

development, while Neanderthal skeletons are comparatively numerous.

Numerous, no doubt, from the Flood in Noah's days.

> Of these Homo sapiens, *Life* magazine states, p. 169:
>
> Even at the time of their earliest known appearance, these men who were inheriting the earth were biologically as advanced as any men who have been born since. In brain size, in posture and in physical organization, the 3 billion human beings who are their descendants today have not basically changed the patterns that evolution had already built into their bodies. [On p. 172 *Life* concludes:] Only today is man recognizing that as he reshapes his world and replaces the relentless but stabilizing action of physical selection with a new, cultural evolution and inheritance, he is taking control of the future. Therein lies the climax of all the eons, the epochs and the years.

What a proud arrogant boast for *Homo sapiens* - The Self-Determining *Wise Man!* All this *without God*. Worse yet is when they refer to mankind as Homo sapiens, sapiens - Super Wise Man.

The *National Geographic* works man up, in four million years from Australopithecus afarensis and africanus (southern ape of Africa) to Homo sapiens (Wise man or modern man). And, oh, how proud modern man is today with his advancement from apelike to manlike! But on the Day of Judgment, I am sure the good Lord will have a different translation for Homo sapiens; namely, Wise Guy or even Smart Aleck. He no doubt will say in the words of Job 38:4: [OK Wise Guy], "Where were you when I laid the foundations of the earth? Tell me if you have understanding?" On the basis of Romans 1:18-22 what a judgment awaits all those who reject what God revealed not only in the Bible but also in the earth and universe, and especially in what that destructive earth-changing Flood in Noah's days screams at us!

I must quote what the Apostle Paul proclaimed to the wordly people of his day in Romans 1:18-22:

> [T]he wrath of God is revealed from heaven against all ungodliness and unrighteousness of men, who hold the truth in unrighteousness; Because that which may be known of God is manifest in them; for God hath showed it unto them. For the invisible things of him from the creation of the world are clearly seen, being understood by the things that are made, even his eternal power and Godhead; so that they are without excuse:

Because that, when they knew God, they glorified him not as God, neither were thankful; but became vain in their imagination, and their foolish heart was darkened. Professing themselves to be wise, they became fools.

According to Webster a fool is: "a person with little or no judgment, common sense, wisdom, etc.; silly person; simpleton."

7.   DINOSAURS AND CONFUSED EVOLUTIONISTS

Fossilized bones of these huge animals are found on almost every continent of this earth. In New Mexico many dinosaur skeletons were found, one on top of another. In the Dinosaur National Monument in Colorado and Utah over 100 dinosaurs of a number of different kinds were found. In one location in Wyoming a hillside was covered with very many dinosaur bones. They were piled up like logs in a river jam. In the Red Deer Valley of Alberta there are thousands of skeletons scattered over what is known as the Canadian Bad Lands. Dinosaur bones have been found in South America, Russia, Belgium, Africa, Antartica and other places. The amount of food that these huge animals ate must have been enormous. Only an extremely productive world, such as prevailed before the Flood, could provide the food these immense animals consumed.

In a short period of time, or even all at once, these great animals became extinct. All kinds of ideas have been given by the evolutionists for their extinction, but none of these assumptions hold up. A run-down of what the news media in the name of science for the benefit of evolution, are feeding the public is here in place. On April 26, 1981, the *Minneapolis Tribune* stated:

> So how did dinosaurs die anyway? Don't blame asteroids or comets striking the earth for their extermination, as a popular, but controversial, theory holds. Changes in the weather were making things tough for the dinosaurs long before then, four top experts concluded in this week's issue of the *Journal of Science*, offering strong new evidence to support their old theory.

On January 6, 1982, the *Minneapolis Tribune* stated:

> The extinction of the dinosaurs may have been caused by a giant asteroid that slammed into the earth 65 million years ago. The asteroid collision kicked up a huge cloud of dust containing iridium. The dust obscured the sun for three to six months, destroying the plants on which the dinosaurs fed.

Then why didn't this cause the death of many other animals; and why did it kill those dinosaurs who were flesh eaters? The same article gave another theory: The extinction

> could have been caused by a volcanic eruption that covered a million square miles of India with lava.

Everything like this could easily have happened at the time of the Flood when the fountains of the deep were broken up, but neither one of the two evolutionary theories above would explain how animals were piled one upon another in certain parts of the earth. The Flood explains this easily, but a universal Flood does not fit in with the thinking of the evolutionists.

On March 16, 1982, The [Mankato] *Free Press,* headlines a story by Robert Locke, AP Science writer:

> Did dinosaurs drown in a giant tidal wave?

Now that is getting a little closer to the Flood! But in this case it was another giant asteroid that was the villian in the fable told by the evolutionists. According to the story, the asteroid hit the ocean.

> Then the dinosaurs would be hit by a 500-foot wall of ocean water — a tidal wave of mind-boggling proportions that would race around the world within 27 hours.

But why did this not kill all the other land animals? This fable, like all their fables, lacks realism in fact and plain common sense in general.

On May 11, 1983, the *Minneapolis Tribune* headline states: "Researchers report most of life on earth somehow wiped out 65 million years ago." They write, "Something happened 65 million years ago that wiped out much of the life on earth," but they give no reason for it happening.

On October 3, 1984, Mankato *Free Press* headline says: "Scientists: Dinosaurs died off gradually." It continues:

> Berkely, California (AP): One of the world's leading fossil experts says dinosaurs died out gradually over millions of years because they couldn't find food during a cooling of the earth, an idea that contradicts the theory that the beasts were killed by a sudden catastrophe.

It took Professor William Clemens of the University of California ten years to come to this conclusion.

On December 12, 1985, the *Minneapolis Tribune* (AP) San Francisco, California stated:

Scientists Wednesday debated what killed the dinosaurs, offering conflicting new evidence against the usual suspects: comets, volcanoes, a death star, acid rain and gradual mass extinction. [See p.p. 427-431]

This time the volcanoes received honorable mention.

On January 29, 1986 in Nova Scotia 100,000 bone pieces of animals were found. "Bones were sticking out all over the place. They were everywhere." This time an asteroid again gets the nod for extinction.

On April 29, 1986, Mankato *Free Press:*

Dinosaurs extinction theory questioned. [It continues] Recent finds suggest that 110 million years ago, dinosaurs lived in the Antarctic Circle where they survived sunless winters lasting three to four months, said Dr. Tome Rich, curator at the Museum of Victoria, Australia. Rich said: "We know a few months of darkness couldn't have knocked them out." Rich said the period of darkness would need to have lasted ten years or more to wipe out the prehistoric reptiles.

But that would have wiped out not only the dinosaurs, but also all other animals and also mankind.

The September 1985 issue of the *Reader's Digest,* p. 99 printed another theory. Physicist Richard Muller and fellow scientists at the University of California, Berkeley, proposed a more intriguing theory: "A 'Death Star' orbits our sun and triggers mass extinctions at strikingly regular intervals." But they are not sure if there is such a death star, and if something like this did happen, the question again is, Why didn't all life on earth end?

The reason I have spent so much space on all these stories is that these stories are being given out week after week to the public via the newspapers, magazines, radio and TV and very likely in the public school system, as if all this were the Gospel truth. The big questions still remain: Why did these dinosaurs die out simultaneously all over this earth, why were they massed together in heaps in huge graveyards, and why was not all other life extinguished at the same time? The only reasonable, common-sense, and logical explanation lies in the universal Flood of Noah's day. Only a flood like that could kill them in masses and bury them in fossilizing sediments world wide. But the evolutionists because of their rebellion against God like *the children of men before the Flood,* just simply cannot tolerate any idea that may come from the Bible, no matter how logical and conformable to common sense and sound geology it may be. See p.p. 427-431.

8.   NO TRANSITIONAL FOSSILS BETWEEN DIFFERENT *KINDS* OF ANIMALS

If animals in the different layers of the earth's sediments died over a period of millions of years, there should be some transitional animals between different *kinds* of animals. However, no transitional animal-fossils have ever been found in spite of a couple of claims of the evolutionists with not a single connecting link between any.

The animals and men that exist today have never changed into other kinds. They are no different from those of the earliest fossils of various species of animals that existed in the very beginning. They appear abruptly in the fossil records and are fully formed and developed like the various species of animals today. Crocodiles, cockroaches, elephants, cats, dogs and many other animals have continued from the beginning without any real change, in much the same form.

9.   COELACANTH

One creature that the evolutionists for some time thought had undergone a change was a large fish called the coelacanth. When this fish was found only in fossil form, the evolutionists claimed it had evolved into a higher form and became extinct some 90 million years ago. They thought this fish developed legs and began to live on earth some fifty million years ago, and since then it became extinct. However, in 1938, one of these fish was caught off the southern coast of Africa. Since then a number of these fish were caught. This fish was five feet long and weighed 127 pounds. So instead of this fish having changed from a water creature to a land creature and becoming extinct, it is still very much alive and unchanged. And so another myth of the evolutionists went poof.

Still the evolutionists do not give up. As late as September 24, 1987, the *Minneapolis Tribune* carried a story on this fish to continue advocating the fable of evolution. They report the same essential facts I gave above regarding this fish; but they still state:

> Coelacanaths are members of a larger group of primitive fishes, crossopterigian, which many zoologists say are an important evolutionary link between aquatic and terrestrial vertebrates. Of the eight fins on these fish, four are paired and have bone structures that may represent the beginning of a transition to the legs of land animals. The extinct rhipidistian fishes, also members of the crossopterigian line and close cousins of coelacanths, are

widely regarded as ancestors of the amphibians, from which all other four-footed land animals are believed to have evolved.

There is no way that fish could have evolved into land animals. There is a tremendous difference between the backbone, or vertebrae, of fish and land animals. Fish lack the pelvis which land animals have, and there is no fish showing any sign of a pelvis. Also, the skulls of fish and land animals are different. There also are no evidences of fins ever turning into arms, legs, wrists, ankles, fingers and toes. No fish ever gradually developed over millions of years into land animals, any more than apelike creatures ever developed into humankind. Coelacanths are still coelacanths and apes are still apes today.

10.   LIKEWISE MAN HAS NEVER CHANGED — EVEN ACCORDING TO EVOLUTIONISTS

The *Minneapolis Tribune* (March 19, 1976) shows a picture of evolutionary fossil-seekers, Donald Johanson and Richard Leakey, and states that they

> Told a news conference in Washington about a newly discovered skull of an early ancestor of man. This and other recent discoveries lead scientists to believe that man 3.75 million years ago was anatomically much more like modern man than was previously thought.

Seven years later, October 19, 1983, the *Minneapolis Tribune* printed another Associated Press story from Nairobi, Kenya, of the skull of a 40-year-old man, who they say lived 150,000 to 300,000 years ago. Richard Leakey stated:

> He was wholly human. If this fellow had come into this room clad, you would not have discovered he was not one of us. He was physically human. He had language, had culture, had certainly by this stage the use of fire, the use of weapons.

The Associated Press continued:

> Leakey and other paleontologists have put the origin of man at between three and four million years ago. . .Leakey said that this man had a brain case of about 1,300 cubic centimeters, only about 50 cubic centimeters less than the average contemporary human.

Accordingly mankind has not undergone any major change in three to four million years. Do evolutionists really believe it took such highly developed man three to four million years to learn to use fire and tools?

How can evolutionists claim that mankind has evolved? The skull referred to no doubt belonged to one of the highly cultured, rebellious "children of men" who were descendants of Adam and Eve and were buried in the sediments of that one Universal Flood.

11.   GAPS AND MISSING LINKS IN THE EVOLUTIONISTS' FAMILY-TREE OF ANIMALS

The evolutionists love to espouse in school books, science books and dictionaries a presumed family tree of animals. But they fail to point out the immense gaps and missing links between all the different kinds of animals. There are no transitional fossils between sea and land creatures or between these and air creatures. There are no transitional forms between different *kinds* of animals, as the book of Genesis in chapter one states in forceful repetition, that various creatures were created *after their kind.* Never has a cat been changed or evolved into a dog, or a dog into a cat; or sheep into a cow or a horse, or vice versa. The same phyla, classes, orders, families, and genera that we have today exist in the fossil records of the past. There are no transitional forms changing from one kind into another kind or evolving into higher forms. The gaps and missing links are *there* as plain as day.

If evolution is a fact, as the evolutionists claim, then there should be some preliminary animals and some transitional forms leading to the animals that lived millions of years ago and to those living today. Originally Darwin and his followers admitted that they did not have enough fossils to fill in the gaps and to find the missing links. Yet today, over 120 years since Darwin, although millions of fossils have been found, not a single fossil of a transitional animal has been found, and, above all, not of one leading to man.

Even the evolutionists admit that there are big gaps between various kinds of animals and big holes in their theories. Allan Broms in his book *Thus Life Began* (1968) on p. 198 writes:

> Though an enormous amount of such work has been done in the century since Darwin and Wallace, there are still many gaps and much uncertainty, in tracing the kinship among those most ancient and primitive progenitors of animal kind.

T. N. George, professor of geology at the University of Glasgow, wrote (January 1960):

> There is no need to apologize any longer for the poverty of the fossil record. In some ways it has become almost unmanageably

rich. . .The fossil record nevertheless continues to be composed mainly of gaps.

More and more evolutionists are admitting that the missing links are still missing and that the huge gaps between kinds of animals are still there and that there is no evidence for a gradual change from one kind to another. Professor Stephen Gould of Harvard University, a leader for the evolutionists today, states:

> All paleontologists know that the fossil record contains precious little in the way of intermediate forms; transitions between major groups are characteristically abrupt.

12.   NO HALF-WAY CREATURES - ARCHAEOPTERYX

There just are no half-way creatures between different "KINDS" of creatures. There was one kind that the evolutionists rely upon to fill in all their gaps, the archaeopteryx, which, translated, means "ancient wings." They claim that this creature had teeth, a lizardlike tail, well developed wings, was covered with feathers, and had feet like a bird that were used for perching on limbs. The claim is made that this creature had certain characteristics of reptiles and became extinct like the dinosaurs. This creature very likely was different from all other creatures, just as the different kinds of creatures are different from each other. There is no evidence that any bird ever evolved from a reptile. And there is no reptile today that might have any tendency to develop into a bird today. Even Stephen Gould of Harvard University and Niles Eldredge who are two prominent promoters of evolution, especially of evolution by jumps (punctuated equilibrium) have stated, "Archaeopteryx does not count." Yet Niles Eldredge does promote the creature as a gap filler. In a book written in 1982 *The Monkey Business* he writes, p. 121:

> The stellar case is Archaeopteryx, the primitive animal so beautifully intermediate. . .between birds and advanced archosaurian reptiles. . .The [five] specimens are about 150 million years old. No earlier birds are known.

But another hoax or fraud: Fred Hoyle and Chandra Wickramasinghe, two well-known scientists in London have written a book *Archaeopteryx, The Primordial Bird (A Case of Fossil Forgery)*. In this book they furnish proof that archaeopteryx is a hoax. They present excellent photographs showing that wings were pasted onto the skeleton. In addition the two sides of the slab do not match. They also state that the London Museum deliberately altered the fossil to make it appear more real.

No fossil has ever been found of a creature with eyes just beginning to develop, or arms or feet beginning to turn into wings, or of scales beginning to turn into feathers. Among the fossils, no reptiles have been found that have begun to turn, or were turning into birds. Reptiles and birds, like so many other different *kinds* mentioned in the Bible, have never developed, evolved or crossbred into another.

13.   MISSING LINKS ARE NOT MISSING

Evolutionists will never find missing links because they never existed. What was never there can hardly be missing. But there really are missing links that are missing and that are very evident. These missing links are not what is missing in the millions of years of so-called evolution. The missing links that evolutionists are rebelliously missing are the people who lived 2500 to 4000 B.C. or even 6000 or 8000 B.C. Certainly apelike people did not suddenly, like "hopeful monsters", arise into highly intelligent and skillful people that suddenly accomplished marvelous feats in architecture in Egypt, Sumer or Babylonia, India, China, etc. The ancestors of these highly technical and learned people are not missing. Read Genesis chapters 1 through 11 for their immediate predecessors.

14.   HOPEFUL MONSTERS AND PUNCTUATED
EQUILIBRIUM

Some evolutionists realized that the slow development of creatures into different kinds just did not make sense and that slow development over even millions of years did not explain gaps and missing links in the fossils found all over the earth. So some in recent years have turned to "Hopeful Monsters" and "punctuated equilibrium" to explain the sudden appearance of all kinds of different creatures.

The National Geographic (November 1985) summarized these two views on p. 600:

> Just how evolution works is the subject of much discussion among today's biologists. One idea is that evolution is gradually taking place all the time because of mutations and changing environmental influences. Another proposal is that long periods of relative evolutionary stability are punctuated by sudden appearances of new species. This hypothesis is called punctuated equilibrium. It may well be, many scientists [rather evolutionists] say, that both kinds of evolution are in operation.

I cannot help but say, if one guess, presumption, theory, or postulation doesn't hold up, try another. One guess isn't any better than another.

This new idea on evolution started when the German evolutionist, Otto Schiendewolf in 1930 developed the idea that evolution took place in sudden leaping-up jumps from one basic kind to another. Then in 1940 Dr. Richard Goldschmidt of Berkeley, California, came up with the "Hopeful Monster." He said evolutionists had been digging for 100 years since Darwin and still had not found any transitional fossils to prove evolution. The missing links were still missing. Goldschmidt noticed that every so often a freak animal is born, such as a sheep with only two legs. It was a monster and it died. Or a turtle was born with two heads; it also was a monster and died. Although all these monstrosities did not survive, *hopefully*, if you had enough of these, you might get a good one. And so the Hopeful Monster idea of evolution was born, whereby a huge change might have occurred all at once. This Hopeful Monster would bridge the jump from one kind of animal to another, and that way evolution would not have the problem of explaining gaps and missing links in the fossils. Out of this was born the idea that one day a reptile laid an egg and a bird instead of another reptile hatched from the egg. Other evolutionists (neo-Darwinists) said that Goldschmidt is the one who laid an egg because there was not one bit of proof to back up his idea. Goldschmidt insisted that the neo-Darwinists also had no proof for their slow-evolution idea. However, neither party of the evolutionists has proof for their evolutionary fables.

Sewall Wright stated:

I have recorded more than 100,000 newborn guinea pigs and had seen many hundreds of monsters of diverse sorts, not one was remotely hopeful, all having died shortly after birth if not earlier.

And even if one monster would have survived, a hopeful mate of the same kind would have to be born at the same time and area and survive. Then they would have to produce offspring that were hopefully fertile.

In 1977 Stephen Gould, in opposition to those who believe in a slow gradual evolution over millions of years, asked what good beginning feet, arms or wings would be to a creature over millions of years. He said, "What good is a half a jaw or half a wing?" Such a creature could not function and live. Because of this, Gould and other colleagues felt they needed another explanation for evolution. And since the hopeful idea was contrary to what is evident in the science of genetics, they developed a new idea called "punctuated equilibrium." It was called "equilibrium" because nothing or very little happens among creatures or they remain the same and equal for millions of years. It is called "punctuated" because suddenly, rapidly, new creatures arise to punctuate or interrupt the equilibrium. These new creatures are assumed to propagate readily, and no evidence of them can be found among the fossils because the new creatures arise rapidly. In essence there is little or no difference between Gould's "punctuated equilibrium" and Goldschmidt's "hopeful monster."

Gould in his article "Evolution as Fact and Theory," printed in *Discovery* (May 1981) stated:

> I count myself among the evolutionists who argue for a jerky or sporadic rather than a smooth gradual pace of change. In 1972 my colleague, Niles Eldredge, and I developed the theory of punctuated equilibrium. (*Discover*, October). We argued that two outstanding facts of the fossil record — geologically "sudden" origin of new species and "failure to change thereafter" (stasis) — reflect the predictions of the fossil record. . .We proposed the theory of punctuated equilibrium largely to provide a different explanation for pervasive trends in the fossil records. . .Since we proposed punctuated equilibrium to explain trends, it is infuriating to be quoted again and again by creationists — whether through design or stupidity, I do not know — as admitting that the fossil record includes no transitional forms. Transitional forms are generally lacking at the species level, but are abundant between larger groups. The evolution from reptiles to mammals, as mentioned earlier, is well documented.

But he does not provide any documentation. He only refers to that old evolutionary story:

> Major evolutionary change required too much time for direct observation on the scale of recorded human history.

Also the missing links and big gaps between the families, orders, classes and phyla are still there in spite of Goldschmidt's "Hopeful Monster" and Gould's "punctuated equilibrium." And so it goes on and on with neither side of the evolutionists providing any scientific proof for their non-proven, non-tested, non-scientific creed or belief. They appear willing to proclaim almost any idea no matter how absurd, illogical and unreasonable just so the idea of evolution can continue to be proclaimed and *even proclaimed as a fact,* and the facts of creation are ignored. This takes us up to another evolutionary fable well publicized in many books and in many ways.

15.   THE GEOLOGICAL TIME TABLE

The sedimentary rock strata, which were laid down in quick succession upon the earth at the time of the Flood, are claimed by the evolutionists to have been laid down gradually over millions and millions of years. These layers of sediment are made up mostly of limestone, sandstone and shale, which can be miles deep, as is evident from the strata of entire mountain ranges such as the Rockies and the Himalayas. Some limestone was changed by pressure, heat, and chemical action into marble. The evolutionists have divided the layers of earth according to what they believe are the oldest to the youngest on top. The oldest are referred to as pre-Cambrian, then comes Paleozoic or Old or Ancient Age, then Mesozoic or Middle Age, and finally on top Cenozoic or Recent Age. Each age is again divided into sub-ages. Young people in school, when they see these charts of geological time tables, may be highly impressed, as if all this had real scientific truth behind it and as if it were beyond question.

The ages of these strata have been determined not by their chemical and physical makeup or other material factors, but by the fossils that are found in the different layers. But these fossils could be an age-determining factor only if certain animals or creatures lived in a specified time in the history of the earth. According to this, different kinds of creatures would have lived in only certain ages and at different times on earth. If a reptile and a cow were found in a stratum, the more recent cow would determine the age of the stratum. But we know that fossils of all kinds of animals have been found inter-mixed in the Flood graveyards of the earth. However, the fossils are a record not of animals that evolved gradually and died and were buried here and there singly over millions of years, but they are a record of animals that died and were buried suddenly in massive quantities and heaps in the Flood. A critique of *The Geological-Ages Hoax*, by Professor George McCready, stated: "In brief McCready's idea is that the geological strata in which the fossils are found are so badly scrambled that it is just as easy to believe that all these animals appeared simultaneously as that the simpler forms of life came first."

There is no scientific evidence for the assumed ages given in the geological time table. It is as Hilbert Siegler so clearly stated in his book, *Evolution or Degeneration — Which?* p. 67:

The student, when first confronted with this table, believes that geologists can actually find these various strata of rocks together in serial order, one on top of the other, in various locations. As Rehwinkel (1951, p. 265) and also Goldring (1960, p. 56) point out, nothing is further from the truth. In fact, nothing resembling such a series has ever been found together in one place on the face of the earth. The full series was devised only by correlating information gathered from studies of rocks and their fossils from all over the globe. In fact, scientists admit that an absolutely complete series cannot yet be arrived at. In other words, the geological time table is an artificial creation which does not actually exist anywhere in nature.

Furthermore many cases are found in which older rock strata, judged to be millions of years older according to the geological time table, are lying on top of younger rocks. In northern Montana and southern Alberta is an area where 20,000 square miles of supposedly older rock is lying upon younger rock. There is no sign of massive destruction between the two layers, where the older rock was supposed to have been lifted up and pushed over the newer rock. This also runs counter to the uniformitarian principle of evolution that change on this earth took place slowly and gradually. It would have taken a violent catastrophe to move such large volumes of rock.

As mentioned before, the ages of the various geological strata in the geological time table or time scale are not determined by their mineral make-up but by the fossils that are found in them. If an evolutionary geologist is asked how old a rock is he will go by what age the biologist gives for the fossils therein. If you ask an evolutionary biologist the age of the fossil he will go by what age the geologist gives the rock.

There just simply are not geological ages. They are a fabrication of the evolution religion and result from misreading the geology of this earth.

16.   CIRCULAR REASONING

Thus the reasoning goes round and round, reasoning in a circle. If the fossil record falls because of all the gaps and missing links in the fossil records, the geological time scale falls with it. The millions of years for the fossils and the millions of years for the geological time scale have no scientific foundation. One might expect a clever lawyer to reason like this, but not a scientist who must work with provable, proven facts.

How did this circular reasoning between evolutionary biologists and evolutionary geologists get started? In the middle of the last century (about 1850) biologists were convinced that evolution was a fact in spite of the gaps and missing links. The geologists began to believe what they heard and began to arrange the strata of the earth on paper so they would conform to the supposed fact of evolution. If a layer of sediment was found that contained fossils of animals or plants which the biologist said were evolved last, the geologist put that layer of sediment on top and named the stratum accordingly. And so fossils are dated, on the one hand, according to the kinds of rocks or strata they are found in; on the other, the strata are dated according to the kind of fossils they contain. It is the fossil that determines the name of the stratum and its age. The degree of hardness of the strata, or the position of the stratum above or beneath other layers of strata, or the type of material the fossil is in, or the mineral composition of the strata, have nothing to do with determining the age of the strata, according to the reasoning of the evolutionists.

In short, the fossils label and date the strata; the strata label and date the fossils. And so round and round we go in circular reasoning, which proves absolutely nothing. If Richard Leakey finds a fossil and wants to know its assumed millions and millions of years of age, all he needs to do is tell the geologist in what kind of rock it was found, even though the stratum was laid down in the Flood about 5,000 to 8,000 years ago.

Evolutionists are notorious for reasoning in a circle and proving nothing regarding their claim that evolution is a fact. Darwin evidently started this illogical reasoning. H. Spencer coined the phrase "survival of the fittest" to prove the theory of the evolution of creatures. When asked who are the fittest, the answer is those who survive. Norman Macbeth, a retired Harvard-trained lawyer states in his book, *Darwin Retried*, pp. 62-3:

> [T]his means that a species survives because it is the fittest and it is the fittest because it survives, which is circular reasoning and equivalent to saying that whatever is, is fit. The gist is that some survive and some die, but we knew this at the outset. Nothing has been explained.

Another example of circular reasoning was given by Sir Peter Medawar, at the Nobel Conference XVIII which I attended at Gustavus Adolphus College, October 1982, and which was celebrating the "Darwin Legacy." He won the Nobel Prize in 1960 for his work in physiology and medicine. He stated:

> Biologists believe in evolutionary theory because the evolutionary conception permeates and informs the whole of biology.

This is the same as saying: The evolutionary conception permeates and informs the whole of biology because biologists believe in the evolutionary theory. Because they believe in the evolutionary theory it must therefore be a fact that has a right to permeate and inform the whole of biology. This again is circular reasoning that proves nothing. In fact, that entire Nobel Conference XVIII held at St. Peter, Minnesota, proved nothing, for no evidence of any kind was given by all the different, internationally-known evolutionary speakers trying to prove evolution to high school teachers from all over the Midwest who attended that Nobel Conference. Some of the speakers were: Richard Leakey of Africa, Stephen Gould of Harvard University, Sir Peter Medawar of England and Jaroslav Pelikan of Yale University.

To me, so far as proving evolution was concerned, it was a total failure. The failure of the speakers and the nastiness of some of the evolutionists was extremely well worded by Sir Peter Medawar himself when he stated at the very end of his paper:

In summary, hypotheses of the stature of evolution are not proved, but to the best of our knowledge and understanding, evolution occurred. The evolutionary notion has entered so deeply into the fabric of our thought that it makes a nonsense today to confute it. For a biologist the alternative to thinking in evolutionary terms is to abstain from thinking altogether - a rather desperate expedient to which some anti-evolutionists seem already to have had recourse.

What a nasty dig the last remark is. It has happened again and again that when the evolutionists cannot prove their theories, they resort to attacking the person holding the opposite viewpoint.

Above all, Sir Peter Medawar provided another example of circular reasoning: "The Evolution Notion has entered so deeply into the fabric of our thought that it makes a nonsense today to confute it." This is the same as saying: it makes a nonsense today to confute evolution because the evolution notion has entered so deeply into the fabric of our thought.

Also "Notion" is a good word to rate the idea of evolution. Webster's New World Dictionary explains "Notion" as "A general idea, vague thought, a belief, opinion, view, a desire, inclination, whim."

XII.   THE BEGINNING OF ALL THINGS

1.   THE ORIGIN OF ALL THINGS

Going back to the very beginning of all things, I ask the primary question: From where did everything come? According to human reasoning all *material* things must have had a beginning. The Bible gives us the answer. Before the 92 natural elements, of which all material things consist, came into existence, there was one Force, one Power in existence: the everlasting, almighty, *non-material being* — God, who created all elements and material substances out of nothing in six natural days.

2.   THE EVOLUTIONISTS AND THE BIG BANG

The evolutionists also have an explanation for the beginning of all things. To them and their creed or belief there were always only material things. Yet, they know that for the material things of this universe there must have been a beginning. So they devised the fantastic story of the Big Bang, in which all material things came into existence in a few unbelievably short seconds more quickly than even God created the earth and universe.

How did this theory get started? In 1927 a Belgian astronomer, George Lemaître (1894-1966), suggested that a number of billions of years ago all matter in the universe was compacted into one small body. He called it a primeval atom. Others have called it a cosmic egg. Joseph Silk, in his book, *The Big Bang* (1980) states, p. 104:

> [A]ll the matter we now see in the universe, comprising some millions of galaxies, was compressed within a sphere of radius equal to one-thousandth of a centimeter, the size of the point of a needle. At this moment, the observable universe was far smaller even than an atomic nucleus.

All this matter was packed together in temperatures of trillions of degrees. How such a cosmic egg could have been formed and how long it lasted, George Lemaître had no idea; but in the course of time it exploded. This assumed explosion has been called the "Big Bang," since it was presumed to be the greatest explosion ever in the universe.

It is believed by astronomers that because of this immense explosion the universe is still expanding today. In 1912, American astronomer Vesto Slipher discovered that about a dozen galaxies around us are moving away from us and from one another at enormous speeds of a million miles an hour. Tracing the movements of these outward-expanding galaxies backward in time or reversing their expansion, the evolutionists believe that the original explosion took place some 20 billion years ago, which is the commonly-accepted age of the universe, according to the evolutionists.

According to the *Minneapolis Tribune* (August 28, 1975), it is claimed that the temperature in that tiny cosmic egg reached 10 million, million degrees or 10 trillion degrees in one-millionth of a second after the Big Bang. Then in one second after the Big Bang, according to Anthony Feldman, in *Space* (1980):

> The temperature was then about 38,000 million degrees Fahrenheit. But, as the universe expanded, the temperature fell rapidly.

My! What a thermometer and clock that must be! But it does make quite a story. Evolutionist Carl Sagan wrote quite a story showing how easily millions, billions and trillions can be fed to some of the gullible public. I will refer to this later. The modesty of the account of creation in Genesis can hardly compete with this. And all this occurred out of only a tiny, little speck of material. In Genesis, it at least took a non-material God to create the universe, and it took six days, which is an unbelievably short time according to the evolutionists.

Isaac Asimov, known for his many science-fiction (or rather evolution-fiction) stories or fables, wrote in his *In the Beginning* (1981) p. 23:

> In tiny fractions of a second, the temperature dropped precipitously. . .A full second after the big bang, the temperature of the Universe had dropped to ten billion degrees, about what it is at the center of the largest stars. . .It was, however, not until about a million years after the big bang, by which time the temperature of the Universe had dropped to five thousand degrees (that of the surface of the sun), . . .

One is tempted to ask: "Were you there, Isaac? And were you also in the center of the hottest star and on the surface of the sun?" What a fable for evolutionists to enjoy! Remember what Carl Sagan said in the previous paragraph. (See also Chapter XVI, Part 1, last two paragraphs.)

Not only are billions and trillions of degrees bandied about with the greatest of ease but also are billionths of a second. James Trefil in "Accidental Universe" in *Science Digest*, June 1984, wrote, p. 54: the universe expanded

> from a size much smaller than a single proton to something approximately the size of a grapefruit in about 10^{-35} second.

That is: In one hundred millionth of a billionth of a billionth of a billionth of a billionth of a second or in .000,000,000,000,000,000,000, 000,000,000,000,035 of a second. Now that is really getting to very fine timing! Only a confirmed disciple of evolution could believe this! Evolutionists can throw around billionths of a second and billions of degrees as easily as they can concoct *billions of years* and other evolutionary fables for the sake of their creed.

According to the *Reader's Digest* (July 1980, p. 49), the theory of evolution has the same sudden beginning as does the account of creation in Genesis. It has an article by Robert Jastrow entitled, "Have Astronomers Found God?" After referring to the Big Bang of astronomy on pp. 50-1 He states:

> The essential elements in the astronomical and Biblical accounts of Genesis are the same: The chain of events leading to man commenced suddenly and sharply at a definite moment in time, in a flash of light and energy. Some scientists are unhappy with the idea that the world began in this way. . .Einstein was disturbed by the idea of a universe that blows up, because it implies that the world had a beginning. In a letter to de Sitter, Einstein wrote, "This circumstance [of an expanding universe] irritates me!". . .I suppose that the idea of a beginning in time annoyed Einstein because of its theological implications.

Preston Cloud in his *Cosmos, Earth and Man* (1978), sized this up correctly when he wrote, pp. 24-25:

> Where the ball (or balls) of neutrons and the accompanying radiation may have come from is a question that transcends the bounds of science. It is the ultimate or penultimate question of first causes, belonging to metaphysics and theology. . .Perhaps the 'big bang', as it is sometimes called, was simply an initiating event in the most recent of a continuing succession of pulsating expansions and contractions within an eternal universe. Perhaps it was a divine act. We have no way of knowing.

What a confession of guessing!

The evolutionists do not like the idea of a definite beginning because it relates to the creation account of the Bible, so they have devised the new assumption of an "oscillating universe." This idea has been well stated by evolutionary fiction writer Isaac Asimov in his *In the Beginning*, p. 25:

> For instance, it may be that the Universe will not expand forever. It is expanding against the pull of its own gravitational

field, which is constantly sapping the rate of expansion. It may be, then, that eventually the expansion will slow to a complete halt and that the Universe will make a slow turnabout and begin to contract again. If so, it may be that the Universe, which is now winding down to chaos as it expands, will begin to wind up again as it contracts and will eventually form a new cosmic egg. Naturally this should happen over and over again and we should have an "oscillating Universe." In this case, there is no true beginning and no true ending; the Universe exists forever, with no problem as to where the infinite number of cosmic eggs came from or where the order came from.

This is not only another guess, assumption and childish fable, but it also goes contrary to science by propagating the idea of perpetual motion, which runs counter to the teachings and laws of science. Perpetual motion is an impossible idea. Only an all-powerful and all-wise Creator could create perpetual motion, and He did. (See Chapter XXV, Part 16d.) Asimov's idea also does not explain the origin of matter, gravity, oscillating power, intense temperature, explosions and many other things. Above all, it does not explain where that original atom of energy, that tiny ball of electrons, protons and neutrons came from. No one has the slightest idea, for there can be only a non-material cause and explanation for the beginning of material things.

In another book that Isaac Asimov wrote, *The Collapsing Universe* (1977), he proposes:

It must be admitted that the notion that the universe is continually recycling is a rather tenuous speculation. If we dismiss it, however, we are left with the big bang — either as a one-time affair if we are living in an open universe, or as an endlessly repeated phenomenon if the universe is closed and oscillating. Either way there is a problem.

He then goes on with the cosmic egg, neutron stars, black holes, etc.

The evolutionists reject the belief that God simply created everything by His own almighty power, without using any preexisting matter or materials. They reject this belief because it involves some supernatural force, which they consider unscientific. At least it is a force over, above and beyond the material things of this earth. Yet the evolutionists believe the universe created itself or evolved out of nothing without any outside force or simply always existed with no beginning at all. That can hardly be scientific. Matter just does not create itself. Above all, where did that original matter come from? Why did the explosion take place? What force produced the original explosion?

Yet, at times some astronomers become reasonable and logical. Astronomer Robert Jastrow stated in his book, *God and the Astronomers,* (1978), pp. 11 and 14:

> The essence of the strange developments is that the Universe had, in some sense, a beginning — that it began at a certain moment in time. [Then referring to the Big Bang, he states:] Now we see how the astronomical evidence leads to a biblical view of the origin of the world. The details differ, but the essential elements in the astronomical and biblical accounts of Genesis are the same. [But they are not the same.]

3.   THE BIG BANG AND ITS PROBLEMS

Another problem the evolutionists have with the Big Bang is the old, unreliable and untrustworty belief in "extrapolation," that is, in estimating or inferring that something has taken place or will take place over billions of years in the same ratio as has happened in recent years. The evolutionary doctrine of uniformitarianism is based on this belief. (Extrapolation will be treated a little more fully further on; in this chapter, part 8.) But the creation of the universe and stars took place with everything complete at once in time and space so that the universe immediately was a mature universe, even though today the galaxies *may be* spreading out in space. Space shall be considered a little further on in Part 4 of this chapter.

Another problem with Big Bang is how could such order as exists in the universe today come forth out of the disorder the Big Bang would have created? Any kind of explosion, and especially one as tremendously big as the Big Bang is assumed to be, does not produce order. It makes garbage and a scrap heap out of everything. An explosion like that would not reaccummulate and reunite all the material the explosion created, into stars and planets, and certainly not put them in such orderly fashion that perfect time can be kept by them. That order should follow out of disorder goes contrary to the second law of thermodynamics, which declares that everything naturally becomes more and more disorderly, as we shall see in a discussion of the Second Law of Thermodynamics (Chapter XVII).

In the final anaylsis the whole theory of the origin of the universe, for the evolutionists, is based on a creed or belief that has no scientific foundation. In fact, it is anti-scientific. It is a rebellious, unscientific creed standing also in opposition to the account of creation given to us by the Creator. This attitude has been nicely summarized by an agnostic, Robert Jastrow, in the *Reader's Digest* (July 1980), pp. 51-2:

Now that evidence pointed to the fact that the universe had a beginning, a few scientists dare to ask, "What came before the beginning?" Some, even bolder, asked "Who was the Prime Mover?" The British theorist, Edward Milne wrote "The first cause of the universe is left for the reader to insert. But our picture is incomplete without Him."

Further on, *Reader's Digest* summarizes, pp. 52-3:

Theologians generally are delighted with the proof that the universe had a beginning, but astronomers are curiously upset. . .I think part of the answer is that scientists cannot bear the thought of a natural phenomenon that cannot be explained. There is a kind of religion in science; it is the religion of a person who believes that every event in the universe can be explained in a rational way as the product of some previous event. This faith is violated by the discovery that the world had a beginning under conditions in which the known laws of physics are not valid, and as a product of forces we cannot discover. When that happens, the scientist has lost control. He reacts by ignoring the implications, or by trivializing and calling it the big bang, as if the universe were a firecracker. Consider the immensity of the problem. Science has proved that the universe exploded into being at a certain moment. It asks, What cause produced this effect? Who or what put the matter and energy into the universe? Was the universe created out of nothing, or was it gathered together out of pre-existing materials? And science cannot answer these questions, . . .The scientists' pursuit of the past ends in the moment of Creation. . .Now we would like to pursue that inquiry further back in time, but the barrier seems insurmountable. For the scientist who has lived by his faith in the power of reason, the story ends like a bad dream. He has scaled the mountains of ignorance; he is about to conquer the highest peak; as he pulls himself over the final rock, he is greeted by a band of theologians who have been sitting there for centuries.

What a beautiful confession! The folly and rebellion of evolutionists could not have been summarized better.

From all this it is quite evident the Big Bang idea is doomed, as has happened to so many of the evolutionary *ideas*. I would not rate them as theories. Before the "big bang" idea, there was "the steady state" explanation of the origin of the universe. This idea believes that new matter is constantly being formed out of nothing somewhere in space and is keeping the universe in a steady state. Sir Fred Hoyle, an outstanding astronomer, originated the idea and promoted it for a long time. He finally gave up his so-called theory and now believes the big bang shall also be discarded on the scrap heap of other ideas regarding the evolution of the universe. He stated in "The Big Bang Under Attack" in the *Science Digest* (May 1984) p. 84:

> I have little hesitation in saying that a sickly pall now hangs over the big bang theory. When a pattern of facts becomes set against a theory, experience shows that the theory rarely recovers.

The Big Bang originally took hold of the evolutionists with tremendous enthusiasm, but there is not one bit of real evidence to prove it. It has no scientific foundation. In essence the Big Bang idea like so many other evolutionary ideas is just another fable for them to read to themselves, after they have read Aesop's Fables to their children.

4.   SPACE

What is space? Even scientists do not always agree on a definition. How far does space extend? Immediately we are faced with an unsolvable problem, as far as science is concerned. We must think of space as infinite or as finite, as having limits or having no limits. And we can do neither. If we think of space as being finite, we at once wonder what lies beyond the most distant stars.

When God created the world, He also created the vast expanse of space. When we think of something, we think of the space that it occupies. Something may be far away or it may be near. Things may be low or high, or they may be to the right or to the left of us, in front or back of us. Each object occupies a certain amount of space in length, thickness and breadth. We cannot think of anything as really existing without occupying some space. Thus we cannot picture God's omnipresence to ourselves, for He lives without being hemmed in by the space He created and that He fills all space and yet occupies no space. Since God created space, space very likely is finite or limited.

The *World Book* under "Universe" states regarding its space and size:

Nobody knows just how large our universe is. Einstein's theory of relativity implies that the universe has a definite size. We cannot see its limits because space itself is curved and, like the surface of the earth, has no definite boundaries. Consequently, a light ray from a star does not go out into space and get lost. Instead, it eventually returns to its starting point, like a traveler who journeys around the world.

The accuracy of astronomers in trying to determine the distance of the stars to the earth is very likely as false as the billions of years given for the age of the earth & universe. There is no direct way of measuring the distance of the stars. The guesses of evolutionists here very likely are very wild as their guesses often are. See pages 252 and 301

5.   TIME

The same is true of time. Before the creation there was no time, only eternity. Eternity is something that is not comprehensible to the mind of man. The human mind is bound by time and space and therefore it cannot reach out beyond time and space. Time and space are connected to creation. St. Augustine said the world was not created in time but with time. The universe and the earth and time and space are coexistent and coextensive. St. Augustine stated:

> If there was no time before heaven and earth, why do they ask what God did then? There was no "then" where there was no time.

On the other hand, time has been made a hero by the evolutionists even though time finally is turned into a villain. Evolutionists originally started with millions of years; and finally having failed to fit the evolution of all things in that space of time, they have extended it to *billions* of years. Now they are playing around with *trillions*. Given enough time, they can make the impossible appear possible, the possible becomes probable, and the probable has finally become certain and an actual fact to them. The evolutionists loudly and insistently proclaim that the evolution of the universe, of the earth, of life and of man is an established fact. (See Chapter XXI, Part 7.)

6.   MATTER AND THE ELEMENTS

Together with space and time goes matter or material elements. We know that this universe is made up of matter. That supposedly dead, lifeless matter could get here by itself without any outside Force, Maker or Designer is simply ridiculous. It goes against common sense to believe this. Of what does matter consist? Matter is most familiarly known to consist of molecules. But molecules in turn consist of atoms grouped together to form molecules. The atoms in turn consist of a nucleus of one or more positively charged protons, surrounded by one or more negatively charged electrons. Generally the nucleus also contains neutrons, uncharged particles. The positively charged protons and uncharged neutrons make up the heavy nuclear center of the atom, but occupy very little space. The tiny electrons in comparison make up only a very small fraction of the mass of the atoms, yet in moving around the nucleus they occupy most of the space of the atom.

The different elements in the universe consist of these atoms made of varying numbers of protons, neutrons and electrons. The simplest atom, hydrogen, consists of a single proton surrounded by a single orbiting electron. All other atoms consist of a nucleus of protons and neutrons (together called nucleons) around which moves a swarm of electrons in orderly fashion. There are 92 different naturally occurring elements (plus other man-made elements) ranging from hydrogen, the lightest and most abundant, to the heavier uranium. Altogether there are over 100 elements. Uranium 238 contains 92 protons and 146 neutrons and 92 electrons. Complex atoms like uranium degenerate into less complex ones like lead. They never go into the reverse order.

Where all these protons, neutrons and electrons and the accompanying positive or negative electrical charges and radiation come from is a question that transcends the bounds of science at every stage of the study of the architecture of the atom. Evidence of a Designer is evident at every stage of the atom. As an explanation of their origin and design any process of a struggle for existence or the survival of the fittest cannot be invoked, as the evolutionists are inclined to do. Atoms are "a universe within a universe!"

The entire universe is made up of these atoms or elements. The most predominant is hydrogen, the lightest and simplest of all, followed by helium. It is claimed that 99 percent of the total mass of our universe now consists of hydrogen and helium. The amazing thing about the tiny atom, which no man can see, is that it contains a universe in miniature with its suns, stars and planets, called protons, neutrons, and electrons. It is a little universe in itself. This tiny universe is as completely organized as the great universe above and around us. Everywhere there is evidence of design, order and thought behind it. Seeing how immense the universe is, people often wonder whether God could be concerned about them, tiny little specks on a tiny earth, which is a speck itself compared to the entire universe. But if God is concerned about the untold endless atoms He created, He certainly is concerned also about me, who consists of trillions of atoms, and above all also of a spirit created in the image of God.

7.   LIGHT

In connection with space, time and matter we should also consider light. Genesis 1:3 states that God created light the first day. Then Genesis 1:14 states that on the fourth day "God said, Let there be lights in the firmament of the heaven to divide the day from the night." Evidently God created two different things on the first and fourth day. On the first day He created the elemental light or the essence of light without any sun, moon or stars. An indication of this light is given in Revelation 21:23-24 where in writing about heaven and eternity, the apostle John wrote: "And the city had no need of the sun, neither of the moon, to shine in it: for the glory of God did lighten it, and the Lamb is the light thereof. And the nations of them which are saved shall walk in the light of it." God could fill the whole universe with the brightest light without suns and stars. There can be light without the sun and stars, as is evident by the light produced by electrical or chemical action. Also fireflies and other insects and fish can throw off light.

On the fourth day God created luminous bodies to cast light upon the earth. Adam and Eve could immediately see these distant heavenly bodies. The original creation evidently was a completed creation. This included a fully functioning universe with all its parts fully in place. The universe had an appearance of age at the very moment of creation.

Appearance of age is evident from a number of acts of creation. Adam was created as a full grown man. Without any education He knew all the different animals and gave them names. If we could go back in time to the Garden of Eden we would find him to be the most knowledgeable man we ever met. Also all the land animals, the fish and the birds were fully mature and were able to reproduce their kind at once. Also plants were created fully mature and bore fruit at the time of creation. There is no question that God created not only a fully mature earth, with rocks appearing as old as today, but also a fully mature universe with the stars and their light beams fully in place as they are today.

One more thing regarding light should be mentioned, and that is the speed of light. Today it is calculated that light travels 186,000 miles per second. Some scientists are thinking that the speed of light has not always been the same, but that it was much faster in the past. As everything else in this universe, the speed of light may be decaying.

Kupal, in his book *Man and His Universe* (1972), states about the same thing when he wrote, p. 294:

Is it, moreover, certain that photons of light reaching us from distant parts of the Universe after a travel-time of hundreds, or thousands of millions of years will do so with their original energy (i.e. wavelength) unchanged — or do they, perchance, lose some of it enroute? We know remarkably little of what light does as it travels through empty spaces.

8.   EXTRAPOLATIONS

Professor E. H. Andrews in *Is Evolution Scientific?* wrote, p. 14, regarding "The Danger of Extrapolation,"

The second abuse is that of extrapolation. That is when a theory, which may be perfectly good in one realm, is extended, without justification into realms where it is not known to apply . . . if we try to extrapolate that theory and force it to apply on an atomic scale, or to things traveling close to the velocity of light, we shall be doing violence to it and our prediction will be false. So there is a danger in extrapolation. . .

Many of the follies of evolution are based on faulty assumptions and extrapolations, in which one estimates what happened in the past or will happen in the future on the basis of what is happening at the present time and assuming that things have always been the same and will be the same in the future.

Another big mistake that evolutionists make in extrapolating is that, in their claim to be scientific, they ignore that there could have been a non-material Force and Designer behind the purely material things the evolutionists base their beliefs on. And as far as the earth is concerned, they ignore the havoc and destruction that that tremendous world-wide Flood had on this earth. The destruction that took place during the Flood makes it impossible to extrapolate the age of the earth, on the basis of the uniformitarian belief in the gradual geological formation of this earth.

9.   THE UNIVERSE

In recent decades astronomers have proclaimed all kinds of fantastic stories regarding the universe. How much of this is based on actual scientific facts is unknown. But knowing how many of the stories that evolutionists have been proclaiming to the public are mere assumptions, presumptions and simple fiction and fables without scientific foundation, one must question much of what astronomers proclaim.

Up to and until the last century the stars that were seen by the naked eye numbered about 3,000. This did not seem to add up to what God promised Abraham, Genesis 22:17: "In blessing I will bless thee, and in multiplying I will multiply thy seed as the stars of the heaven, and as the sand which is upon the seashore." Knowing that the descendants of Abraham run into billions the promise of God that Abraham's seed would be as many as the stars of heaven, did not jibe with only 3,000 stars. But today giant telescopes and other devices have revealed that the stars run into trillions, and counting them would be like trying to count "the sand which is upon the seashore." So God's prophecy was scientifically correct. Genesis 2:1 states: "Thus the heavens and the earth were finished, and all the host of them." Jeremiah 33:22 declares: "[T]he host of heaven cannot be numbered, neither the sand of the sea measured."

Today, with literally billions of galaxies found by giant telescopes, and in turn billions of stars in the galaxies, the number of stars is truly incomprehensible. Equally amazing is the variety of stars: pulsars (pulsating stars), neutron stars, red giants, white dwarfs and many other kinds. It is as I Corinthians 15:41 states: "There is one glory of the sun, and another glory of the moon, and another glory of the stars; for one star differs from another star in glory."

Regarding the number of galaxies and stars, the *Reader's Digest* (September 1974), from a condensed version of a *National Geographic* article states:

> Today we know that galaxies are as common as blades of grass in a meadow. They number perhaps 100 billion. . .The world's largest working optical telescope — can see as many as a million galaxies inside the bowl of the Big Dipper alone.

The complexity and immensity of the awesome universe simply leaves man bewildered. The *National Geographic* (May 1974) in "The Incredible Universe," states that the present knowledge of the universe leaves man "stunned."

10.   QUASARS

Quasars is a shortened name for *Quasi Stellar Radio Sources*. Quasars, which were first discovered in 1963, are mysterious objects that appear in the sky as starlike objects, but seem to create more energy than 100 billion stars, according to some astronomers. About 3,500 quasars have been found, and they are thought to be located near the very edge of time and space. In 1986 one quasar was found which astronomers thought was 73 billion trillion miles from the earth (73,000,000,000,000,000,000,000,000). That's quite a distance. But remember what I said previously about the measurements of astronomers being way off, p. 161. Their estimates of distance may be wilder than their estimates of time with guesses of billions of years and millions of light-years. One writer summed up the quasar problem nicely by saying, "Let us, however, abandon the quasars wherever they may be, and return to the more normal galaxies."

11.   THE UNCERTAINTIES OF SCIENTISTS REGARDING THE UNIVERSE

Furthermore, evolutionists and above all true scientists and astronomers question their own findings.

On November 4, 1985, the *Minneapolis Tribune* printed this commentary by Eugene Mallove, an astronomical engineer:

Scientists puzzle over coincidences of the cosmos. Some scientists are awestruck by the numerous improbable physical coincidences in the universe, without which life could not exist. Their work is forcing them to ask the ultimate philosophical question, long the province of religion: Did the universe come into being by chance or by design?. . .Some cosmologists are proposing that the universe has been perfectly "designed" for life in a way that could not have happened "by chance.". . and evolved on a planetary surface only by the grace of many congenial circumstances [coincidences] — not too warm, not too cold, the right chemicals, the right energies, neither too little nor too much stability in the environment.

Regarding coincidences or coinciding occurrences, the *Reader's Digest* (December 1946) printed an article by Cressy Morrison, former president of the New York Academy of Sciences, entitled "Seven Reasons Why a Scientist Believes in God." He pointed to many coinciding facts well known to science which:

prove that our universe was designed and erected by a great engineering Intelligence. For one, we are just the right distance from the sun. If we were closer to the sun we would roast in heat and if farther away it would be too cold to sustain life. If the earth rotated one tenth as fast as it does, the days and nights would be ten times longer. Then during the day the sun would burn up all the vegetation and at night the temperature would drop so low that the plants that survived the days would freeze. Then also the distance of the moon from the earth is about right. If the moon were only 50,000 miles from us, the ocean tides would be so immense that all continents would be submerged in water twice a day.

Notice how correct is the conclusion of Sir Isaac Newton:

This admirably beautiful structure of sun, planets and comets could not have originated except in the wisdom and sovereignty of an intelligent and powerful Being.

Or as Professor Harlow Shapley, director of Harvard Observatory, said:

I cannot imagine the planets getting together and deciding under what law they would operate. Nor do we find anywhere in the solar or stellar systems the debris that would necessarily accumulate if the universe had been operating at random.

Finally the question is: What is behind this gigantic universe that is so finely arranged and tuned, to keep it in place? The earth revolves on its axis, it moves around the sun in a constantly tilted position, and the entire solar system moves on in space in its Milky Way galaxy among all the other stars, and all the galaxies maintain their distance and place. Can you imagine the stars and galaxies with billions of other stars getting together and deciding to keep out of each others way, especially after all this should have happened as a result of an immense explosion? Could this finely adjusted mechanism of the universe be the result of self-starting, hit and miss action and motion? There must be a Master Designer, there must be a non-material Being greater than the lifeless materials and elements of this universe, there must be a God, a non-material Being, whose tremendous mind and will has planned it all, created it all and still sustains it. It takes a mind, the mind of a supreme Thinker whose will is wise, good and all-powerful to create this universe.

12.   STARS

In regard to the creation of stars Genesis 1:16 states briefly, "He made the stars also." An immense amount of creation is included in those few words, since God compared the number of the stars in heaven to "the sand which is upon the seashore." Jeremiah 33:22 declares: "The host of heaven cannot be numbered." He lived 650 B.C. Ptolemy in A.D. 100 counted only 1022 stars. Galileo in 1742 counted a few thousand. That the stars are as numerous as the sand upon the seashore, and are numberless, is clearly known today. In recent decades giant telescopes and other devices have revealed that this is a scientific fact. God was very generous in His creation of matter.

Men today working in astrophysics (the study of stars) do not know how any of the stars really were formed. In a recent book review a noted astrophysicist, Harwitt, 1986, commented in regard to the origin of stars: "The silent embarrassment of modern astrophysics is that we do not know how even a single one of these stars managed to form. There's no lack of ideas, of course, we just can't substantiate them."

According to the evolutionary theory of the origin of the universe everything was blown to smithereens at the time of the Big Bang. That the stars and galaxies could have condensed out of this debris and finally combined by gravity into balls of fiery hydrogen is totally unreal. How did this immense amount of hydrogen form from such a small cosmic egg and then where did the gravity come from? NASA has available a pamphlet entitled "Lifestyles of the Stars." It starts out:

STAR BIRTH. Stars are believed to originate by the condensation of enormous clouds of cosmic dust and hydrogen gas...There are many such clouds in our universe. The motivating force behind the birth of a star is gravity. [But what is the origin of the clouds of cosmic dust and of gravity? They explain how this mass develops into a star. They say:] At first the cloud contracts rapidly, because the heat released by contraction is easily radiated outward. Then the cloud grows smaller and more dense, so that heat created at the center cannot immediately escape to the exterior. This causes a rapidly rising internal temperature, slowing down but not stopping the constant contraction. At a certain time the interior of the star becomes so dense, and its temperature so high, that thermonuclear fusion begins. This is the actual birth of the star. In thermonuclear fusion two atoms of hydrogen are converted into one atom of helium, the second lightest element, and so on.

But no proof is given for any of this. It is all based on guessing, assuming and presuming. Above all, this runs counter to the laws of thermodynamics, which declare that total mass energy remains unchanged, but that the usefulness of the energy is contantly decreasing.

Then the NASA pamphlet explains how stars may burn up all their nuclear fuel and "may finally become a White Dwarf, Neutron Stars, or a Black Hole." That such degeneration is taking place is very likely according to the second law of thermodynamics.

Mulfinger (1968) writes:

Contrary to popular belief, not a single star, planet or galaxy has ever been seen forming spontaneously out of cosmic debris.

Such imaginary evolutionary processes do not even work on paper. Why, then, are we continually told that we live in an evolutionary universe rather than in a degenerating universe? Because of the implications of such an admission. A universe that is running down demands a Creator who "wound it up" at the beginning. And astronomers today have a morbid fear of the stigma of creationism. . .It is now understood that stars are consuming their fuel at a fantastic rate, losing mass and radiating energy in all directions, never to be recovered. Violent destructive events such as novae and super-novae have been observed — stars blasting fragments of their material into space at incredible velocities. (See page 301 about stars.)

Evidently stars too, like everything on earth, are undergoing a slow degeneration, a slow death, all according to God's second law of thermodynamics imposed at the time of the Fall of Man.

13.   THE STAR OF BETHLEHEM

One specially created star, the Star of Bethlehem, must be considered, because so many false stories have been devised and propagated concerning it. Every year around Christmas time some astronomers go around the country proclaiming that the Star of Bethlehem very likely was a conjunction of two bright planets, Jupiter and Saturn, and perhaps also Mars, a conjunction which occurs only once in eight centuries.

Again, some think that the Star of Bethlehem was Donati's comet blazing over the skies of Bethlehem. They say when Donati's comet raced past the earth in 1858, astronomers calculated that it would take another 1800 years before it would appear again. And so, figuring back about 1800 years from 1858, Donati's comet could have appeared about the time Christ was born.

See how foolish all these theories are! How could a conjunction of planets or a collision of stars, or supernovas, or comets direct the wise men from the East to Jerusalem and then south to Bethlehem and also remain in a fixed position over the place in Bethlehem where the young child was? That star, we are told in Matthew, *went before* them, *moved as a guide,* it *came* or *arrived,* and it *stood.* Furthermore Bethlehem is south of Jerusalem and ordinary stars move from east to west and never stop and stand over a certain place.

What these wise men saw was a startling phenomenon, shining brightly like a star, but so low in the heaven that it could stand above a house to distinguish it from other houses. Man loves to explain away the miracles of God, and then create impossible and contradictory miracles to help out God. There may have been a conjunction of planets or comets at the time, but they certainly had nothing to do with the Star of Bethlehem. That star was a special light, placed by God in the lower regions of our atmosphere close to the earth for the special purpose of guiding and directing the wise men to where the Savior of mankind was.

Above all, if man can place a spaceship or a balloon to go around the earth and glow so that it can be seen from earth, why should it be so unusual or impossible or unbelievable for God, who made all the immense stars of the heaven, to place a small star in the sky at Christ's birth? We have space objects today that appear to stay stationary in one place above the earth as news and weather satellites. Also, since God sent angels to the shepherds to announce the birth of Christ, He could just as easily have created a special star to guide and direct the wise men. Certainly God does not need the help of astronomers to make the Star of Bethlehem appear reasonable and scientific.

14.   BLACK HOLES

One of the most fantastic stories devised by evolutionary astronomers in recent years is the story of black holes. They are important in the evolutionary fable because black holes laid the foundation for the Big Bang fable.

NASA, in its pamphlet, *Lifestyles of the Stars,* says in regard to the stars:

A large dying star shrinks into such incredible density that its gravity becomes so great in proportion to its size that nothing, not even light, can escape its surface. Therefore, it literally becomes a 'black hole' in space. Any matter or light that approaches such a star is sucked downward to its surface and vanishes.

Lloyd Motz, in *The Universe: Its Beginning and End,* expands on the story:

Eventually the collapse of the universe will bring the stars that are not black holes in the galaxies so close together that collisions between them will tear them apart and the stellar matter they contain will be smeared out into a uniform gas. If black holes in the universe collide, they will merge to form larger black holes, and if a star collides with a black hole, the matter in the star will be swallowed up by the black hole. By this time the temperature of the universe will have risen to millions of degrees and the radiation itself will disrupt any stars that are still around. But in time the radiation, too, will be swallowed up by black holes and then the black holes themselves will begin to merge until a single black hole is left, which will be the final state of the universe. Shortly before this happens the universe will resemble the fireball from which it began, but now it will be an imploding and not an expanding fireball. All the matter in the universe must ultimately collapse to a single black hole, but what happens after that?

The *Family Weekly* June 1, 1980, expanded on this:

The material in the squeezed core of the black hole is incredibly dense. One teaspoon weighs a billion tons. The pull of gravity on the surface of this dense plug of matter is inconceivably great; in fact, gravity is so strong that nothing can escape from the squeezed star, not even a ray of light can get away. Since no rays of light can get out, the star is invisible. It has become a *black hole* in space. This is the meaning of the black hole: It is an enormously compressed object whose gravity is so powerful that nothing can escape. Everything inside the black hole is trapped there forever. Once a black hole forms, it will capture anything that falls into it. Black holes are insatiable. As they capture more matter, the pull of their gravity becomes more powerful, and they capture still more matter. Eventually black holes will swallow the universe.

Lloyd Motz on page 312 of his book *The Universe* continues:

If the same ideas are now applied to the collapsing universe, one can argue that as the implosions of the universe continue into the black hole stage and beyond. . .some kind of violent rebound or explosion will again occur and that another expansion phase of the universe will begin, leading ultimately to another cycle of stars - building, synthesis of elements, and finally planets and life itself.

What a fable!

Evolutionary fiction writer, Isaac Asimov, in *The Collapsing Universe* comes forth with the same kind of tale, p. 148:

Even black holes will, little by little, disgorge, and in the end the universe will be a vast, incredibly thin cloud of gravel, dust, and gas growing endlessly vaster and thinner. If this is so, it might seem that the universe began as a huge mass of compressed matter and will end as a huge volume of thin matter. This raises the puzzle of where the compressed matter came from. We needn't worry about the matter as such, for it is just a very compact form of energy, and we might suppose that the energy has always existed and always will exist — much of it in the form of matter. The question is, how did the matter come to be compressed into the cosmic egg to begin with?. . .Why may not this be repeated over and over? Why, in short, might there not be an endlessly *oscillating universe?* [On page 158 he continues with the Cosmic Egg:] It must be admitted that the notion that the universe is continually recycling is a rather tenuous speculation [tenuous means thin, flimsy]. . .If it is true that anything with more than 3.2 times the mass of our Sun must form a black hole when it collapses, then the cosmic egg was the biggest of all black holes. How, then, could it have exploded and yielded the big bang? Black holes do not explode.

And yet *just before this* he said matter is compressed into a cosmic egg and cosmic eggs explode.

All this unproven talk about black holes, cosmic eggs and big bangs was well summarized in the *Minneapolis Tribune* (January 8, 1986) by one of two astronomers who claim they found a third black hole. The *Tribune* reported that Ronald Remillard, of the Massachusetts Institute of Technology after attending a meeting of the American Astronomical Society in Houston:

said the existence of black holes was impossible to prove. Although their presence can only be deduced by observation of the objects around them, "the circumstances can be strong enough in some minds to be proof," he said.

Remillard rightly stated: *There is no proof of black holes.*

15.   THE SUN AND THE SOLAR SYSTEM

How did the sun and its planets get here? The Bible is very clear on this: God created them on the fourth day together with the stars. But since our country's scientific and political powers, controlled by the evolutionists, do not want to believe this, the NASA space program was given many billions of dollars to learn how and when the solar system "evolved." Now after landings on the moon, space probes and other space activities and space instruments, they are no closer to finding an evolutionary origin of the solar system than they were twenty years ago.

But in spite of the billions of dollars spent to help evolutionists try to prove the evolution of the moon and the earth billions of years ago, some of our astronauts, living in a world of realism, logic and common sense, came back from the moon with a different story. Commander

Eugene Cernan of the Apollo 17 flight, who also had been on the Apollo 10 flight to the moon, said shortly after his return to the earth:

When you look at the earth from the moon and you see the perfection of it and the beauty of it and the logic of it all, you know it didn't happen by accident. The earth is moving with beauty and you get a feeling that you are looking at our earth as God envisioned it when He created it. [Cernan also said:] You know the Russians said that they went up in space and looked around and said they proved there was no God, because they didn't see Him. [Then Cernan added:] No, I didn't see any God either, but I know there is someone bigger than us all behind this because of what I saw and felt. Mankato *Free Press* 11-30-92

Commander David Scott of Apollo 15 said:

What impressed me was looking at the earth and finding it is the only color in the universe. You sort of think that you have to take care of our earth, because it is the only home in the reachable vicinity.

Even a physicist mentioned how valuable this planet is, when men realize how disappointing a place the solar system is, except for the earth.

Another astronaut summarized it all very emphatically while preaching to a group of people. In one hand he held a rock he brought back from the moon and in the other hand he held the Bible symbolizing Christ, who is referred to as the Rock in the Bible; and he asked them: "Which Rock are you going to cling to?"

When we consider the heavens, the sun, the moon, the billions of galaxies, and the trillions of stars which God has created, we must humbly confess with Psalm 8,4: "What is man that thou art mindful of him and the son of man that thou visitest him?" Yes, although the universe is great and God who created the universe is infinitely greater, and although this beautiful blue, white, green and brown earth is but a mere speck in this vast universe, nevertheless, God is deeply concerned about this earth, in spite of all its griefs and miseries that man brought upon himself by his sin and rebellion against God. Although we human beings are in turn but mere specks upon this earth and like atoms compared to the rest of the universe, yet, of the entire earth and universe, God is most deeply concerned about us. It is as Psalm 113:4-7 declares:

The LORD is high above all nations, And His glory above the heaven. . .who humbles Himself to behold the things that are in

the heavens and in the earth? He raises the poor out of the dust,
And lifts the needy out of the ash heap. NKJV

All the manned voyages to the moon, as well as the unmanned
missions to various planets, have clearly shown that all the planets and
satellite moons are vastly different from each other, so that they could
hardly be the result of any evolutionary process. The same is true of the
sun and all its sister suns or stars. They too are vastly different from each
other, and so they could hardly result from one evolutionary process.
Although the sun and moon are referred to in Genesis as the great lights
in comparison to the stars, yet there are many stars that are much larger
than our sun. But God presents this from the viewpoint of us on this
earth — from our viewpoint and not from the viewpoint of the entire
universe.

The sun, the moon and the stars were placed in the heavens after
the earth had been created, after elemental light had shown upon it,
and after vegetation had been placed upon the dry land. They were
placed in the heavens for light, for signs and for calendars as Genesis
1:14 declares: "Let there be lights in the firmament of heaven. . .for
signs and for seasons, and for days, and years."

Dr. Alfred Rehwinkel in his wonderful book, *The Wonders of
Creation,* summarizes the purpose and usefulness of the sun very
correctly on p. 139:

> The energy of the sun radiated upon the atmosphere of our
> planet is responsible for the climate and the weather and changes
> in the weather; it gives rise to the winds and storms on land and
> sea. It raises millions and billions of tons of water from the ocean,
> vaporizes and demineralizes it; collects the vapors into clouds,
> moves the clouds thousands of miles over land and sea by the
> energy of the wind, which is also produced by the energy of the
> sun, condenses the vapors, and then scatters them again on the
> dry land to make life possible. The energy of the sun activates the
> germ of life hidden in the seed and causes it to grow, to produce
> the plant and to reproduce itself. The green leaf, with its
> mysterious chlorophyll, would not be possible without the energy
> of the sun. There could be no forests on the mountainsides or
> green meadows for cattle and sheep and there would be no flowers
> or fruit to delight the heart of man without the energy of the sun.

God could have created the necessary light in another way as He
did on the first day when He created elemental light and He will do so

again in eternity for His saved children, as Revelations 21:23 and 22:5 state:

> And the city [the temple of God] had no need of the sun or of the moon to shine in it, for the glory of God illuminated it and the Lamb is its Light. And the nations of those who are saved walk in its light. . .And there shall be no night there: They need no lamp nor light of the sun, for the Lord God gives them light. And they shall reign forever and ever. NKJV

16.   THE PLANETS AND THEIR SATELLITE MOONS

The nine satellite planets of the sun in the solar system, starting with the one closest to the sun are: Mercury, Venus, Earth, Mars, Jupiter, Saturn, Uranus, Neptune, and Pluto. Some of these planets in turn have satellite moons going around them. This entire solar system is just part of a giant galaxy of about 100 billion stars, it is claimed. Our sun is about three-fifths of the way from the center to the edge of the Milky Way. As the sun revolves around the center of this mass of stars, the earth and all the other planets and moons tag along in perfect order, all keeping their places in perfect time and harmony.

What keeps the solar system, the planets and the moon in perfect order without banging into one another? Not only did some Originator, Creator and Designer have to create all these different galaxies, different stars, different planets, different moons, and different comets, He must also design a way of keeping them apart as they speed around in space as a solar system, planet systems and moon systems. To keep them in place two different forces had to be designed and created. The one force is gravity that keeps them from flying off into space and into each other. Then another force had to be created — the right amount of speed around the mother sphere to counteract or balance the force of gravity. According to the evolutionary belief or creed all this was supposed to have happened by itself, by chance.

Furthermore, all the planets are extremely different from each other and different from the sun. They could hardly have resulted from a common evolutionary origin and process. Heinz Haber, in *Our Blue Planet* (1965) translated from German, writes: pp. 10-11

> In earlier times, it was held that the planetary system owed its existence to a kind of birth from the sun. This rather primitive concept had to be abandoned when it was found that the sun, on the one hand, and the planets Mercury, Earth, and Mars, on the other hand, have altogether different chemical compositions. The

sun consists largely of hydrogen and helium, the two simplest, lightest, and most basic chemical elements. The earthlike planets, however, consist mostly of the heavier elements: oxygen, silicon, iron, nickel, and many others. The main ingredients of the sun, hydrogen and helium, are quite rare on the terrestrial planets. This is why those early, naive concepts about the origin of the planets had to be discarded.

Heinz Haber is not a creationist.

Not only are the four inner planets (Mercury, Venus, Earth and Mars) different chemically from the sun, but they are also very different from each other and from the other five planets. As NASA in its space probes penetrated farther and deeper into space, they were more and more amazed at the variations they observed. Not only on the moon and on Mars but also on Venus, Jupiter and Saturn they were continually surprised by the unexpected, and by the variety of differences.

Not only are the planets and their satellites different in makeup, but also different in the directions of their rotations. Venus and Uranus rotate in the opposite direction from the other planets. Also a few of the moons of the planets rotate in a direction opposite from that of their planets.

The final question on this subject is: Why are the planets and their moons and their sun so different from each other? The simple answer is: God made them different for good purposes. Very likely one purpose could be to confuse, confound and condemn the evolutionists when they stand before God with all their human wisdom on the day of judgment. If the planets had evolved, they would all be about the same.

17.   ONE OF THE PURPOSES OF THE SPACE FLIGHTS

The February 1976 *Reader's Digest*, p. 133, mentioned in regard to the Viking flight to Mars:

The Viking assault on Mars is the most ambitious unmanned space venture ever attempted. Though the investment — a hefty $1 billion — is sizeable, the return could have enormous philosophical value. Evidence of life in any form, present or past, on a second planet in our solar system would be proof that life is a cosmic statistic, not a terrestrial miracle. It would also be a convincing argument that the human species is not alone in the universe.

However, Henry Hiebert, in his book *Evolution: Its Collapse in View* (1979), p. 111, states and asks:

The Viking probe of Mars has shown that no organic molecules exist on that planet, in spite of the presence of carbon, nitrogen, oxygen, and hydrogen atoms, these being the constituents of organic matter on earth. Why, if life originated through spontaneous generation, did the same things not happen on the surface of Mars?

18. BRIEF FACTS REGARDING THE PLANETS

A. MERCURY

Mercury is the planet closest to the sun and also the smallest. It has no moon. It is about 1/16 as large as the earth. It moves around the sun in 88 days. Being close to the sun, it has temperatures between 500 to 770 degrees Fahrenheit, which make it one of the hottest planets. The other hot one is Venus with about 860 degrees Fahrenheit.

B. VENUS

Between Mercury and the Earth is Venus, our closest planet and about the same size as the earth. It has volcanic peaks, high plateaus, mountains higher than Mt. Everest, and impact craters. It rotates in reverse of the other planets in a clockwise direction instead of counter-clockwise. Why should it do this if it evolved with the other planets? Russian spacecraft pictures of Venus showed rock slabs, boulders and lava. Clouds of concentrated sulphuric acid covering Venus hide a world so forbidding and so hot that one NASA scientist says the planet fits "the classical view of hell." Besides the heat, the pressure is about equal to being 3,000 feet below sea level. The air is about 50 times as dense as the air on the earth. The question would be, if one went there, whether would one boil first or be crushed to death by the pressure.

The *Minneapolis Tribune* (December 11, 1978) reports about sending space probes to Venus:

Data from Venus surprises experts. Information from earth's latest encounter with Venus may force a complete revision of theories about how the solar system formed, scientists reported. "It was a totally unexpected result that we've come up with," said Dr. M. McElroy, a Harvard University physicists. "It appears that Venus formed of different stuff from earth". . .The scientists found that the Venus atmosphere appears to contain Argon-36 gas in proportions as much as 100 times greater than on earth or Mars. The findings are important because that type of argon — an inert gas — cannot be created after a planet's formation, and if Venus was formed the way Earth and Mars were, it probably would have about the same concentrations. It means that either Venus was formed from substances different from those for the rest of the solar system or the formation process itself was different.

Evidently God did not want to make a monotonous universe, so He made different kinds of stars and planets. Behold the blue, marble-like Earth, the red Mars, the beautiful Jupiter and Saturn as we shall see further on. Why shouldn't God have made the stars and planets as different as He made the animals and plants on this earth different: elephants, ants, whales, horses, redwood trees and tiny plants, all extremely different from each other?

C. MARS

After Venus and the Earth with its moon comes red-colored Mars. (The Moon and the Earth will be considered after the other planets.) Mars is the third smallest planet. Its diameter is about one half that of the Earth. Like the Earth it takes 24 hours to turn on its axis; and like the earth it is tilted about 24 degrees but it takes 682 days to go around the sun compared to 365 for the earth. Its seasons are similiar to those of the Earth but almost twice as long. It is the nearest planet on which an astronaut could land. It has no seas, so it has more land surface than the Earth. The temperature becomes comfortably warm at times, but the nights are very cold. The soil is rich in iron and silicon, and because of the iron it is rust colored. It has pink skies, sand dunes and many boulders. It also has many extinct volcanoes that are larger than any on earth and canyons that would stretch across much of the United States. One volcano is three times higher than Mt. Everest, with a crater big enough to hold the state of Rhode Island.

Before the space landings, it was thought that Mars might have some form of life, since it is a similiar distance from the sun as the earth and because it might have water. After our astronauts landed on the moon they discovered that life on the moon is impossible. That left only Mars as a place for life, since the other planets are either too hot or too cold. Evolutionists believe that if life evolved on earth purely by a number of accidents, then life must exist also on other planets and in other regions of space. In fact, some even believe that life was brought to this earth from other regions of space.

But arch-evolutionist Carl Sagan of Cornell University, a constant spokesman for the evolutionary cause, wrote in a "Special to The *Los Angeles Times,*" as reported in the Mankato, Minnesota, *The (Mankato) Free Press* (August 2, 1976):

. . .Mars must illuminate the question of the origin of life on Earth. For we will then have examined two planets near each other in space, equally old, with rather similiar environments, but life has begun and evolved on one but not on the other. Why?. . .The conditions necessary for the origin of life are now gone irretrievably from both Earth and Mars. . .In the early histories of these planets, however, abundant biological organic chemistry must have occurred.

Why does he say, "*Must have occurred?*" Not because biological organic chemistry or *life* has occurred or evolved, but because the evolutionary explanation for the origin of life demands it. Yes, the failure to find life on Mars is a serious obstacle to the evolutionists and it gives the answer to the question of whether evolution is a fact or merely fables and fiction without any scientific proof.

Regarding life and water being found on Mars, *The (Mankato) Free Press*, printed an article (July 25, 1978), two years after two Viking landers had landed on Mars, entitled "Mars still a Mystery," by George Alexander of *The Los Angeles Times:*

Organic molecules would find it difficult, if not impossible, to maintain chemical links between various carbon, hydrogen, nitrogen, and oxygen atoms under that kind of radioactive onslaught. And that is what an organic chemistry experiment aboard each of the Viking landers found: Nothing. If organic compounds are out of stock on Mars, so too is free running water. What passes for 'bone-dry' on Earth would comparatively speaking be 'wringing wet' on Mars, so arid is the latter.

D. JUPITER

The fifth and sixth planets from the sun are Jupiter and Saturn. Jupiter, 89,000 miles in diameter, and Saturn, 75,000 miles, are giant spheres of atmosphere covering a liquid or solid nucleus about as large as the earth. Both planets rotate about once every 10 hours. Jupiter has 16 satellite moons. The four outer moons move around Jupiter in the opposite direction of the other eight moons. Saturn has 17 moons and the outermost ones move in the opposite direction from the other eight. Planet Uranus and its 15 moons all move in the opposite direction of the earth and other planets. Neptune has 8 satellites, and one of them, Triton, moves in the opposite direction. If all these planets and satellites were of evolutionary origin, they certainly should all be moving in the same direction. But evidently here also the Creator wanted variety in the solar system.

JUPITER and all other planets are strikingly different from each other in numerous ways, so they could hardly have evolved. Jupiter is a rapidly spinning ball of liquid and gas, ten times the size of the earth and larger than all the other planets combined. Because of its enormous mass (318 times as massive as the earth) its gravity is immense also. An astronaut landing on the giant planet would be stuck to the spot by its gravitational pull. But one could not land on Jupiter because it has no surface to land on. The most unusual feature of Jupiter is the Great Red Spot, an orange red oval 15,000 miles long and 8,000 miles wide, about the size of the Pacific Ocean. This spot has been there for 300 years or more. The entire planet is colored and looks like a giant Christmas tree ornament spinning in space. It is just another one of God's endlessly beautiful objects in space, another jewel.

E. SATURN

Just as beautiful, unusual and striking is Saturn with its many magnificient majestic rings. These are not solid, but are composed of billions of small objects, ranging in size from marbles to basketballs and larger, each orbiting in its own orbit around the planet. As they orbit they appear to be like twisted strands of material shimmering in the light of the sun, criss-crossing each other. Saturns rings are made up of many different brightly colored rings. If Saturn evolved, the rings most likely would all be of one color and material.

F. URANUS, NEPTUNE AND PLUTO

The solar system's three outer planets are Uranus with 15 moons, Neptune with 8 and Pluto with one. Pluto has been observed, so far only from earth-based telescopes.

Regarding all these planets and moons, Dr. David Morrison, a planetary astronomer at the University of Hawaii, said in a 1981 news report that the exploration of the solar system has

> produced a revolution in our concept of the solar system and the earth's place in it. Most outstanding to me is the incredible diversity of what we've seen. Each of the two dozen bodies we've looked at is unique.

Truly, it is a majestic and diverse earth and solar system and universe that God created for the delight of mankind.

19.   THE MOON

The moon's diameter is 2,160 miles, or about one-fourth the diameter of the earth. It travels around the earth at about 2288 miles per hour. While the moon travels around the earth it also rotates just fast enough so that the same side of the moon is always turned to the earth. Because of this we see only one side of the moon from the earth.

While one of the basic reasons for spending all those billions of dollars in sending men to the moon was to find evidence for the origin of the moon and earth and the universe, and also to find the origin of life, yet an AP news release from the *Houston Space Center* stated, July 18, 1979: "The basic question of its origin remains unanswered."

Three different theories have been given for the origin of the moon. First, according to the "fission," splitting apart, or escape theory, the moon is a daughter of the earth. Originally, they claim, the earth and moon were together in the shape of a sausage and finally the smaller end broke off to form the moon. A later version of this theory was that the moon was torn or exploded out of the Pacific Ocean basin. This theory has been disproved because geological evidence shows that the ocean basin, even according to evolutionary thinking, cannot be older than 200 million years, which is much too young for the claimed age of over four billion years for the moon. That the ocean basin shows such young age, even according to evolution, is no doubt due to the sedimentation from the Flood. Charles Darwin's son, George, according to *Cosmos, Earth and Man* by Preston Cloud, p. 102, also concluded:

that the moon had somehow become detached from Earth, leaving the Pacific Ocean as a birthmark. That would certainly have been enough to split the Earth. Indeed, as geophysics now tells us, it is unlikely that either Earth or moon could have survived such an event.

Such fables are appealing to young children. One day, while I was teaching in a school, an eighth grader was very insistent that this is the origin of the moon. But if the moon exploded from the Pacific Ocean, the force should certainly have taken a large amount of water with it. Furthermore, as the Associated Press stated July 18, 1979:

Most experts now discount the fission theory because the chemical composition of the Earth and moon are so different.

The "double planet" theory believes that the earth and moon condensed into separate bodies when the solar system was formed, and that they are sister planets. Then why are they chemically and structurally so different as we shall see further on?

According to the "capture" theory, the moon was formed elsewhere and was captured by the earth's gravity. But a large body like the moon passing close to the earth would more likely smash into the earth or miss it completely, not slowing down enough to go into orbit.

H. C. Urey, a Nobel-prize-winning chemist, summed up the different theories by saying in The *Moon Book* by B. French, p. 56:

All explanations for the origin of the moon are improbable.

Dr. Michael Drake reported:

Although it has been fourteen years since the first lunar samples were returned to Earth by the Appolo mission, the origin of the moon remains unsolved.

B. French (not a creationist) wrote in his *The Moon Book* (1977), p. 126:

The moon rocks contain no water-bearing minerals, no clays, and no rusty iron oxides. Geologists were startled to discover that a lunar basalt believed to be 3 ½ billion years old actually looked fresher than warm lava collected from a terrestrial volcano only a few days after an eruption.

Being created 6,000 to 8,000 years ago, the lunar basalt would naturally look fresher and younger than the evolutionist's claim of 3 ½ billion years.

The size and distance away from the moon is very important for the earth. If the moon were twice as large or only one-half the distance away from the earth, the tides would be much higher so that not only many islands but also much coastal land would be covered as tidal waves would sweep inland many miles twice a day. Many harbors as they exist today would be useless.

Regarding conditions on the moon, the astronauts found no winds, no storms, no water, no magnetic field and only the thinnest atmosphere. According to an AP report from the Space Center in Houston, July 24, 1984, "Scientists believe the moon has no water now, and never did. The chemistry of the Apollo samples indicate that the rocks formed in the absence of water." Without any atmosphere, the moon is baked by day and frozen by night in temperatures of 270 degrees F above zero to 230 degrees below zero, a difference of 500 degrees in only a few days.

How could evolutionists believe that life would exist in such extreme temperatures. We know what happened to the frozen mammoths in Siberia and Alaska. There just was no indication that life ever existed on the moon, in spite of all the dreams of the evolutionists. It is just a lifeless world. Astronaut Frank Borman in the Apollo 8 flight summed it all up in a few words:

> My own impression is that the moon is a vast, forbidding expanse of nothing. . .It would not appear to be a very inviting place to live and work.

Then what would it be like to try to live and work on those other fiery planets going around the sun? Astronaut James Lovell compared the moon with the earth:

> The loneliness up there is awe-inspiring, and it makes you realize just what you have back there on earth. The earth from here is a grand oasis in the great vastness of space.

Although one of the great purposes of space exploration, and of trips to the moon, was to help find the origin of the universe, of the earth and of life; and although the evolutionists have always had and still have all kinds of assumptions, presumptions, guesses, theories, hypotheses, postulations, and claimed facts on the origin of all things, their trips to the moon (that cost the American taxpayer 33 billion of dollars for 400,000 engineers, technicians and workers) have backfired. Instead of proving evolution, they provided additional evidence that there was a wise, all-powerful Designer behind everything. At the Kennedy Space Center in Florida, April 1980, I found this little statement:

> Until Apollo, it turned out, we knew very little about the moon. Apollo completely changed our lunar perspective from one of conjecture to one of fact.

Notice the word "conjecture," a nice way of saying "guessing." Webster's dictionary explains conjecture: "inferring, theorizing, or predicting from incomplete or uncertain evidence. A guess, inference, theory, or prediction based on guesswork."

What an exact description of the ideas of evolution! It certainly is not scientific. And the "fact" is, as mentioned above, that the differences between the earth and the moon disproves evolution.

With the sun burning down upon the moon for 15 days and then not having any sun for another 15 days; and no atmosphere to somewhat disperse and check the burning rays of the sun, how could evolutionists ever surmise, guess or conjecture, that some form of life might be found there? The AP from Space Center, Houston, July 24, 1984, stated:

> Nor is there any indication of life on the moon. An exhaustive chemical analysis of lunar samples never turned up any of the compounds associated with living organisms.

B. French in his *The Moon Book* (1977) states on p. 118:

Analysis of lunar rock found no organic compounds and only tiny amounts of inorganic carbon. Just like the observable surface of the moon, the lunar rocks were devoid of life.

If the atmospheric conditions on earth, and life on earth, are due to the evolutionary process, why isn't there also atmosphere and life on the nearby moon and the planet Mars?

The evolutionists, in the time before space endeavors, had dreamed up all kinds of queer guesses and conjectures regarding the moon. One of their oddest, based on the moon, earth and universe being billions of years old, is that the moon would be covered with a very thick layer of cosmic dust that fell upon it from outer space. It is known that a constant rate of cosmic dust settles on the earth's surface from space. It has been estimated that in the assumed five billion years age of the earth, enough dust should have fallen to cover the earth with a 182 foot-thick layer of dust. But there is no sign of a cosmic dust layer anywhere on earth. Evolutionists have argued that wind and water erosion have covered up the cosmic dust.

In 1960, when space travel to the moon was being planned, the cosmic dust layer began to become a frightening prospect with no water and no windy atmosphere to wash and blow it away. R. Lyttleton, a respected astronomer and consultant to the space program wrote in the 1950s:

. . .the lunar surface is exposed to direct sunlight, and strong ultra-violet light and x-rays can destroy the surface layers of exposed rock and reduce them to dust at the rate of a few ten-thousands of an inch per year. But even this minute amount could during the age of the moon be sufficient to form a layer over it several miles deep.

That is, if the moon were really 4.5 billion years old. Others thought the dust might be 50 feet thick. On the basis of such thinking it was feared that men would sink into the dust when they stepped onto the moon.

When Bob Hope asked Neil Armstrong what his greatest fear might be when he stepped onto the moon, Armstrong said without hesitation that his greatest fear was the layer of moon dust that he was told by experts to expect. Therefore huge duck-feet landing pods were attached to the legs of the lunar lander, so it would not sink into the supposed dust. But the December 1966 *Reader's Digest* stated, p. 104:

So a man could walk on the moon! He would not sink into dust up to his knees — or to his neck. [The June 1969 issue asked,

p. 135:] Would 'lunar quicksand' swallow a vehicle? (Radar reflections from the moon had indicated that the surface might be covered with a deep layer of fluffy volcanic ash, little more substantial than soapsuds.)

But the dust accumulation was found to be very small, measuring only a fraction of an inch, clearly indicating that the moon is only a few thousand years old as the Bible states. What a credibility gap exists between the actual facts and the conjectures of the evolutionists!

Another amusing conjecture of the evolutionists regarding the moon was revealed in the AP report from the Space Center in Houston, July 24, 1984. This report raised the possibility of the astronauts carrying back germs and poison on their return from the moon:

> For awhile when Apollo 11 returned from the first landing 15 years ago, the moon rock and dust were treated as hazardous substances. Some scientists warned of moon germs that could rage unchecked across a defenseless Earth. Others were concerned that moon dust could be poison. These views were considered extreme, but NASA took no chances. The men of Apollo 11 and their moon rocks were quarantined for 21 days in the Lunar Receiving Laboratory at the Johnson Space Center. The rocks were unpacked and treated as if they were contaminated with a deadly plague. Gowned, gloved and masked scientists tested the moon samples for disease, toxicity and for other hazards. The astronauts, meanwhile, were poked, probed and punctured daily for blood. At the end of three weeks, the astronauts, healthy and unaffected by moon dust, went home.

And still they did not trust those possible moon germs and that possible poison, for

> NASA repeated the quarantine for the second and third Apollo landings before deciding that the lunar material was harmless.

Amazing what men will do, with enough money on hand, to overcome those probably evolved germs on the moon that might have survived a 500 degrees variation in temperature! The *Reader's Digest* (1968), p. 146, states:

> Nothing will be allowed to escape into the atmosphere without being purified. Body wastes will be sterilized, and the very air the astronauts have breathed will be filtered and treated as it passes through the air-conditioning system. . .

That should take care of those nasty little "evolved" germs. It is odd that some of them couldn't have evolved into larger forms, so we could see more advanced life on the moon, if evolution is a fact.

Finally, the earth and moon have been found to be so different in physical composition and structure that they could not possibly have had a common evolutionary origin. Jerry Bishop, in "New Theories of Creation," *Science Digest*, October 1972, p. 42, states:

> To the surprise of scientists, the chemical makeup of the moon rocks is distinctly different from that of rocks on earth. This difference implies that the moon formed under different conditions. . .and means that any theory on the origin of the planets now will have to create the moon and the earth in different ways.

Above all, in going to the National Museum of Natural History, Washington, D.C. in October 1982, I saw this statement:

> Any explanation of the moon's origin must explain one of the most important discoveries of the Apollo program: the moon is very different in composition from the earth. . .If the moon and earth accreted together [i.e., formed, grew or came together] in the same part of the solar nebula at the same temperature, why are they so different in composition? The formation of the moon is still far from being understood.

Yes, the moon and the earth have different physical compositions and structure. This is a very important scientific discovery. And this difference is even greater between Saturn and its moons and Jupiter and its moons. In addition, each of the moons of each planet is very different from the others. Evidently God loved variety in the make-up of the solar system as well as variety all over the earth in landscape, in plants and in animals. Evolution certainly would not evolve such extreme, and so many, beautiful varieties. These many varieties throughout the universe are a hard fact of science that contradicts the entire evolutionary creed and belief.

20.   THE EARTH

What is the origin of the earth? The Bible gives a very simple and reasonable answer: "In the beginning *God* created the heaven and the earth." Gen. 1:1 These few words tell all that needs to be known about the origin of all things. These words give all the answers regarding origins that "the children of *men*" have been searching for in vain throughout the centuries.

Matter just cannot create itself. All matter has been assumed to come from the simplest element, hydrogen. But what is the origin of hydrogen, and especially the endless amount of it which is behind the entire universe? Certainly hydrogen and all other elements of matter cannot form or create themselves. Reasonably, there must be some power greater than nature or material things, there must be some invisible, untouchable, intangible, all-powerful, *non-material* power or source behind all the material things of this earth and universe. For this reason the *fourth word of the Bible, "God,"* gives the only sensible, reasonable, logical answer to the source of all material things — "in the beginning *GOD."*

But mankind, ever since "the children of *men"* rebelled against God and rejected Him, has tried to find another explanation for the origin of all things. So man has continually devised a different answer from what the Bible gives. Evolutionists during the last century have devised a number of ideas. One of them called the *nebular* theory. It was formulated in 1796 by the French mathematician Pierre Laplace. He thought that the solar system began as a ball-shaped cloud of hot gas, a nebula, which rotated rapidly and spread out into space. As the temperature decreased, the nebula tended to shrink. This caused it to whirl faster and thus throw off rings of matter from the outer edge. These rings formed into balls which finally became planets. The gas that remained in the center condensed and became the sun.

But new discoveries proved that Laplace's theory was false. Astronomers found that the nebula never could have been so large or so hot as Laplace supposed. Physicists discovered that a ball of gas could not form into rings, nor could rings roll themselves into planets. Also the sun's rate of rotation was not rapid enough compared to the speed with which the planets move around the sun today.

A new theory, called the *planetesimal* theory, was formulated by two University of Chicago professors, Chamberlin and Moulton. They said that millions, perhaps billions of years ago, a star larger than the sun passed close enough to the sun to pull out large chunks of sun by gravity. At a certain distance the pull of the passing star and the pull of the sun were balanced and the sun's material stopped following the star. After that, the chunks of matter began revolving around the sun to form the planets. But other professors have discredited this theory, plus some other things that have been found scientifically unacceptable. Ruth Moore, in her book *The Earth We Live On* (1956), p. 292, states:

With the conclusion that the earth, its moon, the sun, and the planets evolved from a primordial cloud of dust, agreement ends. Beyond this point the uncertainties, the unknown, the conflicts are limitless. How did the earth and the other planets accumulate from the beginning nebula?. . .What happened after the earth rounded into form? What went before, and how the nebulae came into existence is another profound mystery and point of conflict. [Last sentence is a footnote.]

Richard Carrington, 1956, states in *The Story of Our Earth*, p. 10:

Even today no sure answer can be given to the problem of the Earth's origin, and many time-honoured theories are rapidly being superseded. [On p. 13:] This theory of Jeans's. . .has been assailed by the entirely revolutionary view that the Earth and the other planets were not produced from the sun at all. . .[P]lanetary material contains elements of a very different kind from those normally found in the sun.

Then on p. 24, Ruth Moore, quoted above, presents a fantastic tale how the atmosphere could have developed, then clouds and rain, without any scientific explanation. It all ends in: evolutionists just do not know the origin of the earth and universe.

21.   AGE OF THE EARTH

Various methods have been used to try to determine the age of the earth. A British physicist tried to determine how long it would take the earth to cool off, if it had started as a molten sphere. He estimated 20 to 40 million years. Another method tried was to determine how long it would take to dissolve all the salt that is now found in oceans and seas. Figures were arrived at, from 97 to 330 million years. But they do not know how much salt was on the earth originally, and how much was in the water. Another method was the denudation method, or how long it would take to denude the earth from a supposed crust of 70 miles to the present surface of the earth. But the earth has eroded sometimes very fast by floods and winds, so this method also has been rejected by scientists. Another method tried was the deposition theory, or figuring how fast deltas are built up at the mouths of big rivers. But deltas can be built up very fast at times; and this method was proven false also in a recent case. The remains of an Indian were found deep in the sands of the Mississippi delta at New Orleans. It was estimated by Dr. B. Dowler as being 57,000 years old. A little later, a piece of wood, which was identified as a piece from the gunwales of a Kentucky flatboat was found at a still greater depth. Those 57,000 years for the bones of the

Indian were quickly cut down to about 200 years. This shows how wild the age-guesses of the evolutionists can be. But even these wild guesses are not wild enough for them. They need time, and much of it, billions of years to make their ideas of origins work out. By assuming enough time, the impossible can be made to look possible and even inevitable.

But there are all kinds of evidences that the earth is young. One obvious evidence is the age of the trees that lived and are still living on this earth. Many of the giant sequoia trees in California are over 3,000 years old and they seem to be immune from pests and diseases. Bristlecone pines have been found in the White Mountains of California which have been estimated to be over 4,600 years old. Since there are no other living things older, they very likely began growing from some seed or sprout shortly after the Flood. Forty-six hundred years is very near to the time of that tremendous Flood mentioned in the Bible and evident in the geology of the earth.

The genealogies of the Bible cannot be taken exactly as they are given there, as Bishop Ussher tried to do in establishing that the creation of the earth, the universe, and Adam and Even was at 4004 B.C. These genealogies were not meant to give exact historical dates, but to give the lines of descent from Adam and Eve onward, from whom the Savior, the seed of the woman, was to come. The families of those days, very likely, were very large, in obedience to God's command to be fruitful and multiply and replenish the earth. And God meant replenish the entire earth. Because the descendants were so very many, the Bible gives merely the main line of descent, so some generations could have been omitted in the Bible. Nevertheless, the creation of the earth can hardly be more than a few hundred to a couple of thousand years earlier than Ussher's date.

That the earth is young is evident also from the active volcanoes erupting and arising from the surface of the earth. If the earth were 4.5 billions of years old and started from a fiery ball, it would have cooled enough so no volcanoes would erupt so near the surface as one did recently in Mexico. A 1981 folder from the Yellowstone National Park does not speak of billions of years like most National Park folders used to do, but more modestly states:

> Although thousands of years have passed since Yellowstone's violent birth, the thermal features in the park bear testimony that at a comparatively shallow depth beneath us the fiery heart of the volcanos still beats. Literally thousands of hot springs dot the

thermal basin; gigantic columns of boiling geysers. . lava flows. .
.less than 100,000 years ago.

Their estimated age has decreased considerably from billions of years.

Other evidences of a young earth are: 1) the rate of the
accumulations at the delta of the Mississippi show that it could hardly
be more than 5,000 years old; 2) petroleum and natural gas deposits
could hardly be more than a few thousand years old, since they are held
underground at high pressure in porous sedimentary rock and would
have leaked through long ago if they had been there millions and billions
of years; 3) evolution of the earth, of plants, animals and man could
hardly have taken place in a few thousand or even millions of years. The
only reason for believing that the earth is billions of years old is the
necessity of long ages to support the idea of evolution. Even with the
billions of years concocted the past 100 years, evolution has no
reasonable scientific possibility.

22.   APPEARANCE OF AGE

Although the earth is young and was created by God, yet it has the
appearance of age. Adam and Eve were not created from seeds or
embryoes or even as a babies but as a fully mature man and woman.
Likewise everything else was fully mature. Plants and trees at once had
fruit on them. There was no question of which was first: the chicken or
the egg. The ability to lay eggs or produce seed was fully inherent in the
plants and animals.

Also, the soil of the earth was extremely fertile so it could luxuriantly
and abundantly bring forth vegetation more richly than it does today.
In every way the earth appeared fully developed and with the
appearance of age, as if the earth had been here for hundreds of years.

Likewise the sun, the moon and the stars were fully visible (mature)
at the very instant of their creation, as they are today. Some astronomers
believe that the boundary of the universe is only a few hundred light
years from the earth. The great distances that have been deduced from
red shifts and the size of the stars could easily be as greatly exaggerated
as are many of the evolutionists' other wild figures.

23.   THE EARTH IS UNIQUE — DIFFERENT FROM
ALL OTHERS

The earth is very different from any other planet. It is the only planet
that has life. The temperature is just right for life to exist. If the average
temperature rose or fell only a few degrees, life would soon freeze or

roast. There are a number of factors that keep the right temperature, as I mentioned previously. One is the distance of the earth from the sun. If the earth were too close to the sun the heat would be unbearable; if it were too far away life on earth would freeze. Another factor that benefits the earth is the tilt of the earth, so that the earth rotates at 23 ½ degrees from the perpendicular of the earth's orbit around the sun. This gives the earth the four seasons of the year. If there were no tilt, the earth's temperature would be the same year around, the poles would be rather cold and the equator region would be very hot all year. Because of the water vapor canopy that very likely encompassed the earth before the Flood, the temperatures were most likely very pleasant and growth productive, as confirmed by evidences from pre-Flood geology.

Also the speed of rotation of the earth is just right. If the earth rotated more slowly, all life would die either by burning during longer days from too much sun or by freezing at night because of lack of heat during longer nights.

The earth also has an abundant and right amount of oxygen which makes life possible. On other planets, only very small amounts of oxygen have been discovered. Other important life-benefiting gases found on earth are carbon dioxide and nitrogen.

Another important substance found on earth and not on other planets is the abundant supply of water. Certainly that did not get here by accident or by outgasing from volcanoes as the evolutionists claim — not 340 million cubic miles of water! After all, where could gas for so much outgasing come from? There is enough water on earth that if the land surfaces were leveled, the water would cover the entire earth 8,000 feet deep or about 1 ½ miles. Also the earth has many minerals not found on other planets. Because of all the features mentioned above, our earth, like no other planet, is covered with a beautiful variety of color and mixtures that no other planet has: blue oceans, seas, rivers, streams, green vegetation, mountains, valleys, prairies, plains, brown deserts and white clouds. All other planets are covered with lifeless matter.

Another striking feature of the earth is its continents and high mountains. How were they formed? The *Reader's Digest* (January 1978 and again recently in September 1987), printed articles by Ronald Schiller, in which he tries to show how the continents were closely massed together, and then in the course of time some parts of the continents broke away and slammed, rammed and collided with other land masses. The January 1978 issue, p. 113, states:

Half a billion years ago according to geological reconstruction, there appear to have been three continents, corresponding to present-day North America, Europe and Asia spaced out along the equator. The rest of the continents were welded together in a fourth plate in the Southern Hemisphere. Then, about 400 million years ago, the scattered plates began coming together into a single huge continent which scientists call "Pangaea" (Greek for "all lands"). It was no gentle meeting.

Page 113 also states just before the above:

Most spectacular of all is what happens when two continents collide. Since they have the same buoyancy, and neither can sink beneath the other, their edges pile up into stupendous jagged masses. The Alps were formed this way when Africa bashed into Europe 130 million years ago; and the Himalayas arose when India rammed into the belly of Asia 80 million years later. Thus all of the earth's mountains, and perhaps the continents themselves, were created by collision of crustal plates. . .

In the September 1987 *Reader's Digest*, Schiller states, p. 155:

[A]bout 180 million years ago, rifts opened up under Pangaea and the enormous landmass began to break up into the continents of today.

But what force would make these continents decide to do all this reconstruction and landscaping work? Certainly there must have been some outside force to create such a reconstruction or "banging about." Large masses of earth could not do that of their own accord.

Although movements of land masses such as Schiller describes were done by the decision of God at the time of the Flood, the evolutionists have a special reason for such a movement of continents. For one thing, it would make the recent rising of the mountains to such immense heights seem plausible. But they have a bigger problem to explain, which they try to get around. In the September 1987 issue, Schiller gives the reasoning for all this. It is those misplaced fossils that they cannot explain otherwise but that developed at the time of the Flood. Schiller states in a heading, on p. 152:

Canadian geologist James Monger was baffled; how could fossils native to China, Japan and Indonesia have gotten into the mountains of California and British Columbia?. . .And what were 500-million-year-old fossils from Europe and Africa doing on the east coast of North America? Among scientists, these and other strange discoveries were a source of wild speculation until . . . geologists published studies with revolutionary implications. They believed that parts of other continents collided with North America.

What these geologists have conjectured could have happened — not millions of years ago without any Designer or guiding force behind it, but by God, in less than a year, at the time of the Flood. Professor Rehwinkel in *The Flood* gives a description of what very likely happened at that time of the Flood, pp. 290-1:

When the "waters returned continually" after the Flood, a miracle similiar to that performed on the third day of creation was repeated. Land and water were again separated and dry land once more appeared. . .Think of the enormous volume of water rushing on with ever-increasing speed toward the newer lower levels as the bottom of the sea slowly gave way and great land masses were forced up and new mountain ranges were being born. . .Imagine a supergiant lifting up the basin of the Pacific Ocean on its western shore and pouring its water over the American continent in one great splash. . .The second period of mountain building began when the waters abated, when the bottom of the sea dropped to new levels and the continents of the modern world were pushed upward out of the water.

It could very likely be that all continents were joined together at one time, as the geologists believe (but before the Flood), and for that reason fossils of animals are found in North America that are also native to China, Japan and Indonesia today. Then during and toward the end of the Flood, the continents were separated and formed as they are today. All this took place not over millions of years but in the space of about one year. Because the Bible is historical and factual, the geologists must come to the same conclusion, as the geology of the earth naturally shows and proves.

XIII. ENERGY FORCES AND LIFE ON THIS EARTH

1. FIRE

In connection with the earth, there are a number of energy forces that could not have evolved by themselves. One of them is fire. Although fire is not mentioned in the creation account, it is one of the most mysterious forces in the universe. We see it in the fiery elements of the sun and stars and in the volcanos. Since the time of the Flood, we see it in the lightning bolts of thunderstorms. Fire is a perplexing force that is hard to explain. Its result is more simple: heat and light from the combustion of materials or elements. Fire is the heat and light that comes from burning, the uniting of oxygen with organic substances or liquids like petroleum or gases or gun powder or dynamite. When fire consumes substances like wood, made of organic and inorganic matter, the organic is converted into a gas, which mixes with the air and the inorganic is reduced to ashes. Fire was known and used by man long before what the evolutionists believe. We are told in Genesis that Tubal-cain, a grandson of Adam, was a worker in brass and iron. This indicates that he knew the use of fire long before what evolutionists call the Neanderthal man. But when the weather changed at the time of the Flood, mankind saw fires that God set and created through lightning bolts. Certainly man knew about fire many centuries earlier than evolutionists give man credit for.

2. ELECTRICITY

Electricity likewise is a mysterious energy force. We know what it does, but no one really knows what it is. We know that it can produce heat, light and power, but we really do not know what it is. We know that it works through negative electron and positive proton charges. Electricity is evident in the lightning bolts that pass from negative to positive charges in clouds, and between clouds and the earth. This force in nature is a mystery to man and certainly could not have evolved by itself any more than weather systems would have evolved before God changed the climatic conditions on earth at the time of the Flood.

3. PLANTS

Most plants come from seeds, roots or branches of parent plants. Seeds come from the union of male and female elements in the parent plant. Seeds appear to be lifeless. They can lie dormant and be stored for many years and still be reactivated to life by planting in soil, even if they have been frozen or exposed to extreme heat. A pile of sand and a pile of wheat look very much alike, and both look lifeless. But when the wheat is planted it springs forth with roots and shoots to produce new plants and fruits. And the growth of these shoots can become immense. A giant redwood can grow from a seed one sixteenth of an inch in diameter to become a tree 300 feet tall. Or in the animal world a whale 100 feet long comes from an egg so small that it can be seen only with a microscope.

4.   DIFFERENT KINDS OF PLANTS

Each seed will reproduce only its own kind. One seed can never cross over into another or get combined with another *kind* of seed. Corn will produce only corn and never soybeans. Pine trees will produce only pines and never another kind of tree. A radish seed and a turnip may be planted side by side but each will produce only its original kind. Botanists cannot create new *kinds* of plants, only different varieties of the same kind of plant. Hybrids cannot reproduce themselves. If left to themselves, they will soon revert to the original parent stock.

Throughout the world there are thousands of different kinds of plant life. There is an endless variety of small plants, there are many kinds of trees, some that grow hundreds of feet high. There are seaweeds whose roots are at the bottom of the ocean but grow a thousand feet in the water until their shoots and branches reach the surface. Different plants produce grain, fruits, wine, oil, coffee, tea, cotton, spices, medicines, etc., to feed, clothe and furnish fuel for mankind. W. Bell Dawson, M.A., D.Sc., in the *Presbyterian* for March 10, 1938, presented some reasons to show how weak, from the viewpoint of scientists, the idea of evolution proves to be. Referring to plants and trees, he wrote:

We can also see in the world a wonderful variety of vegetation. There are humble kinds of mosses and ferns which have no flowers; there are pine-trees and spruces which do not bear any nuts or fruits; and there are fruit-trees and plants with their seeds inside their fruits, as currants and apples have. So, when we look over the different plants and vegetables and trees, what comes out most clearly is the contrast between the different kinds. The leaves of the pine and the oak, and the way their seeds are formed could hardly be more different. Everywhere we look we see opposites and no connecting links. How, then, can we suppose that one kind of plant developed from another? The great vegetable world of plants and trees is an immense puzzle to the evolutionists; and in consequence very few botanists who study these things believe in evolution.

Hundreds of different kinds of trees and shrubs can grow side by side and never change into another. In some jungles of the world, trees, shrubs, and many other varieties of vegetation grow so close together that they intertwine and form a mass so thick that nothing but maybe a small animal or snake can crawl through. None of these plants has ever changed into another or semi-other plant, but all have retained their original properties. If evolution ever had a chance to prove itself, it is in these jungles, but there is no evidence of any cross-breeding between kinds of plants. Every plant kind has remained distinctly separate from every other kind, even though the roots, branches, flowers, fruits and seed have been thickly mixed in with many other kinds.

The seeds of all the different kinds of vegetation are spread around the world in many different ways. Seeds are spread by winds, birds and animals. Winds are powerful carriers and spreaders of seeds. Some seeds like dandelions have tufts that are easily carried far and wide. Bird and animal dung can easily spread seeds. The tumbleweed with its large ball-full of seeds easily spreads its seed. Then again seeds can fall into creeks and streams and be carried down rivers. Certainly all the different kinds of seeds that are found in plant life could hardly have developed by themselves and have propagated life as the evolutionists assume.

Many seeds can increase and multiply thousands of times in a year or two. Watermelons, peas, beans and corn can produce hundreds and thousands of seeds in one year. One kernel of corn can produce 680 or more seeds in one year. In three generations one seed of corn can produce over 300,000,000 seeds. A maple tree can produce over a million seeds in one year. Such are the growth and reproduction factors that God stored in the plant life of this world. Such reproduction could hardly have evolved by itself.

But we are seeing only the degenerated state of the plant life that God created. Just as the animal life before the Flood was more abundant, larger and more vigorous than today, so also was plant life. In the sedimentary rocks throughout the world there is fossil evidence that there was a great variety of plants, and that they were larger and more widely dispersed throughout the world than today.

Professor Rehwinkel in *The Flood*, p. 21 writes:

Trees such as the oak, beech, myrtle, laurel, walnut, palms, banana trees, magnolias, breadfruit, grape vines, sequoias like those of modern California, and others like them were not only found in the northwestern states of Wyoming, Montana, and western Canada, but also in Alaska, Greenland and up to the very polar regions. The abundance and the great varieties of plant life found in Arctic Siberia have even suggested to some that the Garden of Eden might have been in that region. An irrefutable proof for the unparalleled luxuriance of plant life in that prehistoric world is the great coal beds found in every continent of the earth today. The recent Byrd Antarctic Expedition discovered a whole mountain of coal at the South Pole.

According to the evolutionists, life first appeared on this earth in very simple forms such as the single cell. Since animals need food to live on, the one-celled creatures first had to be plants. But when and how did plants turn into animals, or how did one-cell life develop into plants and animals simultaneously, just as they presuppose that man and apes came originally from some apelike creature? But just as apes and man are totally different creatures and cannot be crossed, so also plant life and animal life are totally different and cannot be crossed.

The distinction between plant and animal life is clearly seen in how they nourish themselves. A plant can get all it needs to live and grow from the ground, water and air. Animals cannot do this. Animals must have for their food what has been produced in plants. If an animal eats the meat, eggs or milk that has been produced by other animals, then that food also has been produced from the plants the first animal has eaten. In other words, plants make food and animals eat that food to live. In every way, plant and animal life are totally different; one cannot produce the other, and there is an immense gap between them.

5. FISH

In creating the earth, God subdivided it into three different spheres in which animal life could exist: the sea for fish, the air for birds and the dry land for land animals. The earth's surface is one-fourth dry land and three-fourths water. In considering the seas and oceans, in which the fish live, we find that to a great extent, it is an unknown area. This is due to the great pressure that makes exploration of the deep difficult. In these waters we find all kinds of creatures. The number and variety of them is greater than of those found on land.

In these waters are found wonderful and strange creatures. Some are very large like the whale, weighing many tons, and larger than any land animals; some are beautiful and others grotesque; some frightful like the shark and others very shy, all living and playing together in the same water. Like land animals, the different kinds of sea creatures do not crossbreed but stay within their own kinds. Whales are sea creatures that are entirely different from the ordinary fish. Unlike fish, they do not propagate by means of eggs, but like land animals the young whale develops within its mother, and the infant whale is fed by milk from its mother like a calf from a cow. The young are born in water, weigh almost a ton, and are over 10 to 12 feet in length. As soon as a baby whale is born it rises to the surface to breathe. How did this non-fish mammal originate and develop in the waters of the sea? The vast difference between whales and land mammals clearly shows that both were created differently by God.

In regard to the creatures of the sea, Professor Rehwinkel in *The Wonders of Creation* poses a number of important questions for the evolutionists. On p. 81:

> How do you account for the countless species, forms, and colors among these creatures of the sea? And how did the butterfly-fish learn to dress himself in such gorgeous array of dazzling colors and style? And then, finally, why aren't some modern crocodiles growing feathers and wings and getting ready to take to the air? Why did they stop this practice?

6.   BIRDS

As with the land animals and fish, so also with birds, there are many different kinds. It is estimated that there are about 9,000 species of birds and many subspecies. Each species is distinct from the others so that there are endless forms and varieties of birds. Leviticus 11:13-16 mentions "the eagle, the vulture, the buzzard, the kite, and the falcon after its kind; every raven after its kind, the ostrich, the short-eared owl, the seagull, and the hawk after its kind," etc. NKJV And all these kinds and varieties have existed side by side and there has been no crossing from one to the other.

The beauty of many of these birds is remarkable to behold. There is the strutting, beautiful peacock in all his colors, the proud Plymouth Rock rooster as he struts among his hens, then there are the robins, the bluejays, the cardinals, the beautiful bird of paradise, and many others. The songs of these birds are a pleasure to hear, as they sing their songs that sound so cheerful to us. The cardinal's song makes you look up to see where he is in the tree, the meadow lark sings his cheerful song and all appear to sing in unison their praise of their Creator, and yet each is different in structure, in looks, in color and in song.

Their migratory habits are extremely and unbelievably remarkable. For centuries men have marvelled at the twice-yearly migration of birds.

How do billions of these tiny birds find their way to distant parts of the world annually and some species endure grueling flights as long as 12,500 miles from pole to pole? Some of these birds go to the same spot where they wintered the year before, and in springtime they fly back to the same spot and even to the same tree they had the previous spring. Some species breed in our country's heartland, then in fall fly to the Atlantic coast, and from there fly 2,300 miles nonstop for 86 hours over water to South America. The arctic tern breeds about 500 miles from the North Pole and then flies over 12,000 miles to the Antarctic. Men have devised all kinds of contraptions in cages to confuse some of these migratory birds and have tagged them but they still found their way to their desired destinations. They seem to use the sun and the stars to find their way. Only a fool can believe that this ability to fly and find their way over such vast distances happened by chance.

Yet, evolutionists believe that all these different kinds of birds evolved from reptiles. Preston Cloud, in his *Cosmos, Earth and Man,* states that old unproven evolutionary belief by declaring, on p. 228:

> As in the case of the transition from fish to amphibian and from amphibian to reptile, a combination of luck, persistence, and incisive scholarship has established convincing evidence of gradations from reptiles through intermediate form, to birds and to mammals . . . Likewise the acquisition of feathers and wings, and the extinction of the flying reptiles, endowed birds with a new dominion above Earth's solid surface.

But he provides no "evidence of gradations from reptiles," and no proof for "the acquisition of feathers and wings." Where did the feathers and wings come from? The feathers and wings are also of such masterful construction that only an all-wise Designer could have constructed them and made them reproducible.

Evolutionists give no explanation of how a reptile could change its tough scales into soft, delicate and light feathers, and its clumsy front legs into wings that can fly, and its heavy bones into hollow, light bones, and its grunts into the beautiful song of birds. And how could a reptile change into all the different kinds of birds: powerful bald eagles, tiny hummingbirds, proud peacocks, cardinals, crows, cranes with long legs and web-footed ducks and geese? Yet evolutionists claim all this happened by chance, even though there has been no sign the past 6,000 years of anything nearly like this taking place. But children in school and adults in newspapers and TV broadcasts are being told that they are not modern and up-to-date if they do not accept this as a scientific fact.

But it all comes from the smart "Homo sapiens sapiens" evolutionists who have doctoral degrees and proclaim that this is how it all happened over millions of years. Our children are being brainwashed by evolutionists who have turned our public schools into their own parochial schools of the evolutionary faith. It all sounds so wise and impressive to the young to hear teachers or their books explain how all this evolution of birds and animals took place. But no scientific evidence shows that evolution or change from one kind of fish, bird or animal to another kind ever took place.

7.   ANIMALS

Animals usually develop from the eggs of their parents and feed on the food that plants provide, and on other animals. Unlike plants, animals usually have minds with which they can decide what they wish to do although they cannot progress in reasoning as mankind does. For thousands of years we have observed domestic animals, but we have never seen any trace of intellect such as mankind has; and even with constant training, animals never step out of their original sphere and approach anything close to even the simplest human savage. Neither by their own efforts nor through the help of man can they develop ideas of human mentality and culture. They will always remain just animals, including the ape animals. There will be more on the difference between animals and mankind later.

8.   KINDS OR SPECIES OF ANIMALS AND VARIETIES WITHIN SPECIES

There has been much misunderstanding regarding kinds, species and varieties. Ten times in the first 25 verses, the Bible states that God created grass, trees, sea creatures, birds, cattle, creeping things and beasts of the earth, *all according to their kinds*. Leviticus 11:13-16 again subdivides birds according to various kinds. I Corinthians 15:39 also divides all flesh in a general way:

All flesh is not the same flesh, but there is one kind of flesh of men, another flesh of beasts, another of fish and another of birds.

In Genesis, God again subdivided fish, birds, cattle, creeping things and beasts into different kinds. In Genesis 1:11 God divides the kinds into those "whose seed is in itself." From this it is evident that God put into each kind the seed or ability to reproduce only its own kind. Reproduction is one of the keys to what designates the kinds.

The Swedish botanist, Carolus Linnaeus, over 200 years ago, in setting up a table for plants and animals used double Latin words to designate different plants and animals. The first Latin word named the genus or general grouping, and the second word the species or subdivisions. This second word, *species,* he used to represent the Bible word *kind.* Byron Nelson in his *After Its Kind,* states, p. 190:

> EVOLUTIONISTS HAVE NO EXPLANATION OF THE ORIGIN OF SPECIES. Evolutionists have many unsolved problems . . . Why, from purely natural causes, there have come to be what so clearly are natural species, i.e. groups of plants and animals composed of varieties freely interbreeding according to Mendel's laws and separated by walls of various degrees of sterility from other groups of plants and animals. Darwin sought by "natural selection" to account for the nonmiraculous origin of the present world of plants and animals, and he sought by "natural selection" to account for the phenomenon of sterility between species. He was unable to do so.

Evolutionists today also have this problem with "kinds" and "basic kinds." Niles Eldredge in his book, *The Monkey Business* (1982), p. 116, quotes creationist Dr. Duane Gish:

> Among the vertebrates, the fishes, amphibians, reptiles, birds and mammals are obviously different basic kinds. Among the reptiles, the turtles, crocodiles, dinosaurs . . . would be placed in different kinds. Each one of these major groups of reptiles could be further subdivided into the basic kinds within each. Within the mammalian class . . . bats, hedgehogs, rats, rabbits, dogs, cats, lemurs, monkeys, apes and men are easily assignable to different basic kinds.

But Eldredge does not realize this in trying to correct or belittle Gish's presentation, p. 117:

> By his [Gish's] very words, then, bats, whales, mankind and the rest of the mammals he cites could have arisen as variations within the basic mammalian "kind." But he then defines these sub-groups of mammals as *themselves* constituting "basic kinds" — which means they cannot have shared a common ancestor by creationist tenets. Bats beget bats, whales beget whales, and so forth, but Gish implies there is no common ancestral connection between these basic sub-units of mammals. This, of course, is inconsistent at best and at worst senseless. One cannot but agree that creationists indeed have trouble with the notion of "basic kinds."

No, it is not the creationists but the evolutionists that have trouble with basic kinds. Evolutionists are so bogged down in their belief that all things actually *evolved* from one common source into a treelike pattern of evolution that they just cannot understand that in creation all the different kinds were created like individual trees in a forest. The different species arose *not like a tree* with branches of evolution, but they rose as a *grove of trees*. There is no evidence that creatures evolved gradually from simple to more complex, or that one kind or species evolved into another kind. Instead all evidence from the fossils shows that all species appeared on the earth at the same time in the same form as they exist today. Missing links never existed or could have existed. If the theory of evolution is true, there should be at least one instance of one species evolving into another.

According to Eldredge and other evolutionists, everything must have had a common ancestor, or as he says of Gish: "which means they cannot have shared a common ancestor" and "Gish implies there is no common ancestral connection." That bats, whales and mankind are *vertebrates* does not imply that they should have common ancestors, except according to faulty evolutionary thinking. Again, going down the evolutionary line of thinking still further, although bats, whales and mankind are *mammals,* this does not imply that they should have common ancestors. On the other hand, although all three are vertebrates and all three are mammals, they still were created "different basic kinds." Pigs, sheep, goats, cows, horses, dogs and cats all have a backbone, four legs, a heart, a brain, and a reproductive system, and they all are similar in other ways; but that does not prove that these animals are identical and have a common ancestral connection.

9.   WHAT ARE KINDS OR SPECIES?

The term kind, or species, can be defined as a group of individual plants or animals which are interfertile or breed together freely and reproduce fertile offspring. The Standard Dictionary defines "species" with the words:

A classificatory group of animals or plants subordinate to a genus, and having members that differ among themselves only in minor details of proportion and color, and are capable of fertile interbreeding indefinitely.

Within each species or kind of animal are again *varieties* of animals, which are interfertile with each other. If one looked at only the external features or appearances, the same varieties would in many cases not be recognized as belonging to the same species. The various breeds or varieties of dogs, cats, horses, cattle, pigs, sheep, peas, etc., often differ more from each other than do they from the original wild stock they came from. If a draft horse and a Shetland pony, a Great Dane dog and a poodle, or a Poland China pig and a razorback were found in a state of nature, one would hardly think of them as belonging to the same species. Yet the two horses, the two dogs and the two pigs came from the same stock, are interfertile and are therefore, of the same species, although they are different varieties of the same species.

A new species would originate only if a variety could no longer be crossed with brother and sister and parent varieties. If a small Shetland pony could not be crossed with a large draft horse because of size or other reasons, it would still not be a new variety, so long as it could be crossed with other varieties of horses or parent type horse.

Among the many different kinds or species there are many varieties. There are about 6,000 varieties of roses which can be crossbred. But it is impossible to cross a rose with a tomato or apple tree. Cauliflower, cabbage, kale and Brussels sprouts all have come from the wild cabbage of southern Europe. They all belong to the same kind, for they are interfertile. There are many varieties of cats, dogs, cattle, horses, sheep, pigs, etc., yet all the varieties of cats belong to the cat kind or species. The same is true of the dog kind, etc. Cats have always been cats, and dogs have always been dogs. And what is true of animals is also true of mankind. God did not create Chinese, Negroes or Indians, but he created man. All races of men, regardless of size, speech or color are one species or kind. All are capable of reproducing human beings.

What varieties are possible within kinds or species is evident in the cat family. Over 50 varieties of cats have been identified in the world. From the house-cat through lynx, cougars, tigers and lions there is a gradual increase in size. Yet from outward appearances, hunting habits, actions, and structure they are closely related and of one species. All cats, small and large, catch their prey in exactly the same manner. House-cats have been crossed with wild cats and bobcats, and produced litters of kittens. Jaguars and leopards and tigers and lions have been crossed.

10.   KINDS DO NOT CHANGE INTO OTHER KINDS

No kind or species has ever evolved into another kind or species. There is no evidence anywhere in this world as far back as evolutionists want to go that any real evolution from one kind to another has ever taken place. There have only been variations only within kinds or species.

Darwin, already in his day, realized that his theory of gradual evolution from one kind to another could not find support in the fossils that have been found. Since then millions of fossils have been found, but the missing links between kinds remain missing. Darwin himself said:

There are 2 or 3 million species on earth, sufficient field one might think for observation. But it must be said today that in spite of all the efforts of trained observers not one change of a species into another is on record.

Darwin in his book, *The Origin of Species,* never dealt with the *origin* of species, in spite of the title of his book.

There just has been no crossing over from one kind to another, and above all there is no evidence of any evolution moving upward. The changes have been horizontal within kinds and not vertically upward toward more complex and advanced kinds. If a new species were ever to come forth out of the dog species, a number of puppies would have to be born that would not be able to cross back with other dogs, and yet be able to cross with each other. These new different puppies would then be a new species or kind. So how could evolution have any possibilities at all, especially as we shall see in Part 11 of this chapter? Only degeneration has taken place, according to the second law of thermodynamics and history. A farmer said: "When I cross pigs, I get pigs, and not dogs or cats or horses."

Billions of dollars and the work of thousands of men have been used to find a way to develop a new kind, but none has been found. Members of two different species cannot be mated. If they can be, the offspring, like the mule, is nearly always sterile.

While kinds or species do not change from one to another, there are, however, many varieties within the kinds. There are thousands of pigeons that have come forth from the common rock pigeon, and if all these varieties would breed together they would soon be back to the common original pigeon, the same blue rock pigeon with the black bars across the wings. The same is true of dogs. Over 200 distinct varieties of dogs have been brought forth from a few wild dogs, such as the dachshund, poodle, collie, Great Dane, etc. Since 1700 over 500 varieties of peas have been produced from one type of pea.

While kinds have not changed from one to another, they also have not changed from the very beginning of time. Fossils of various kinds from the very earliest time do not differ from the same kinds living today. Fossils of many kinds of animals are embedded in the sedimentary rocks. They are the same kinds of animals that still exist today. While dinosaurs died out completely and are remembered only from their fossil bones, there however are numerous other animals that are living today which lived from the earliest of times. The royal cats of the Egyptian pharaohs were the same as our modern alley cat.

11. VARIETIES DEGENERATE—REVERT BACK TO ORIGINAL KIND

Evolutionists teach that on the basis of natural selection plants and animals will eliminate the inferior ones and preserve the superior ones and thereby plants and animals have improved and evolved. But left to itself, the exact opposite is true according to science. There has been no advancement of kinds but there has been a deterioration or degeneration of the kinds, when left to themselves. A farmer can develop superior qualities inherent in cows, pigs, chickens, etc., and maintain them with proper care and watchfulness. But if the different varieties of pigs or chickens are allowed to intermingle, the superior qualities will disappear.

Here one thing must be stressed, as Hilbert Siegler in his book *Evolution or Degeneration — Which?* states, p. 29:

However, no plant or animal group will ever again equal the hereditary potential of its originally created parents.

Dr. Theodore Graebner, in *God and the Cosmos* (1932), states p. 195:

We know that grasses, grains, fruits and animals are far superior to serve man's need today than one hundred years ago. How has this great improvement come about? By leaving nature to work alone? No. It was wholly by the toil of man in rejecting the inferior and preserving the superior that this great improvement has been made. Let man cease his mental and physical toil and leave Nature to work unguided, and the gain of a hundred years will quickly be lost. If left to Nature, the best plants and animals not only do not improve but rapidly deteriorate. Some three hundred years ago the Spanish turned loose some well bred horses on the plains of the Southwest. The small worthless range ponies are the result. The worthless wild hogs of the Southern States are the direct descendants of at least fairly well-bred domesticated swine.

The most beautiful flowers that have been produced after years of experimentation and watchfulness have always, when not cultivated, returned to their original stock. There have been many disappointed breeders who carried their work to a certain point and then only saw the animals or plant revert to where they began. Burbank produced about 40,000 hybrids but hardly any are in existence now. Hybrid chickens are amazing. New breeds every so often come into existence; but if they are turned loose in the barnyard, these fancy breeds soon degenerate or revert to the former inferior stock. A farmer knows that it doesn't pay to keep seed from his crop of hybrid corn. It will only produce a crop of less desirable quality.

12.   HYBRID VARIETIES ARE STERILE

Whenever two close species of animals are crossed, which rarely can be done, the offspring, which is hybrid, is a sterile creature which cannot reproduce itself. Natural hybridization between animals is not common, for different animals in the wild state have a tendency to avoid each other in reproduction. The cross between an ass and a mare is quite common and results in a hybrid mule. But if you try to breed a male and female mule you can get no offspring whatever. The two mules are sterile. Lions and tigers have been crossed, but the hybrid that resulted was not only sterile but inherited all the vicious tendencies of both parents. Crosses have been made between guinea pigs and rabbits, but the young died before they matured. A California rancher raising Hereford breeding cattle stated that the females became sterile after the fourth generation or they died shortly after birth. If they survived, they reverted back to the original kind.

In the fall of 1986 a love-sick moose fell in love with Jessica, a cow, in Shrewsburg, Vermont. He stayed close to the cow for 53 days, even though the moose and the cow could produce no offspring.

13.   HEREDITY

Gregor Mendel, an Austrian monk (1822-84), discovered the biological law which governs heredity. He ended up not with a theory, but a fact, a biological law called the Mendelian Law. By experimenting with plants in the cloister garden, he demonstrated that the varieties of sweet peas he discovered were not, as Darwin had believed, simply a matter of chance evolution, but that they followed a definite law in producing varieties. By crossing various types of plants and animals he found that the characteristics of the parents would appear in the descendants according to a definite mathematical law or sequence. Others have found that in crossing a black fowl with a white one, all the chicks were white splashed. When the white splashed chickens bred among themselves, they produced chicks in a definite mathematical number: 25 percent black, 25 percent white and 50 percent white splashed. The white chicks when crossed among themselves produced white ones, the black produced only black; but the white-splashed again produced 25 percent black, 25 percent white and 50 percent white splashed. Thus it is evident that there are hereditary traits that continue down from offspring to offspring. However, the offspring can produce no greater number of different types of offspring than there are factors that can be combined.

What Mendel proved by his statement is that no variation outside the limits of the species is possible. It is now a simple law of biology that "the factors which the individual receives, and no other, are those which he can transmit to his offspring." Also, "an organism cannot pass on to an offspring a factor which it did not itself receive." Thus Mendel's facts expressed in Mendelian Law overthrew the false supposition and theory proposed by Darwin, that creatures changed from one kind to another kind by chance.

August Weismann (1834-1914), a German biologist, pointed out how for many generations the tails of certain breeds of sheep and the combs of fighting cocks have been cut off with no effect upon the tails and combs of the sheep and cocks which descended from them. He himself cut off the tails of mice for nineteen generations and then gave up in disgust. The tails of the last were as long as the first.

14.   NATURAL SELECTION

In connection with kinds or species on one hand and varieties within species on the other hand, we need to consider Charles Darwin's evolutionary ideas regarding "natural selection." This idea means: There is not enough food, space, shelter, etc., for all the sprouts and offspring of living things. Therefore living things constantly compete with each other to live. In their struggle for existence some will live and others die quickly. The fittest will produce favorable variations and the unfavorable will die out. And so they claim, that after many thousands of years, the surviving members may be greatly different from their ancestors.

The *purpose* of Darwin's idea of natural selection was put rather bluntly by Sir Julian Huxley, a modern leader of evolutionary thinking; (from "The Remarkable Birth of Planet Earth," H. Morris, p. 6:)

Darwinism removed the whole idea of God and the Creator of organisms from the sphere of rational discussion. Darwin pointed out that no supernatural designer was needed; since natural selection could account for any known form of life; there is no room for a supernatural agency in its evolution.

Dr. George Romanes of Cambridge, England in 1910, in *Darwin and After Darwin* p. 256 states, in regard to natural selection:

If one may estimate the importance of an idea by the change of thought which it effects, this idea of natural selection is unquestionably the most important idea that has ever been conceived by the mind of man. Yet the wonder is that it should not have been hit upon long before.

But this man of science later changed his mind completely. Later in life after more study, he wrote *Thoughts on Religion,* and admitted it was "reasonable to be a Christian believer," and he returned, says Bishop Charles Gore, to the "full deliberate communion with the Church of Jesus Christ." Romanes also said, "unbelief is usually due to indolence, often to prejudice, and never a thing to be proud of."

Going back to Darwin's theory of "survival of the fittest" and "natural selection," we must state that neither in nature itself nor by the help of men in artificial selection and breeding do survival of the fittest and natural selection produce new kinds or species as is claimed. Even if the premise of natural selection were correct, the conclusion of new kinds or species would be false. The logic is wrong. From survival of the fittest and natural selection do not follow new kinds and evolution of new kinds. While it is true that the "fittest of the kind" may and do survive, this does not explain how the kind originally arrived or began.

Also in regard to the survival of the fittest, one must bear in mind that animals do not ordinarily overpopulate the territories they occupy. The Mankato, Minnesota area is simply overrun with countless squirrels; but one seldom sees more than two or three in one block. There also is very little warfare or struggle among animals in trying to exist. In fact, there is much cooperation among them. The unfit often survive, and many times they do so because members of their own species assist them in surviving. So Darwin's idea "the survival of the fittest" runs counter to actual scientific fact.

15.   MUTATIONS

What are mutations? They are the sudden changes or accidental appearance of new features or characteristics in animals and plants. These new characteristics are transmitted to the next generation. Mutations have been considered the basis of evolution. The theory regarding mutations was developed by Hugo de Vries. A famous example of a mutant or change was the Ancon ram, which first appeared in 1791 in Massachusetts. Its body was long and its legs short. The farmer used it for breeding, and in a few years he had a number of sheep with short legs. They were bred together to produce a new breed of sheep that could not jump fences. But they still were only sheep. They were not a new species but only a new variety of sheep. Usually mutants are not different from their parents, except for size or color, etc. Scientists do not know what causes mutants, but the number of mutants can be increased by heat, x-rays and other means. Luther Burbank used the principal of mutants in originating the thornless blackberry by using a wild dewberry mutant which had no thorns. Clover was produced by mutants with three to seven leaves on one plant, but it still was only clover.

De Vries succeeded by selection in creating an ear of corn with extra rows of kernels. But as soon as he stopped crossing the mutation with other multi-row corn "the excellence of the race at once disappeared." Within two or three years the corn was back to its average number of rows. He did not believe in Darwin's "natural selection." He said that only after a species is created does natural selection play in. He said: "Natural selection creates nothing, it only sifts" the dying from the remaining plants. The evolutionists argued among themselves as to which could produce new species: natural selection or mutation. Neither has done so. They have helped produce merely new varieties of the same species.

In no case have mutations formed new and more highly developed species. Mutations never change species into something else, or into something entirely different. Since fruitflies can generate many generations in a few years, they have been experimented with to try to prove evolution. Over many generations, fruitflies have never generated anything new. They may have developed malformed wings, legs, and bodies, or other malformations, but they still remain fruitflies. Evolutionist Richard Goldschmidt, after observing mutation in fruitflies for many years, admitted: the changes were so hopelessly micro or little that if a thousand mutations were combined into one fruitfly, there still would be no new species.

Usually mutations are genetic mistakes. In almost all cases mutations have a negative effect upon the creatures. Mutations are harmful to the creature, and many are fatal. This is the reason for the concern over the increasing amount of radioactive fallout. Radiation produces mutations. Geneticists definitely claim that an increase in mutations will damage the human race. A mutation is a random change in a gene. Every individual organism inherits a set of genes from its parents. Genes contain coded instructions for building proteins in living cells. Genes can contain from 600 to 186,000 code letters. A mutation that changes a single letter can change the code message and thereby change the protein and cause it to function poorly or not at all. Because of this, the plant or animal may not be able to live as the parent did and thus will die. In most cases mutations are harmful to the plant or animal. They are injuries that make the animal act below par.

James Crow, in "Genetic Effect of Radiation" in the bulletin of atomic scientists, January 1955, stated:

> Mutation and mutation rates have been studied in a wide variety of experimental plants and animals and in man. There is one general result that clearly emerges: Almost all mutations are harmful. The degree of harm ranges from mutant genes that kill their carrier, to those that cause only minor impairment.

That Ancon ram with its short legs could no longer run and jump as its parents did. A midget also is disadvantaged by its small size. It has at least one advantage, as someone said, "It is less likely to be hit on a battlefield," or never gets into the front lines.

In short, mutations are another evidence of the degeneration that is taking place on the earth, another good example of the second law of thermodynamics which teaches that all things are falling into disorder and are degenerating, as we shall see when we touch on that subject. Dr. Sewall Wright of the University of Chicago states:

> Evidences that degeneration is taking place on the earth instead of evolution through mutations is seen in the animals that lived before the Flood from the records of the fossils. The animals that lived then were much larger than those living today, as we see when we examine the giant animals like the dinosaurs, the giant bison, the mammoths of Siberia, the large saber-toothed tigers, giant beavers, cockroaches, cave bears and many other animals.

Professor J. Muller, who received a nobel prize in 1946 for his work on mutations wrote: "Most of the mutations are bad, in fact the good ones are so rare that we can consider them all as bad", (Time, Nov. 11, 1946, p. 38).

XIV. LIFE

1. LIFE IS EVERYWHERE ON EARTH

Although no life has been found on other planets of our solar system or anywhere else in the universe, it is all around us on this earth. Life is so widespread, so varied and so abundant that it is beyond our grasp. We find it in the fish of the sea, the birds of the air and from the smallest insects to the largest animals on land. It is found in the highest mountains, in the deserts and in the coldest polar regions. Even in the ground unbelieveable multitudes of the tiniest creatures are working in the soil to make it more productive for growing plants.

2. ORIGIN OF LIFE (BIOGENESIS)

What is life? What is its essence? Where is it located in the bodies of creatures? Life is the mystery of mysteries. Understanding the essence of life eludes and baffles us. Its essence cannot be defined and comprehended. Because of this we cannot find the difference between the living and the nonliving. How did life arise? Science does not know. We can see only the manifestations of life. Certain characteristics are common to all living things: 1) They react to contacts and conditions around them; 2) They secure food to derive necessary energies for remaining alive and growing; 3) They get rid of unused waste materials; 4) They perpetuate themselves by reproducing themselves.

Scientists have found that plants and animals consist of cells. Within the cells are nuclei. Within the nuclei are chromosomes and within the chromosomes are genes. And genes may be divided into smaller parts. But these are all material things. The wonder of the cell is remarkable when we consider that out of it can come chickens, frogs, sheep, cows, horses, lions and human bodies. Byron Nelson in *After Its Kind*, p. 27 states:

> No expensive watch can begin to compare with a single cell for complexity of structure. A cell has been described as "a little universe formed of a host of self-propagating organisms, inconceivably minute and numerous as the stars of heaven." The material of the cell cannot be analyzed. It baffles all attempts to take it apart or put it together; for as soon as such things are attempted the life within it flees and only such dead material as might be swept up off the floor remains.

Life is a spark of some mysterious power that God created in making plants and animals, this spark makes alive the body of material elements making it a living thing, but it is distinct from the material elements.

Professor Alfred Rehwinkel in his remarkable book, *The Wonder of Creation,* stated, p. 116:

It is not possible to see or observe this spark of life, not even with a high-powered microscope, nor can it be isolated by chemical analysis. It can be destroyed with its material body, but when destroyed its body decays and returns to the original chemical substance from which it had been formed. In some respects life can be compared with electricity. Electricity also is a mysterious force whose manifestation we are able to observe and experience, as in the light bulb or in the form of a shock which we might receive, but no one really knows what electricity is. We can produce it by different devices but its essence remains a mystery. And so it is with life. Life can never come from lifeless matter. The fact has been established over and over again. Only a living organism can reproduce a living thing. Only God, the source of all life, could have been the creator of life.

3.   SPONTANEOUS ORIGIN OF LIFE

And yet people in earlier days have come up with queer ideas regarding the origin of life. In ancient and medieval eras, many people believed that living things could arise from non-living matter, by spontaneous generation. For example, some thought that maggots developed from decaying meat and manure, flies from fruit, insects and mice from filthy rags and mud, and worms from wood and cheese. But scientists like Redi of Italy, Needham of England, and especially Pasteur of France showed that bacteria and other forms of life could not develop in materials that were sterilized, and they disproved the theory of spontaneous generation.

After Pasteur's work, most scientists realized that spontaneous generation was impossible under any circumstances. They stated that life must come from other life, or that life can come only from life. This is why the question of how life *originally* appeared was difficult for scientists especially those after Pasteur to answer.

But the evolutionists would not give up. They could not accept the answer given in the Bible. So some of them concocted the idea that life came from outer space. They said that spores and other stages of small organisms wandered about in space and landed on the earth and began to grow and develop. Many scientists do not accept this theory because of the hazards the organisms would meet in space, and because it does not explain the origin of organisms that would be in space. It only shoved the problem farther away without solving it. If life came from outer space, why isn't there life on the moon or Mars, just as there is life in our deserts?

After Darwin's ideas of evolution gained control, an inevitable consequence was the following conviction among evolutionists, as Allan Broms in *Thus Life Began* states, p. 150:

Life must somehow have originated from non-living matter, presumably by some natural process.

But after Pasteur in 1862 disproved spontaneous generation, scientific opinion agreed on the opposite dogma: "All life comes from life," expressed in Latin "Omne vivum ex vivo." A clash of opinions resulted. But the staunch evolutionists began looking for exceptions to Pasteur's factual evidence. In 1866 evolutionist Haeckel held that some time in earth's early history the very simplest kind of life could have arisen.

On page 151 Allan Broms continues:

Less cautious was Henry Bastian, who in 1872 began defying Pasteur's proofs, asserting that life must somehow have had to originate from non-living matter by natural process, and indeed probably can and is doing so today. But his eager experimental efforts to prove this were unconvincing, as Pasteur and others readily proved them carelessly done.

For forty years Bastian fought for this idea.

Today evolutionists believe that at an early age of the earth's history, billions of years ago, conditions on earth were quite different, which is also assumed. Here I will refer to an article in the *Minneapolis Tribune* (April 14, 1979) by Robert Jastrow, director of NASA's Goddard Institute for Space Studies at the time of Voyager's trips to the planet Jupiter, as well as to other planets. The headline states:

"Dead" Jupiter may be hiding life's secrets. There is every reason to believe that Jupiter is nature's laboratory for chemical evolution. It is a crucible of life . . . The planet is a huge, rapidly spinning ball of liquid and gas about 90,000 miles in diameter, more than 10 times the size of the earth, and 318 times as massive.

Then Jastrow tries to use Jupiter as an example of how life could have started on earth. He continues:

As mentioned earlier, the atmosphere of Jupiter contains abundant amounts of the gases ammonia and methane, in addition to hydrogen and water.

Water on Jupiter is assumed because one of its moons, Io, has volcanoes, and volcanoes are assumed to have produced all the water on earth. Jastrow adds:

> According to the theory, the earth's atmosphere was composed of substantial amounts of methane and ammonia 4.5 billion years ago, when our planet was newly formed. Strokes of lightning, represented by the electric sparks in the laboratory experiment, energized the gases of the earth's atmosphere and produced a rich yield of amino acids. The amino acids, accumulating in the oceans, built up a nutritional broth. Random collisions in the broth, occurring again and again over millions of years, linked small molecules into long ones and finally produced a molecule on the threshold of life. Once the threshold of life was crossed, evolution commenced and the laws of natural selection came into play to produce the variety of plants and animals that exist on our planet.

Just like that! Quite a tale. I hope that this princely molecule found a princess molecule so they could live happily ever after. How many billions of dollars were spent by us sons and daughters of Uncle Sam so that this anti-creation, anti-religious tale could be told!

Even if a lucky combination of amino acids in some primeval pool of water and a stroke of lightning by chance created a spark of life, why has not the same process been repeated again and again? Evolutionists may say that the physical and chemical conditions were different then. However, creationists scientists have shown rather conclusively that the early atmosphere was not substantially different from our own. But if conditions were artificially reproduced today, would life appear? Even if the origin of life were a possibility in the laboratories, some intelligent being would have had to produce it. All this is only more evidence that an intelligent all-wise Creator created life.

Evolutionist Carl Sagan of Cornell University said on August 2, 1976:

> If we find life on the planet [Mars], it will be, I think, a monumental event in human history, as well as the most significant discovery in the history of the biological sciences.

But then years later, July 24, 1986, the *Minneapolis Tribune* reported:

> Scientists have demonstrated a possible new source of the gases that led to the origin of life: the rocks on Earth that were cracked open as meteorites bombarded the planet . . . The hypothesis presented yesterday is more down to earth. The chemicals needed

for life already were here, but the impact of meteorites freed them. [That is, the necessary elements of carbon, hydrogen, oxygen and nitrogen.]

But why go through all these rituals of trying to find gases, elements and material for life? The world is full of them today in the world of the dead. Dead animals, blood, meat and vegetables are full of the ingredients evolutionists are looking for to produce life. These dead products contain cells, nuclei, chromosomes, genes, DNAs, but they are dead. No matter how much mixing, stirring, heating and electricity is shot through them, they remain dead. Nothing man does can restore life to these cells, chromosomes, etc. All the dead creatures in the world are evidences that life is not a material thing but a supernatural essence that is not producible or restorable by man. The old, old theory of the origin of maggots, flies and mice is more logical and reasonable. Why must men become unreasonable and illogical just to deny their supernatural Creator? It is rebellion against God and a deifying of men that is as old as the Earth, as old as "the children of men," the close descendants of Adam and Eve, who also opposed and denied their Creator when they rebelled against Him.

This attitude exists in spite of statements like the following from evolutionist Julian Huxley:

Of the causes which led to the origination of living matter it may be said that we know absolutely nothing . . . The present state of knowledge furnishes us with no link between the living and the not living.

Even Robert Jastrow said:

The origin of life is beyond the reach of scientific inquiry.

The *Journal of Theoretical Biology* (1981), p. 26, admits:

One must conclude that no valid scientific explanation on the origin of life exists at present.

Boodin reduces the idea to absurdity:

If it is absurd to suppose that the structure of inorganic matter originated by chance, how much more absurd it is to suppose that life compounds so originate . . . Of all philosophies, materialism makes the greatest demands on man's credulity. [That is, the tendency to believe too readily.]

Yet the evolutionists will stick to their theory that life must somehow have originated from natural causes. Going back to that article that

Robert Jastrow wrote, April 14, 1979, regarding Jupiter (see p. 213), he says:

> The elements of living matter accumulate in the flask, but no life climbs out. Why does the experiment fail? Because it lacks a key ingredient. The missing ingredient is time — millions on millions of years of ceaseless experimentation.

Yes, given enough millions and billions of years, the evolutionists believe that they can make all their theories sound plausible. Evolutionary geologists and astronomers have already given evolutionary biologists billions of years, but even that is not enough for their theories to work out as assumed.

Not only are their assumptions not reasonable, but their arrogance is as defiant over against God as that of the giant Goliath over against the God of Israel. Listen to Richard Carrington in his *The Story of Our Earth,* p. 51:

> Man seems to have hung on to the barrier between living and non-living matter with extreme tenacity, and apparently without any suspicion that it might be artificially erected. As a result the question of the (origin) of life has been and still is a fundamental enigma to the vast majority of mankind. In religion it has led to the many charming legends of the creation, in which God is assumed to have produced the different classes of living things by a kind of celestial conjuring trick.

How arrogant and conceited can little Homo sapiens, sapiens (Smart Wise Guy) get! "Celestial conjuring tricks" — yet these evolutionists are doing exactly that: — conjuring all kinds of tricks (fables) to explain the origin of the universe, earth and life out of nothing, that is out of non-life. Above all, the entire idea goes contrary to an established law of science. "All life comes from life."

The idols that the evolutionists have conjured and molded are no better than the idols the heathen made in the Old Testament. They have been aptly described in Psalm 115:4-8:

> Their idols are silver and gold. The works of men's hands. They have mouths, but they do not speak; Eyes they have, but they do not see; They have ears, but they do not hear . . . Nor do they mutter through their throat. Those who make them are like them. So is everyone who trusts in them. NKJV

There is only one explanation for the origin of life, and that is the explanation that scientific experiments proved after Pasteur's work: "All life comes from life" and that is the life that God created. Life produces its own kind, as God states again and again in Genesis and elsewhere. All living things come from parent plants and animals of their own kind. This is true of the simplest forms of life to the most complex.

Hilbert Siegler, a biological scientist, summed up the entire issue correctly and to the point in stating in *Evolution or Degeneration — Which?*, p. 84:

> A third law of science, as firmly established as the two Laws of Thermodynamics, is the Law of Biogenesis, which states that *life comes from life*. Every living organism came from some other living organisms. There are no known violations of this law. How do evolutionists, then, account for the world's first living organism? Do they contend that there was one time when nature went contrary to the Law of Biogenesis?

4.   ANIMALS DO NOT COME FROM PLANTS

Another problem for evolutionists in regard to life is: How did animals arise from plants, as they claim and assume? In plant life we see non-living soil and water with the help of the energy of the sun turn seeds, with the life inherent in them, into the living tissues of plants. The seed is raised in time by the natural forces that have been placed into it by God. The plant world is the only areas in which inorganic materials are converted directly into living organic tissues, through the life that is inherent in the seed.

The animal cannot do this. It is entirely dependent upon the plants directly, or indirectly through other animals, for the organic materials out of which its own tissues are constructed. The advance of the vegetable kingdom to the animal kingdom is according to Darwin's co-evolutionists:

> completely beyond all possibility of explanation of *matter*, its laws and forces. It is the introduction of sensation or consciousness, constituting the fundamental distinction between the animal and vegetable kingdom.

Plants live, animals live *and feel*, and they have consciousness. Only an outside "above-natural" force, such as God, could cause such consciousness to come into existence.

5.   EGGS

Then there are the living creatures producing eggs that are found in animals and mankind. Outside the chicken eggs, which are used mainly for food, all other eggs are used mainly to produce offspring. In all ranks of animals above the very lowest, it is impossible for young animals to be produced except from eggs. Most animals, including worms, fishes, reptiles, whales, insects and mammals produce ova and sperm. The eggs of birds, insects, fishes, chickens, etc. are forced out of the body of the female, and the young develop from the food that is in the egg until it hatches. In the case of nearly all mammals, the egg develops within the body of the female until it is ready to be born.

What a remarkable thing happens within the newly developing young. The fertilized germ cell in the female develops two things: the body of the animal that is to be born, and at the same time, cells within the body of the female young, and sperm within the male young, so that when the new body is formed, the germ cells for the next generation are also formed. Certainly evolution could not have thought of all these things for the perpetuation of offspring and could not have done all these marvelous things by chance! How could man be so gullible as to believe such tales? Aesop's fables are more reasonable.

To believe, that all the thousands of species could develop similar male and female counterparts at the same time that could reproduce future generations, is scientifically absurd, ridiculous and foolish.

XV.   HUMANITY IN GENERAL

1.   MANKIND

We must now say more about the most remarkable part of the creation, mankind. A good place to begin is with the biblical statement, "[Man is] fearfully and wonderfully made" (Psalm 139:14). Man's moral and intellectual faculties, the mysteries surrounding his body and mind, how his soul relates to these — all are still mysterious in spite of his achievements in intellectual, medical, technological, and space-age pursuits. These amazing characteristics of man can be accounted for only by their being the work of a supreme Creator. Man's sense of right and wrong, his expanding inventiveness, and especially his religious inclinations, make man fundamentally different from animals. They make him infinitely superior to all other creatures on earth. From the very beginning, and still today, even in the most savage areas of the earth, men are still men. The archeological findings we considered earlier reveal that even the earliest "savages" have stood mountain-high over the animals. All this is in compliance with God's instruction to "have dominion over the fish of the sea, over the birds of the air, and over every living thing that moves on the earth" (Genesis 1:28). NKJV The very first humans, Adam and Eve, were the real *Homo sapiens* of all time, including us today, no matter how educated and advanced we may be.

2.   SOUL

Man's superiority springs from his being made in God's image. God gave man a soul so that he might be His representative having dominion over all. Nothing like this is said of any other creature. That man might have dominion is the message of Genesis 1:26. The soul makes the difference. This non-material part of man is referred to in three different ways: spirit is the word for the principle of life, such as animals also have; mind is used of man's intelligence and sometimes of that of animals; and soul refers to man's distinct nature which was made "in the image of God." The distinctive element in man is not that God "breathed into His nostrils the breath of life; and man became a living soul," Gen. 2:7 but it is in the way that God created him, and in the fact that man was created in the image of God. The Word of God raised man above the level of animals by creating him "a little lower than the angels, And You have crowned him with honor and glory. You have made him to have dominion over the works of Your hands; You have put all things under His feet" (Psalm 8:5). NKJV.

3.   CONSCIENCE

There is another aspect of man that makes him distinct from other living creatures: the conscience. Although the essence and functions of conscience are expressed in many places of the Bible, it is very well summarized in Romans 2:14-15:

> When Gentiles, who do not have the law [of Moses] by nature do the things contained in the law, these, although not having the law, are a law to themselves, who show the work of the law written in their hearts, *their conscience* also bearing witness, and their thoughts the meanwhile accusing or else excusing one another.

Although the Gentiles did not have the laws of Moses as the children of Israel did in the Old Testament, they however had a knowledge of God's law or will written in their hearts, and thereby they also had a natural knowledge that "there is a God" to whom they must give an account. Whenever they did things agreeable to this natural knowledge, their conscience would approve. Many of them, not having a *clear* knowledge of God's law, did not consider wrong desires, thoughts and words as sins nor wrong deeds as sins. Because of this they became proud of their outward deeds and became self-righteous. At other times, however, when they committed deeds that they knew were wrong, their conscience accused and disturbed them. Walt Whitman once said: "Cows do not worry about their sins or wrong deeds, but man does."

The conscience acts like a judge within us. It either accuses us or excuses us, it declares us guilty or not guilty. Conscience is the voice in man which tells him that certain things are right and certain things are wrong, that there is a Supreme Lawgiver to whom he is responsible, that there is a Superior Being, a God, who rewards good on earth and punishes evil. Therefore conscience is that faculty of the soul which makes a person conscious of God as One to whom man is accountable, as One who is holy, righteous and just, and who demands holiness, righteousness, obedience and fairness of all mankind. Conscience is not a product of our own mind and will. There is One above us who implanted a conscience in us, who is the Supreme Lawgiver and Judge and whose holy and wise will and law is absolute. Thank God that He has also provided a Savior in Jesus Christ to save us from our disobedience.

The word conscience does not appear in the Old Testament, but its functions are referred to a number of times, as in the case of Adam and Eve after their sin, of Cain both before and after the murder of his brother Abel, of the brothers of Joseph after their crime against Joseph, and of David after his sins of adultery and murder.

The voice of conscience is found in every man. Atheists have never yet found a tribe, race or nation of fellow atheists. Because every man knows that he is responsible to a superior Lawgiver, he knows that there is a god. There are backward tribes who are so ignorant that they can barely count to ten, but who acknowledge a god whom they fear because their conscience upbraids them for the things they have done which they acknowledge as wrong. It is for this reason that the heathen try to propitiate or please their gods by idol worship and sacrifices in order to gain their favor and to appease their anger. For the same reason learned men try to appease and pacify a god of their own imagination with their own self-ordained, imagined good works.

The fact of God's existence is as certain to all races of men as the fact of the existence of the universe and of man himself. Only atheists try to deny the existence of God. But they do it only in fair weather, when all is going well with them. "Thou hast conquered, Galilean," cried the apostate emperor as he died.

There was a young man who could curse and swear a continuous blue streak in the harvest field. One day a severe lightning and thundercloud came over the field. Everyone got into a car. The young man crawled into the back seat while the lightning flashed and the thunder rolled, and he hunched up like a beaten puppy and never said a word all the while. Someone asked, Why he was not taking God's name in vain now?

4.   THE PERPETUATION OF MANKIND

Where did human beings come from? The Bible states very clearly that Adam and Eve were the beginning of mankind. Although evolutionists do not believe this, there are geneticists who believe that all humans descended from one woman. According to the Associated Press, January 1, 1987:

> Alan Wilson of the University of California at Berkeley said that studies of the genes of 147 people from around the world allowed him to construct a family tree relating the individuals to one another. The family tree springs from one woman who lived in Africa between 140,000 and 280,000 years ago.

At least he was not off into millions of years as other evolutionists are.

First of all, man, like all other living things, is made of billions and trillions of tiny cells. Every cell is a distinct unit that works in perfect harmony with every other cell. The odds of all these cells arranging themselves in the exact order they have, by mere chance, are so small that it is totally impossible without a superior Designer behind it with super-wonderful intelligence.

In order to understand the small probability of anything like this ever happening by chance, we need to look at some of all the almost unbelievable organs in the human body.

5.   BODY CELLS

First we should consider cells a little more before considering the body and its organs. The cells of plants, animals and human beings are extremely complex. There is zero possibility that they could have developed by themselves. Scientists state that all living things are made of non-living chemical atoms of hydrogen, oxygen, nitrogen and carbon, some of them coming together and linking up to form pieces of DNA or deoxyribonucleic acid. I. L. Cohen in his book *Darwin Was Wrong,* p. 206 states: "Chemical molecules are dumb — they have no brains — they cannot design super sophisticated systems by their own volition." . . . p. 212: "There is no mathematical probability whatever for evolution to have been the mechanism that created 6,000,000 sources [of plants and animals] on this earth." The nucleus of every cell has a rolled-up coil of DNA, which is a highly sensitive tape-like molecule that carries the code of life the way a magnetic tape carries music. DNA is like a dictator of the cell. It regulates all the other chemicals in the cell. All forms of life on earth from bacteria to whales have DNA in their cells to direct their activities. It is claimed that there are 60 trillion cells in a human body. These cells are far from being the simple blobs of jelly-like substance they appear to be. They are vastly complex entities, each with a specific mission in the life of the body. Each tiny little cell is a marvelous creation of God, beyond comprehension, endowed with almost unbelieveable properties and powers. The cells are often called the basic element of life. Each kind of cell has a different function to perform. They are as different in function and in form as an elephant and an insect. They come in all sizes, from the ostrich egg down to the ones where a million could be placed on the head of a pin. Their shapes also vary: discs, rods and spheres. Whenever we do something, billions of cells are put to work by instructions from the cells that are in the brain.

The most remarkable of all the cells is the female egg. Once it is fertilized, this simple cell divides again and again, until there are trillions of cells in the body. How this one reproductive egg knows whether the offspring should be a horse, or dog, or whale or a human is something beyond comprehension. And how all the different 60 trillion cells can live in harmony — each minding its own work and business, efficiently performing the task it is to do — is an unbelievable supreme wonder. Only an almighty, all-wise Designer could create something like this. Although millions of these cells die each second, new ones are formed to take their places until they all die at the death of the creature. Scientists have not been able to create a single cell or even a DNA molecule. Even a virus which is a protein molecule consisting of protein and nucleic acid, has not been produced that can live. See p.p. 256, 406.

6.   THE HUMAN BODY

That all those trillions of cells could arrange themselves in a particular order to compose a body merely by chance is beyond all reason and logic. Yet evolutionists believe as a matter of faith, without any scientific experimental evidence, that all living forms evolved out of nonliving matter by chance.

The human body consists of thousands of organs and individual parts, tiny, small and large, and yet all work together in remarkable unison. In spite of the billions of human beings, there never have been two alike. An ancient Greek philosopher said, "The world is full of wonders but nothing is more wonderful than man."

Norman Macbeth in *Darwin Retried*, p. 88, beautifully describes the marvels of the human body:

> [H]ere is a far more wonderful thing than a watch, a man with all his organs ingeniously contrived, cords and levers, girders and kingposts, circulating systems of pipes and valves, dialyzing membranes, chemical retorts, carburetors, ventilators, inlets and outlets, telephone transmitters in his ears, light recorders and lenses in his eyes; is it conceivable that this is the work of chance? that no artificer has wrought here? that there is no purpose in this, no design, no guiding intelligence?

7.   SKELETONS AND SPINES

The skeletons of mankind consist of about 200 different bones of different shapes and sizes joined together with sockets and balls which are lined with a cartilage to eliminate friction between the bones. The bones of the hands and feet, and especially of the spine, are wonderful in their structure.

The spine or backbone should receive special consideration. The backbone is a marvel of biological engineering. It is the body's principal scaffolding on which the skull, ribs, shoulder bones, pelvis, arms and legs are all anchored. Those 24 highly specialized bones of the spinal column are remarkably constructed so that they fit into each other and they are joined to protect the spinal cord, which is a bundle of nerves that links the brain with other parts of the nervous system. The spinal column is flexible enough so it can bend and turn and yet give the body enough support so man can stand and sit in an upright position. A system of muscles, ligaments and tendons keeps the column of bones from collapsing. How could any logical, reasonable person say all this happened or evolved by chance?

8.   THE BRAIN AND NERVOUS SYSTEM

Connected with the spinal cord are the brain and all the nerves connected with it. The nervous system is so complex that it is beyond imagination and comprehension. Scientists have said, "the wiring diagram for the brain is too complex ever to be drawn. The human brain is a bewildering mass of 10 billion neurons, which are single nerve cells with all their processes. Then there are the synapses which are the points of contact between adjacent neurons." Robert Cook, 1941, describes the neurons as being essentially like an electrical system, the complexity of which is beyond imagination. He says that a building as large as the Pentagon in Washington, D.C., would not be large enough to house the computing machine needed to replicate it with as many synapses as are found in the human brain. How could an evolutionist ever believe that such a complex system could evolve without a most brilliant Designer, to make not only one brain, but also to make these brains reproducible?

Evolutionist Carl Sagan in *Cosmos* (1980), p. 278, states that the information stored in billions of neurons in the brain "would fill some 20 million volumes, as many as in the world's largest libraries." *Science News Letter* (September 5, 1955, p. 148), states that the brain of man "is different and immeasurably more complicated than anything else in the known universe." Anthropologist Henry Osborn wrote, "The human brain is the most marvelous object in the whole universe." Science editor Dr. Irving Bengelsdorf wrote: "Anyone who speaks of a computer as an electronic brain has never seen a brain. Our active memories hold several billion times more information than a large contemporary research computer."

Just imagine all the information a skilled piano player must have stored in the brain to play musical compositions with the fingers flying over the keys at the right moment at the right keys and with the right amount of force to execute the composition properly. What an immense amount of programming is stored in that pianist's brain!

The two original evolutionists 125 years ago summed up the brain and their own folly of evolution very correctly, when Alfred Wallace wrote to Charles Darwin regarding the brains of humans and apes (found in *Darwin Retried* by Norman MacBeth, p. 103):

> Natural Selection could only have endowed the savage with a brain a little superior to that of the ape, whereas he [the savage] actually possesses one very little inferior to that of the average member of our learned societies.

Darwin answered Wallace (Darwin Retried) by N. MacBeth, p. 103:

> I hope you have not murdered too completely your own and my child [that is evolution].

9.   EYES

Another of God's organ creations is the eye, which also is most amazing. Its iris dilates and contracts according to the needs of vision. It is a marvel of tender nerves and muscles, which receives millions of light rays and pictures and tell us how the outside world looks and make it possible to learn through reading. It is claimed that an eye can visualize 35,000 different color sensations, multitudes more than paint charts could produce. Dr. David Menton, who is an associate professor of anatomy at Washington University in St. Louis, states in an article in The *Wall Street Journal* (July 15, 1979):

> Incredible structures such as the human eye make our most complicated computers look like beer-can openers.

HOW THE EYE WORKS

The eye has at least four main parts, each having an important delicate function to perform. There is the retina, on which the picture is formed. The lens focuses the rays of light on the retina, and it adjusts itself to near and distant scenes. An opaque curtain, or iris, regulates the amount of light admitted. There are delicate muscles to control the iris and lens. An outer coat with a transparent window in the front encases the whole mechanism. If only one of these parts fails to function — if the retina is missing or the lens becomes opaque or anything else fails with all its multitude of cells, the eye is useless. No part of the eye would be of any value without all the other parts. The retina would not accomplish anything without the cornea and the pupil, nor the pupil and the cornea without the retina, nor all of these put together without the optic nerve feeding all the sensitive sensations of sight to the brain and the brain turning all this into pictures and images.

Everything must be present and work in unison to produce sight. The iris, by expanding and contracting, adapts to the different degrees of light, adjusting to strong and weak light. The eye can also be adjusted so it can see objects at different distances, varying from inches to miles. This is done by slightly changing the shape of the lens, making it more or less convex. A landscape of several miles can be brought within a space of half an inch in diameter and yet all the distant objects can be distinguished in space, color, position and size. The same eye can read printed matter only a few inches away. No optical instrument today could match the workings and capabilities of the eye.

Evolutionists believe that everything in the universe, the earth and all the creatures and organs of man, just evolved. How could such a complex organ as the eye ever evolve? Was there first an eyeball and then an optic nerve that started growing back to the brain? But none of the parts of the eyeball or optic nerve are of any use without all the other parts. They could not wait for each other to develop. All parts had to come into existence simultaneously for the purpose of seeing. When did the millions of atoms and cells, that form the cornea, pupil, retina, optic nerve and other parts of the eye, decide to form an eye, even in an insect? Even if a nerve had already been in existence, extending from the brain, how could that nerve divide to build up an eyeball with all its intricate and delicate parts, and make it possible for all this. There just had to be an outside force or intelligence behind all of it. There had to be an all-intelligent, wise and capable Designer. Then what about all the other organs that are needed to create and maintain a living body?

10.   CHANCES OF AN EYE FORMING BY ITSELF

It is totally impossible that an eye could develop piecemeal even over billions of years. To believe that a fully formed eye could have developed instantly is simply ludicrous. No wonder more and more down to earth scientists like Dr. David Menton of Washington University in St. Louis are compelled to say in disgust, as he did in *The Wall Street Journal* (June 15, 1979): "More and more reasonable scientists are speaking out against this silly theory of evolution." Webster's Dictionary explains *silly* as "having or showing little sense, judgment, or sobriety; foolish, stupid, absurd, ludicrous, etc."

11.   DARWIN AND THE EYE

Even Darwin saw this. Darwin conceded that the human eye constituted a severe strain on his theory of evolution. He said that the thought of the eye, and how it possibly could have evolved by natural selection, made him ill. Of all the organs of extreme complexity and perfection within the human body, the most worrisome to him was the human eye. Harding, another evolutionist, referred to the eye as "*that damned eye.*" [Emphasis His]

The *Readers Digest* (September 1982) in "Where Darwin Went Wrong," by Francis Hitching, p.o. 13-4 observes:

> For the eye to work it must be clean and moist. Light passes through the protective outer coating (the cornea) and continues via a self-adjusting aperture (the pupil) to a similarly automatic lens, which focuses it on the back of the retina. Here 130 million light-sensitive rods and cones cause photochemical reactions that transform the light into electrical impulses. These are then transmitted to the brain at terrific speed. How is it possible that thousands upon thousands of lucky mutations happened coincidentally so that the lens and the retina — which cannot work without each other — evolved in synchrony? At this point we might fairly conclude that the evolutionary theory has reached an impass.

Then the author goes on and fosters a still more ridiculous theory of evolution by the "Hopeful Monster" idea in place of Darwin's gradual evolution. But he just could not condescend to the reasonable idea of, or belief in, a Designer or Creator.

12.   THE EAR

The ear, like the eye, is a very complicated, sensitive organ. The outer odd-shaped shells on the two sides of the head are only a small part of the organ of hearing. They only collect the sounds and direct them to the rest of the hearing-organ inside the head, to the eardrum first of all, which is still part of the outer ear. The eardrum is a vibrating membrane sending sounds to the middle ear, which is a small cavity containing three small bones called the hammer, anvil and stirrup, which help send the sound on to the inner ear. There the real process of hearing takes place. This inner ear with its spiral cochlea, tubes, membranes, rods, and hair cells working together with the hearing nerves is an intricately complex mechanism, which is a miracle that is hard to understand, and a miracle that could hardly have developed by chance, all by itself. It has 4,300 delicate rods, which vibrate with every sound given. It is one of the wonders of creation which could never have developed by itself in billions of years.

Whittaker Chambers, who was known for his cloak and dagger existence as a Soviet spy in Washington, was converted from Marxism and evolution. One day, as he was watching his little daughter eat breakfast, it suddenly occurred to him that everything about his little girl, even those delicate sensitive, intricate ears, starting with the outer ear, was an absolute miracle of design and could not possibly have happened by chance.

13.   THE VOICE

Another miracle that goes hand in hand with the ear, so that men can communicate with each other, is the voice, the wonderful ability to speak. Voice proceeds through the organs of the voice box, lungs, mouth, throat, tongue and teeth. Voice is produced by the vocal cords which are delicate membranes that are stretched across the wind pipe in the throat and are caused to vibrate by air pressure from the lungs. The mouth, tongue and teeth are also necessary to make intelligible speech and music. The voice can let us show various kinds of expression. With it one can command, encourage, lament, express joy, anger, displeasure, grief, etc. Millions of people have been led, misled and amused by the voices of others. No two people have exactly the same timbre or sound of voice so that a person whom we know can usually be detected at once over the phone. Voices are as different as the outward faces and bodies. And then there are people who think that this varied instrument of speech and song just happened by itself.

14.   THE THROAT

In connection with the voice box is the throat in which it is located. Some may consider the throat as a simple hose, like a garden hose. But it contains switching devices that move and sort the air, and the fluids and the solids that go into our bodies from the nose and the mouth. If one should laugh while swallowing a piece of meat, as happened to me one time at a banquet, the throat instead of directing the meat to the stomach might let it slip into or near the windpipe, blocking the air to the lungs. One could collapse from what looked like a heart attack. This so-called "cafe coronary" could kill one unless the meat were dislodged. The throat has two tubes, each about one inch in diameter: the trachea which leads to the lungs and the esophagus which leads to one's stomach. The esophagus does not let the food drop directly into one's stomach. It moves the food on in a wave-like manner gradually and only as fast as the stomach can handle it. Also the entire throat system (for directing air to the lungs and food and liquid to the stomach, and for helping to produce speech) could hardly have happened by chance.

15.   THE TONGUE

The tongue not only helps us in our speech and singing but it also helps us in delivering food to our throats and stomachs. Just as importantly it helps us to distinguish different tastes: sour, bitter, salty, sweet, some pleasant, some distasteful.

16.   THE NOSE

With the sense of taste goes the sense of smell, which the nose provides. The sense of smell warns us of many dangers that may confront us, such as deadly gas and smoke. The sense of smell is not as highly developed in mankind as it is in certain animals, such as dogs, especially those used by the police. Certain odors are repulsive and can cause nausea and disgust, while others give delight, especially food that is being prepared. The sense of smell has been referred to as a certified neuron belonging to the brain nosing around out in the open air.

Another major task for the nose is to clear the air of dust and bacteria and to control its temperature for the lungs. This is done by the hairs in the nose and by sticky mucus that lines its passages to trap bacteria and dust that may get past the hairs of the nose. Every twenty minutes a new clean blanket of mucus is produced by the mucus membrane and the old mucus is washed away. This is another evidence of a most remarkable engineering device that just could not have happened by chance.

17.   SKIN AND TOUCH

Another sensitive sense organ is the skin which conveys to us not only the presence of other people and objects but also brings to us sensations of heat, cold, pain, pressure, pleasure and other sensations that may be hurtful or helpful to us. Although there are countless nerve cells giving us reports of the world, there are two very sensitive spots: the tip of the tongue and the tips of the fingers.

18.   THE LUNGS

There are many wonderful organs in the human body, all of which are vital for living. How long could a person live without the lungs and heart? Man's lungs are some of his largest organs and are quite complex. Most of the real work done by the lungs takes place in the alveoli, which are grape-like bunches of tiny air sacs. There are 250 million of these sacs, and if they were flattened out they would cover an area of 2,600 square feet or about as much floor space as in a house of 45 by 60 feet.

Each one of these millions of alveoli is covered with a web of capillaries. Blood is pumped into one end of a capillary. Red blood cells pass through single file, about one every second. As they go through, the cells get rid of their carbon dioxide brought in from the rest of the body. At the same time the red blood cells pick up oxygen going the other way. It is like a swap place, where impurities are exchanged for pure oxygen, so we can continue to live. Without lungs man could not live. How could such a wonderful organ come into being with all the other organs at the same time merely by chance?

19.   THE HEART

Furthermore, to show how still more complicated the whole body system is, the process of getting rid of the carbon dioxide and taking in the necessary oxygen depends not only on effective lung action but also on quick movement of these two gases between lungs and body tissue by means of vigorous action by the heart. The heart is the most powerful organ in the human body. Every day this powerful muscle pumps more than 1,800 gallons of blood through 60,000 miles of blood vessels.

The body is composed of billions of cells, which require a constant removal of waste and fresh supplies of oxygen and nourishment provided by the digestive system. The heart and the blood vessels are the means for providing all the service required by the cells. The heart is a strong muscle that acts like a pump contracting and relaxing, and like every pump it has valves to keep the blood from flowing backwards.

20.   THE BLOOD

Equally amazing, mysterious and marvelous is the *blood* that is being pumped through the body by the heart. It consists of two kinds of corpuscles, the red and the white. In every drop of blood are millions of red corpuscles which remove waste matter from the cells and carry oxygen and food to the cells. The white corpuscles are less numerous. They protect the cells from disease germs, acting as bodyguards. Then there are other wonderful mysterious elements in the blood which modern medical men still do not fully understand.

When Barney Clark, the man with the first artificial heart, died, it was reported: "His colon failed. Then his kidneys failed. Then his lungs failed. Then his brain failed and lastly when the key was turned off, his heart failed." Seeing how complicated the heart and the entire blood system is, the vital work that it performs, and knowing that life ends suddenly when the heart ceases working — how can evolutionists believe and teach innocent, gullible children that the heart and other body organs developed by themselves, when even a living heart can be kept alive only for a certain time? The heart, the blood system, and all the other organs of the body ought to convince every person that only an all-wise, all-capable and all-powerful Designer could have conceived, designed and created them and that it is unreasonable to believe that the human heart and its blood vessels and corpuscles could have happened by chance as a process of evolution, either gradually or in big jumps. On the other hand, a child of God, who knows what is involved in the heart and what happens to one's life as soon as the heart fails to work properly for only a few minutes, can only exclaim with the Psalmist: How fearfully and wonderfully my heart and my entire body is made! (Psalm 139:14)

21.   THE STOMACH AND DIGESTIVE SYSTEM

The basic organ of the digestive system, supplying the necessary nourishment and energy to the rest of the body, is the stomach. Working with it are the small and large intestines, the pancreas, liver, and salivary glands of the mouth. This food-processing system is the most wonderful chemical laboratory known to man. It is used to help convert vegetables, fruit and the flesh of animals, fish and poultry into blood, flesh, bones, cells, muscles, hair, brains, nerves and nails for fingers and toes. It also produces heat and energy to keep the body going. The lining of the stomach contains 35 million glands which may secrete about three quarts of gastric juice, mainly hydrochloric acid. This acid helps create other acids necessary to break down food and turn it into nourishment for the body and start protein digestion.

Another remarkable thing about the stomach is, How can this fleshy organ digest other proteins and other flesh and *not digest itself?* The reason is that the delicate lining of the stomach is coated with a protective mucus. If it were missing, the stomach would cannibalize and digest itself. Surely this protective feature could not have developed by itself. Chance development is an impossible answer.

22.   THE REPRODUCTIVE SYSTEM

When God created Adam and Eve, He created two very different and distinct forms of human beings. Though they were different, they were created for each other, they attracted one another and they complemented and completed each other. How could two distinct sexes develop side by side with complementary sexual organs and instincts? And how could the number of men and women remain worldwide almost constantly equal in numbers, even though the human race increased by billions over the centuries? No evolutionist can ever explain this perpetual approximate balance between the two sexes.

God wanted this beautiful planet populated with people for whom He created the earth. This earth was to be a material home for a material body. Therefore He gave the command, "Be fruitful, and multiply." He did even more than that. He instilled in each sex such a powerful attraction for the other, and such a strong sex desire, that His command and will would be fulfilled.

Still, the attraction of men and women for each other is not limited to the perpetuation of the human race. Sexual attraction is also the source of the fatherly and motherly instinct in men and women. In fact, most of the better qualities associated with an ideal home have their roots in the mysterious sexual drive. In the later teens, children are already considering establishing their own homes and families and having children that they can love and care for.

However, the reproduction of the human race (as well as of animals) is a remarkable ability that chance simply cannot have produced. The fertilized egg of a woman derives half of its chromosomes and genes from the mother and half from the father, which determine its future development. These few microscopic molecules will determine how the future cells will divide and multiply and will determine whether the new body will be male or female, what color of skin it will have, and what facial features and body it will have. It will also determine all the other features of the body, such as height, its legs, its arms, its teeth, its bones, its skeleton and all the organs of the body. This body will also be endowed by the Creator with a soul that will live on forever, even though the physical body may some time in the future be dead.

The marvels of the development of the human body after conception has been excellently expressed by Dr. Joseph Krimsky in *The Doctor's Soliloquy*, pages 7-9. He has seen many children physically born. He wrote:

> The years of my life as a physician are filled with abundant testimony to the truth and estheticism of miracles. Conception and birth are miracles beyond our understanding, even though we can plot out the steps and stages in the process. The rapid movement of the microscopic spermatozoon towards the ovum, as if guided

and directed by some impelling intelligence bent on the propagation and perpetuation of life — that is a miracle. And let not the materialistic skeptic prate of chemical and physical reactions.

No amount of scientific rationalization can reveal the secret that shrouds the problem of beginning life, whether on earth or in the living womb. The very emotion of love and ecstasy that brings about the union of male and female germ cells is a mystery and an enigma that science cannot explain.

Consider also how the seed is lodged in the womb, how cells and fibers, tissues and blood vessels are prepared to form the uteruarian nest. What foresight, what tender care, what clever and efficient use of materials! But here in the womb of the human mother, the nest is built by some invisible and automatic force endowed by more than human intelligence or animal instinct. The newly fertilized egg, which by some strange magnetism has been drawn and propelled to its destination, is lodged in a wall of warm, palpitating, living flesh, which is supplied with vital strength and nourishment.

Reflect upon the wonder of harmony and adjustment that arouses every gland of the body to cooperate in a common effort for the security and growth of the tiny embryo. Think of the mystery of life in the womb, how here in a period of a few months the evolution — from the single homogeneous single-celled bit of protoplasm to the infinite complexity of structure and function in the child at birth.

The Darwinists tell us that it all came about through mutations and variations, through adaptation and selection. But science is learning that these mutations and combinations of mutations are not haphazard or accidental, not the product of blind chance. They occur in response to vital and functional needs. They emerge, or are evoked, whenever life has need of them for the more perfect and more efficient performance of its task. The bricks do not just spring up in place by a design and purpose; those who have eyes to see and a mind to understand must acknowledge with reverence and awe though the great Architect is beyond the scope of moral vision.

How beautifully expressed!

In addition, how could just the right kind of sex organs develop within a woman, and within a man, or other living creatures, so they could produce the elements of new life? And how could two people of different sex appear at exactly the same time and in the same place on this earth in the imagined billions of years, within about a 50 year period of history in those billions of years, so that they could continue life? And how could the sexes in animals appear within each other in approximately the same time? Mathematically the chances of anything like this happening are almost zero I said, *mathematically*. Certainly the theory of evolution has rightly been called by a doctor of anatomy, a silly, absurd, ridiculous theory!

23.   ALL THE OTHER HUMAN ORGANS

Besides, behold all the other marvelous organs of the human body and also of all other creatures. Consider the teeth, the liver, the glands, the bladder, the pancreas, the feet, the hands, the fingers, the joints of the body, the germ-fighting abilities of the body, reposing sleep for the body, and many other remarkable features that just could not have fallen together by chance. The Bible has stated twice in Psalm 14:1 and Psalm 53, as a forceful introduction to those Psalms: "The *fool* has said in his heart, 'There is no God.' " NKJV Yes, only a fool in fair weather will say such a thing and actually believe it. May God give him *intelligence before it is too late*.

24.   EMBRYOLOGY AND RECAPITULATION

Related to the organs of the body is the old evolutionary theory of recapitulation in the embryo. Almost all evolutionists used to believe (and many still do) that the human embryo as well as other embryos take on, during their development, the shape and form of their evolutionary ancestors. They claimed that there is a striking resemblance between the embryos of other creatures and human beings. This similiarity, they said, points to their common origin.

Embryology was important to Darwin in his theory of evolution. In *The Origin of Species* he devoted twelve pages to it, and made many other references elsewhere. He wrote:

> The structure of the embryo is even more important for classification than that of the adult. For the embryo is the animal in its less modified state; and in so far it reveals the structure of its progenitor. In two groups of animals, however much they may at present differ from each other in structure and habits, if they pass through the same or similiar embryonic stages, we may feel assured that they both descend from the same or nearly similiar parents, and are therefore in that degree closely related.

Ernest Haeckel carried Darwin's thoughts much further. He proposed what is called the biogenetic law, which declared that the growth of the embryo recapitulated the history of the species. The implication was that the embryo indicates lines of descent that are not apparent in adults. Many of the comparative diagrams he drew were not completely honest.

The claim is made that embryos of different creatures show similarities. But similarity does not prove evolution. Most animals and man have many organs of the body that are similar, head, arms, legs, body, eyes, nose, lungs, stomach, etc., but that does not prove that they came from the same ancestors. Although these organs show that certain animals may resemble each other because we live in the same surroundings, eat the same food and breathe the same air, they do not give the information which evolutionists are trying to squeeze out of these similarities.

Informed biologists know that the DNA molecules of various animals are so different, so dissimilar that they cannot come from the same ancestors. The DNA of a cow is so different from that of a dog, and the DNA of a chicken is so totally different from that of a lizard that only the same *kind* of animals can develop from its embryo. Such genetic programs as are coded into the different creatures could never have evolved by chance. The structure of the DNA is so designed that one type of DNA could never evolve into the DNA for another type of species.

Much has been written by evolutionists about "gill slits" that are said to be found in the human embryo at a certain period of its development. They claim that this shows that at a certain period of evolution man passed through what they claim was the fish stage of existence. But these supposed gill-slits never develop into gills or slits in humans, they are structures that develop into various glands, the lower jaw, and structures in the inner ear that have nothing to do with fish.

Haeckel of Germany, who was a close follower of Darwin, compiled 26 stages in the development of man from the lowest forms of animal life and said these 26 stages were recapitulated or repeated in the development of the human embryo. But he manufactured certain stages of development to propose his claimed parallel development of human and animal development. He was guilty of deliberate manipulations to bolster up his claims.

Although this theory was wrong, like hundreds of other evolutionary theories, and although most knowledgeable embryologists now completely discredit this theory, it is still found in many high school and college texts, imposed upon the students. Walter Bock, of the Department of Biological Sciences of Columbia University, said:

> The biogenetic law has become so deeply rooted in biological thought that it cannot be weeded out in spite of its having been demonstrated to be wrong by numerous subsequent scholars.

Yet, in 1956 Carrington, in his book, *The Story of Our Earth,* p. 64, wrote:

> This principle, that the individual embryo relives the story of the race, is known as the law of recapitulation. It is perhaps *the most conclusive proof* we have of the truth of evolution.

Even as late as October 12, 1985, Dr. E. Sillman, professor of biology at Duquesne University, in a debate with Dr. Duane Gish used this old theory. Dr. Gish was surprised (Acts & Facts, Dec. 1985, p. 7)

> that Sillman would use embryological recapitulation as an argument for evolution, since few knowledgeable evolutionists any longer use this thoroughly discredited idea as evidence for evolution.

25.   VESTIGIAL ORGANS AND EVOLUTION

Vestigial organs are organs that have been assumed to be useless vestiges or remains or traces of something that once was useful in a former assumed evolutionary stage, but that have passed away as no longer serving a purpose, such as the appendix, tonsils, thyroid gland, tail bone, etc. They were considered survivals or remnants of an earlier animal stage in man's life. They were considered useful in the animal stage but through disuse or for other reasons they have become practically useless. They were cited by evolutionists as evidence of evolution. But many of these organs have been found to be not only useful but essential in life, especially the tonsils in fighting disease. The tonsils are no longer removed as they used to be, because medical science has found that they play a role in protecting the body from disease, and that the tonsils have a designed plan and purpose for the body.

The appendix contains tissue similar to that found in the tonsils and also helps fight against diseases, especially those that affect the intestines. Both the tonsils and appendix are important in early life to fight against disease more common to children. Later in life they become less necessary. Such organs which provide antibodies for the young can hardly be called useless or without any function. Because one can live without tonsils and appendix does not make them useless. We can get along without arms, eyes and legs, but that does not make them useless.

The tail bone also is not the useless remnant of a tail, but it serves as an anchor for important muscles of the pelvic region that provide a floor for that region. These muscles attached to the tail bone provide support for the pelvic organs. Without these muscles these organs would drop down. In addition, without the tail bone one cannot sit comfortably. All in all, the evolutionists lose many proofs for their false misleading ideas.

26.   LIFE ON OTHER PLANETS

Evolutionists are more and more becoming filled with the obsession that life must exist on other planets. Because there are billions of stars, they assume there also must be billions of other planets. For evolutionists, intelligent life elsewhere is not only a mathematical probability, it is a critical *must* for them. If the earth is only one of many planets, then it is assumed that life has evolved in other planets outside of the solar system, especially since no life has been found on the moon and Mars and other solar planets and moons.

This search for life on other planets is intensified by two false assumptions. First, because they assume that life evolved on the earth it must also have evolved elsewhere in the universe. Secondly, because the evolution of life on the earth has not been proven, and because knowledgeable scientists have stated that evolution of life from non-life on this earth is impossible, they are searching for life coming here from life that might have evolved outside of this earth.

The Free Press, Mankato, Minnesota, (April 4, 1987) reported a meeting of 1,200 people in Pasadena, California. Carl Sagan of Cornell University stated:

> In a universe of 100 billion galaxies each of which have a few hundred billion stars, the idea that our sun is the only star with an inhabitable planet is laughable. Where do we come off to imagine we're the only kind of life in the universe?

That statement seems plausible, but it is based on the old unproven premise and conclusion that

> because the chemical evolution that produced life on Earth exists throughout the known universe, the probability for intelligent life elsewhere is 100 percent.

This was stated by Frank Drake, dean of natural science at the University of California, Santa Cruz. Al Hibbs, retired from NASA, said:

> I'd be willing to bet 100 bucks that between now and the time
> I die we'll find evidence of intelligent life.

I certainly would bet a lot more if I were that certain. On the other hand these evolutionists are seeking a handout of more millions of dollars from the rest of us taxpayers besides the billions already spent to search for "signs of an alien civilization." They are already thinking of sending out a self-contained heterosexual space crew to continue for several generations the search for life beyond this earth.

The entire belief or creed that there is life elsewhere in the universe is based on the false assumption that life began here on earth by chance through chemical action out of non-living material. *The Free Press,* Mankato, Minnesota, (September 10, 1979) quoted the AP from Washington, D.C.:

> Scientists have found the chemical precursors of life in two rare meteorites discovered in the Antarctic, giving strength to the idea that life could have developed somewhere in addition to Earth, they say . . . the findings add weight to the theory that life on Earth began through a chemical percolation in primordial oceans billions of years ago.

To many evolutionists, the statement that life came on earth by "chemical action" is not merely a theory. It is to them a postulated fact. Postulate means: "to assume without proof to be true, real, or necessary, especially as a basis for argument." *The Free Press,* a week later, (September 17, 1979) stated in a report given to the American Chemical Society:

> The findings [regarding the meteorites] give scientific credence of the theory that the chemical evolutionary process postulated for Earth has taken place elsewhere, according to the report.

Notice how fast they jumped to wrong conclusions: from the false "chemical evolutionary process postulated for Earth" they jump to the false conclusion that therefore this same "chemical evolutionary process" must also have produced life elsewhere. But before spending billions of dollars to go out into space to prove the beginning of life, let them first prove that such chemical action produced life on the earth. Because molecules in meteorites and space have been found which are also found in living materials, they have jumped to the conclusion that somehow this proves evolution of life has occurred in space also. But such molecules are far from being alive. The moon and Mars also have molecules and chemicals, but no life is found there.

But suppose that there would be people in outer space, would it be wise for us to try to find them? If these beings would be far superior to us, they could be far more dangerous to us than any enemies ever faced on earth. One wise man said that should we ever hear the "space-phone" ringing from outer space, please, for mankind's sake, don't answer the phone. Rather, avoid attracting their attention, make ourselves as inconspicuous as we can.

To see what could happen if we got too nosey, *The Free Press* (September 17, 1979), which was quoted before, contained another story, this time regarding aliens to this earth:

> More physical evidence that can be used to build a case for extra-terrestrial life comes in the "close encounter of the second kind" that happened to Marshal County Deputy, Val Johnson, on August 27. Johnson was attacked by what he called "an unidentified thing." It dove at his car and smashed the windshield and one headlight. There was a small dent in the hood, the red light atop the car was broken, and two spring-mounted antennas were bent at angles of nearly 90 degrees. The deputy suffered burns on his eyes from the bright light of the object, and he was treated by a physician for this condition . . . No explanation of the case has been offered. There is no question that something very unusual happened to the deputy and his patrol car. The hypothesis that the "thing" that hit the car and injured the deputy's eyes was a vehicle manned or controlled by beings from another planet is certainly as good as explanation as any other that has been offered.

If all this were true, it certainly would be wise to avoid such creatures and civilization (?) and not answer a phone call from them, and much less spend billions of dollars trying to find them.

On the other hand, that same news report stated:

> Although mankind here has made great strides in science, we are yet unable to come up with a cure for the cold. We may find help from friends in outer space. Surely a civilization that is capable of putting men on the moon should be able to find a cure for the common cold.

What dreamers these evolutionists can be, jumping from one false premise and conclusion to another.

On the other hand, there are people who, instead of believing that life evolved somewhere else, wonder whether God might have placed some form of life elsewhere in the universe and created intelligent creatures there. Nowhere does the Bible indicate that there are intelligent creatures on other planets. Just the very opposite impression is given. In Genesis chapter one, we are told that the earth was made first and three days later God made the Sun, the moon and the stars. Genesis 1:16 reads: "And God made two great lights; the greater light to rule the day, and the lesser light to rule the night: he made *the stars also.*" The word *stars* includes also the planets. From this it is evident that God made all these heavenly bodies for the sake of this earth and for the service of man on this earth. Genesis 1:14 states: "Let them be for signs and for seasons, and for days, and years." From all indications given in the Bible, there are no men or manlike creatures living on other planets near stars. Psalm 115:16 states:

> The heaven, even the heavens, are the LORD'S; but the earth
> He has given to the children of men. NKJV

Furthermore, II Peter 3:10 states:

> But the day of Lord will come as a thief in the night, in which
> the heavens will pass away with a great noise. NKJV

The heavens (stars and planets) will pass away with the earth. Matthew 24:29 states regarding the end of the world:

> The stars will fall from heaven, and the powers of the heavens
> will be shaken. NKJV

Now, if there were people or other creatures on other planets near stars, would it be just and fair to destroy their planet and them also because of our sinful rebellion against God? The whole universe will be destroyed only because of man's rebellion.

On the other hand, it is wonderfully comforting for Christians to know that our almighty God and Savior Jesus Christ is in charge of this entire universe, so that we need not fear invasion from space or encounters of the third kind. Time and space can be left in the hands of God together with the care of our bodies and souls.

27.   LIFE IN OUTER SPACE — ANGELS

On the other hand THERE IS LIFE BEYOND the material things of this universe. These living beings are the non-material angels, good and bad ones. They do not breathe air, drink water or clothe themselves. The good angels never experience pain or sorrow or death. They are not limited to time and are not restricted to one place. They are not governed by the laws of gravity. There are millions, myriads or hosts of them. These super-intelligent creatures need no radio communication from us to know what we are doing. Because they are spirits they have no body and occupy no space. Yet they are not omnipresent as God is, for at any one particular time they are only at some one place. Although the good angels live in another world about the throne and presence of God, they did, and do at times appear on earth in human form to serve mankind. They are "ministering spirits, sent forth to minister for them who shall be heirs of salvation," (Hebrews 1:14) and they are "His angels, that excel in strength" (Psalm 103:20).

28.   THE EVIL ANGELS

The evil angels rebelled against God and led many people to do the same — to become rebellious and defiant humanistic wise-guys, *Homo sapiens, sapiens*, the biblical "children of men." Because of the evil which these angels insinuated or introduced into mankind, we now see people making war against their fellowmen, nation against nation. We certainly do not want to make our world hospitable to these deceivers. Someone wrote a poem years ago with this observation: If the devil is not supposed to be, who is doing all the evil for which he is blamed?

XVI.   DATING METHODS IN GENERAL

1.   DATING METHODS

In determining the age of this earth and universe, the evolutionists make one mistake in their radiometric method of determining the age of uranium and other radioactive elements. Since they totally ignore the creation of the world by God, they falsely assume that all these elements started out 100 percent pure parent-substances. However, God in creating this earth created a *mature earth*.

In considering the creation of elements and of all other things, we must remember that there is a vast difference between the *apparent age* or the age they *appear to be* and the *true age*. Adam and Eve very likely appeared to be from about 20 to 50 years old when they were created but their true actual age was *zero* years. When Jesus fed the 4,000 and 5,000, the bread and fish appeared to have matured over months and years, but they were zero years old. The wine that Jesus made out of water appeared to have been made from grapes that had grown years ago and were aged into superior wine. The trees and shrubs and flowers and the four rivers in the Garden of Eden appeared to be many years old but they also had a true age of zero years. The light that God created would appear to "evolutionists," if there had been any, to have traveled millions and billions of years, but the light was there instantly just as the stars were. If such evolutionists had existed on the day of creation and had looked out upon the sky, they would have come up with the same billions of years as they do today for the age of the earth and the universe.

The same is true of the substances containing radioactive materials by which the evolutionists are claiming billions of years for their age and for the age of the earth. Scientists have found that radioactive materials like uranium slowly produce decay products or elements such as lead, so that in the course of years there is a certain ratio of parent elements and daughter elements. But when God created a mature earth and universe, He also very likely created substances of this earth with the appearance of age of billions of years that the evolutionists assume. Yet they were only zero years old. Their appearance of age was due not to decay but to their original creation of God.

For evolutionists to determine the age of uranium and its daughter-decay element, lead, or the age of any other element, they must make three special assumptions: 1) the radioactive material must not originally have contained any intermediate or final decay products; 2) it must have been part of a closed system in which nothing was removed and in which nothing was added; and 3) its rate of decay must have been constant.

1) There must have been only parent uranium with no decay material, lead. But, as mentioned before, when God created the materials of the earth, He most likely created mature, apparently aged materials like everything else He created. The evolutionists, in order to get their billions of years necessary for their theory of evolution, assume that there were originally very little or none of the intermediate or final decay products. Evolutionist Niles Eldredge, in *The Monkey Business* (1982) writes, on p. 102:

> *If* [he italicized the IF] we know the original amount of the "parent" and "daughter" isotopes at the time a rock was formed, and *if* we know the rate at which the parent isotope decays to its daughter isotopic form, we would be able to measure the current ratio of daughter to parent and thus calculate how long ago the rock was in its initial state. Aha! cry the creationists, lots of assumptions there! How do we know that decay rates are constant.

Then he goes to that old circular reasoning trick of comparing the age of the rock to the fossils found in it, which has no scientific foundation. The fossil and rock method is compared with the radioactive method, and he declares they agree. This faulty circular reasoning has been used by the evolutionists again and again. Using one faulty premise together with another faulty premise proves nothing.

That large amounts of radiogenic daughter products very likely were present at the time of creation is evident by what happened in recent years. Henry Hiebert in his book, *Evolution: Its Collapse in View*, stated on p. 30:

> It has been found that radiogenic lead exists with uranimum minerals even in recently formed volcanic rock. In the Journal of Geophysical Research, July 15, 1968, an instance is cited where lava from Kaupuleho, Hawaii, which was *known to be 168 years*, was predicted by the potassium-argon method to be 2,960,000,000 years old! This is no rare occurrence. When modern volcanic rocks are dated radiometrically, their lead-uranium ages are commonly over a billion years! If rocks of known ages yield such unrealistic dates, why should we accept gullibly the ages yielded by rocks of unknown ages?

There is a 17-million-times-difference between 168 years and 2,960,000,000 years. Quite a fable!

2) Radioactive decay takes place in a closed system, with nothing removed and with nothing added. This is not likely, especially in the light of all the violent turmoil the rocks of the earth underwent at the time of the violent Flood, when the fountains of the deep were broken up. When the entire rock system was smashed, crushed, and torn into pieces in that intermixing, much could have been lost and much added that could have changed the composition of the radioactive rocks. At such a time many of these rocks could have been leached. The idea that everything could have remained unchanged over millions of years is ridiculous. Even over a period of 6,000 to 8,000 years much could have changed, especially during the turbulent Flood.

3) A third assumption that evolutionists have made in radioactive dating is that the rate of decay or disintegration must always have been constant. At the time of the Flood the radioactive decay rates could have been changed greatly. Who knows what changes were brought about by that Flood within a very short period of time? The Flood, by mixing radioactive elements and increasing the deposits of the sediments, could have raised havoc with the possibility of using dating methods. Also, there was a vast climatic change at the time of the Flood as is evident from the remains of fossils. This also changed the atmosphere at the time of the Flood. This would result also in a change of cosmic radiation, and if the cosmic radiation is no longer the same, the radioactive method of dating is not trustworthy. And above all, as mentioned before, who knows how much radioactivity there was at the time of creation when a mature world was created? Therefore, the assumption that decay rates remained constant is not provable and certainly not testable.

In general, the dating methods have very shaky assumptions and premises. The premises and conclusions assumed in the dating methods are as shaky as the entire evolutionary theory is. In fact, the dates calculated by these dating methods can be no stronger than the weakest assumption that they used in their calculations. After reviewing a book on evolution and seeing the lack of evidence for evolution, Malcolm Muggeridge stated that the millions of years claimed for evolution "cannot but strike anyone not caught up in the myth as pure fantasy." By myth he meant evolution. Muggeridge continued:

> Posterity will surely be amazed, and I hope vastly amused, that such slipshod and unconvincing theorizing should have so easily captivated twentieth-century minds and been so wildly and recklessly applied.

But the billions of years of time assumed in those dating methods are very important to the evolutionists, because all other methods for having millions and billions of years for evolution to take place have failed them. The billions of years that have been concocted the past hundred years are necessary to support the theory of evolution. Given enough billions of years, they can make the impossible look possible! Then they can make the possible look probable, and finally they can make the probable look almost absolutely sure.

The following from *Clocks for the Ages* by Robert Silverberg, p. 75, shows what fantasies the evolutionists can think of with enough billions of years:

> In any case the pattern of geological history seems clear. According to what is perhaps the most widely accepted theory, at first the earth was a ball of fire; then it cooled and solidified and, as water condensed out of the atmosphere, a rain began that lasted millions of years without interruption, creating the oceans. A billion years or more went by, and then, inexplicably, chemicals mingled in the sea and became a living cell, which thrived and reproduced, and gave rise to more complex but still microscopic living things. Two billion years passed while these simple creatures were taking possession of the waters; but suddenly the pace of evolution quickened, so that the last 600 million years of the earth's existence have brought forth incredible hosts of life forms, trilobites and worms and fishes and amphibians and reptiles and birds and mammals, and, one of the most recent arrivals of all, the mammal known as man, the only creature capable of contemplating such problems as who he is and what has come before him.

But where did the ball of fire come from, where did the water for those millions of years of rain come from, where did that life in that living cell come from, where did its power and capability of reproduction come from, what caused one species to change into thousands of other species, although no species changes into another species today? Above all, where did the billions of years come from? I am sure many children could come up with better tales than that. At least he says that many of his evolutionary ideas are unexplainable, "inexplicable."

One of the best explanations for those billions of years came from the pen of the present day archbiship of the evolutionists, Carl Sagan. In the May 31, 1987, issue of *Parade Magazine* he wrote an article entitled "Billions and Billions," stating:

I never said it, honest. Oh, I said there were maybe 100 billion galaxies and 10 billion trillion stars. It's hard to talk about the Cosmos without using big numbers. I said "billions" a lot in the Cosmos television series. But I never said "billions and billions." For one thing its too imprecise. How many billions are "billions and billions"? A few billion? "Billions and billions" is a little vague . . . People like the sound of it. Sometimes, when I'm asked to inscribe a copy of the Cosmos book, I'm even requested to write "billions and billions" on the title page. "You know I didn't actually say that," I tell them. "It's okay" they reply. "Write it down anyway." . . . In 1980 when the Cosmos television series was first shown, people were ready for billions. Mere millions had become a little downscale, unfashionable, miserly . . . A much more fashionable number is now on the horizon or closer. The *trillion* is almost upon us.

This shows how easy it is to feed the evolutionary fantasy to many people today, and why evolutionists can spread the belief that the earth is 4,500,000,000 years old; and why many swallow the evolutionary fable as an actual fact, as even Sir Peter Medawar, Nobel Prize winner in 1960, does. See Chapter XI, Part 16.

Our national debt was once millions of dollars, then billions and now trillions, and as people are getting accustomed to such figures, so evolutionists soon may also begin using trillions. I would not be surprised if trillions will be used before too long, if the evolutionists see that billions are not long enough to turn impossible to possible to probable to an absolute fact.

2.   URANIUM TO LEAD DATING METHOD

Regarding the uranium method of dating *The World Book* states, in the article "Earth":

Uranium is a radioactive element which breaks up, or *disintegrates*, at a constant rate that can be measured. It gives off helium atoms and leaves lead behind. By measuring the amount of uranium and lead in uranium-bearing rock, scientists can find the number of years ago that the uranium was formed, assuming it started as pure uranium.

Did you notice the false premise or starting point: *"assuming it started as pure* uranium"?

How accurate is this "uranium clock," this method of determining the age of the rock and of the earth? Actually, too much is assumed or taken for granted without any proof. First, it is assumed that the uranium bearing rock in the beginning contained only uranium and lead that was nonradiogenic. Nonradiogenic lead is lead that was not formed by radioactive decay. But God in creating uranium very likely placed both radiogenic and nonradiogenic lead into the rock at the time of creation, so that it, like the rest of the earth and universe, was mature from the very beginning. This gave the rock the appearance of having some age right at the very beginning, at "zero time" for the earth and universe. As mentioned before, it would be natural for God to do so, just as he created Adam and Eve as adults with the appearance of age and not as infants.

Secondly, it has been assumed that the rate of radioactive decay of the created isotopes of uranium has always been the same or constant and as slow as it is at present, so that one half of it decays each 4 $\frac{1}{2}$ billions of years. But who knows if the rate has always been the same? No one could actually watch uranium decaying for millions of years, as they suppose, to see what happens. H. C. Dudley, in *Radioactivity Re-Examined*, April 7, 1975, reported that there is good laboratory evidence that external influences can change the decay rates. Fourteen different radionuclides had their decay properties changed by such things as temperature, pressure, electric and magnetic fields, etc. Uranium dating has made some gross errors, often giving billion-year ages for lava rocks that were known to be only a few centuries old. If much of the lead, which evolutionists claim to have originally been uranium, was really created lead, as it most likely was, and if the rate of decay was once very rapid, there is no reason for believing that the uranium and lead are 4 $\frac{1}{2}$ billion (4,500,000,000) years old.

Since evolutionists have found that uranium on earth might be contaminated, they hoped they would find sources of uranium elsewhere. They finally found meteorites that came from outer space and landed on the earth. But there is no proof that the original earth had the same kinds of materials as the meteorites. That still is also only an assumption.

Radium also has been used as a clock to time the so-called ages. *Our Blue Planet* (1965) by Heinz Haber states:

> If you have a piece of radium, you only need determine its mass and you know at once how much time elapsed, provided the quantity of original radium is known.

But who knows how much the piece of radium weighed?

3.   POTASSIUIM — ARGON DATING METHOD

Potassium is a metal-like element and argon is a gas. Radioactive potassium breaks down very gradually into argon and calcium. This method of determining age can be used only with rocks that were formed by great heat, such as in volcanic flows. Scientists measure the amount of argon in a lava rock and then compute how long it took the potassium to decay into argon gas. Then they give an age for the rock. But this method of dating is also subject to great error. By studying new volcanic rock it has been found that free argon often gets trapped in the rock. This occurs when the rock is originally formed and is not the result of the potassium decaying. Because of this, many rocks are not old although they may appear to be old.

This potassium—argon method has been widely used, and many of the fossils discovered by the Leakeys have been dated in this way. Physical anthropology professor W. Strauss and geography professor Charles Hunt of Johns Hopkins University have found many variables in dating according to the potassium method when they reviewed dates obtained from Olduvai Gorge by Dr. L. Leakey. They concluded: (See *Remember Thy Creator*, Culp, p. 174)

Because some of the Olduvai Gorge dates are inconsistent, some must be inaccurate, they may all be . . . The indicated ages must be taken with a grain of salt . . . The dates are of doubtful value in formulating hypotheses about the rates of evolution of man and his culture, rates of other vertebrate evolution.

Furthermore, lava from Hawaiian and other volcanoes around the world have been dated by the potassium-argon method to be 22 million years old when they actually were only 200 years old. This certainly shows that the assumptions used in dating are not only truly assumptions but also are totally wrong.

Professor Robert Whitlaw, nuclear consultant at Virginia Polytechnic Institute, indicated that the potassium-argon method cannot be used to determine dates older than about 7,000 years, which is the approximate age of this earth.

4.   CARBON 14 DATING METHOD

This method was developed by W. F. Libby, an American physicist. Carbon 14 is a radioactive variety of the element carbon. Ordinary Carbon 12 atoms are not radioactive. The carbon 14 method of dating is based on the principle that cosmic rays are entering the earth's atmosphere and producing carbon 14 atoms that are absorbed eventually by the waters of the earth and from there carried over into growing plants. As the animals and men eat the plants, they absorb some of the carbon 14. Plants and animals and man absorb carbon 14 until they die. At death this absorption of Carbon 14 ends and then the carbon 14 in the bodies begin to disintegrate at a certain assumed rate. The longer the animal or plant has been dead, the less carbon 14 will remain in the fossil. Dr. Libby figured that in 5,568 years half of the carbon 14 will have disintegrated. While this method has been used successfully on redwood trees of known age and on wood used in the tombs of Pharaohs in Egypt, other tests have not been accurate. This has been especially so with things that lived more than 5,000 years ago.

There are too many assumptions in this method that can make it unreliable. Richard Culp, in his *Remember Thy Creator* (1975) states in regard to this method, p. 169 & 172:

> This assumes that: (1) the carbon-14 concentration in the carbon dioxide is constant; (2) the cosmic ray flux has remained unchanged; (3) the rate of decay of carbon atoms has remained unaltered; (4) the relative amount of carbon dioxide in the ocean and atmosphere have not changed; (5) biologic activity, or external processes, have not affected carbon 14 amounts; (6) no contamination with modern carbon has occurred. All assumptions are open to question . . . Most important, the great flood in the time of Noah may have greatly altered these readings. If a humid, cloud-like canopy surrounded the earth, the cosmic ray filtration would be much higher and the carbon 14 formation lower. Such a canopy has been postulated not only by many evangelical Christians but also by many evolutionists in search of a way to explain fossils of tropical flora and fauna all over the earth — even near the poles . . .

There are other assumptions, and all these assumptions are highly questionable. So the carbon 14 method of finding an immense age for the earth and for plants and animals is another method that has failed the evolutionists in their efforts to find a basis for their creed.

5.   PLEOCHROIC HALOS

In recent years, Robert Gentry, a physics professor, has provided evidence, to the consternation of the evolutionists, that the material for this earth must have been formed or created in the space of the very short time of three minutes. This nullifies the old evolutionary belief (uniformitarianism) that everything evolved slowly, gradually, uniformly over billions of years. He found this evidence in the pleochroic halos, which means many (pleo) and colors (chroic) halos. They are spherically concentric shells that are many-colored. Under the microscope they appear merely as rings. They vary in colors, size, number, character and spacing, depending on the substance that produce them. Under the microscope the tiny ring patterns resemble a miniature archery target, with a tiny grain of other minerals at the center as the bull's eye. because of their halo-like appearance and because they showed colored variations, they became known as pleochroic halos.

After studying and analyzing these halos for a number of years, Gentry concluded that the polonium halos disprove the theory that the earth was formed by a hot gaseous mass, cooling and solidifying gradually over hundreds of millions of years. He wrote in his book, *Creation's Tiny Mystery* (October 1986), p. 32:

> Was it possible that the granites had not crystallized out of a slowly cooling magma? Was it possible that the earth had not begun as a molten sphere? Was it even possible that the chemical elements of our planet were not the result of nucleosynthesis in some distant supernova at all - but instead were created instantly when the Creator spoke the planet into existence.

> Were the polonium halos mute evidence of extinct natural radioactivity? Was, then, the half life of 218Po — just three brief minutes — the measure of time that elapsed from the creation of the chemical elements to the time that God formed the granites? In my search for the truth about the age of the earth, had I discovered evidence for its instantaneous creation? Were the tiny polonium halos God's fingerprints in Earth's primordial rocks? Could it be that the Precambrian granites were the Genesis rocks of our planet?

> [He also stated elsewhere:] Further, by virtue of the very short half-life (of radioactivity associated with halos), the radioactivity and formation of the rocks must be almost instantaneous. Incredible? Perhaps. I have been wondering about the idea for some time, and have often asked myself: Is it conceivable that one of the oldest cosmological theories known to man is correct after all? Could the earth have been created by fiat? . . . Geologically speaking, it is usually assumed that all the igneous rock of the earth's crust is of volcanic origin, but if the fiat creation hypothesis is correct, then the rock systems in which the variant short half-life halos are found would constitute the earth's primordial matter formed *in situ*.

"Formed *in situ*" means formed in its original place.

Therefore, because this particular atomic particle has a half-life of only three minutes, it has virtually disappeared in fifteen minutes. Because these halos appear only in solid rock and not in molten rock, the solid granite foundation-rock of the earth must have formed within fifteen minutes and not over billions of years.

6.   A BRIEF LOOK AT OTHER DATING METHODS

The salt in the ocean method. The oceans contain a certain amount of salt. So the scientists measure the rate at which salt is carried into the oceans and then figure the length of time it took to accumulate all the salt that is in the ocean now. This method begins with the false assumption that the oceans started out as bodies of fresh water.

Another method is to determine the length of time it took to lay down the *sedimentary rocks* of the earth on the basis of the false, uniformitarian belief that the strata were laid down slowly and gradually. But from folded rocks, from fossils of all kinds buried in these rocks, and from trees standing through several strata, it is evident that the strata were laid down very rapidly.

Other methods use the rate at which the moon is assumed to be receding from the earth, figure how long it took running water and glaciers to erode gorges, or how long it took to accumulate the meteorite dust on the earth and moon, and count the tree rings in old trees, although more than one ring could have been formed in one year.

But all of these theories, either separately or all put together, cannot shake the foundation statements of the Bible that the earth and universe are only from about 6,000 to 8,000 years old.

7.   DATING FRAUDS

On the other hand, we do have cases of dating errors and even frauds. For example, as mentioned before, rocks that recently erupted from volcanoes have been falsely dated millions and billions of years old when they actually were only 200 years old.

Then there was the Piltdown man. Evolutionist Ruth Moore, *as late as 1953* in her book, *Man, Time and Fossils*, states, p. 349, that on the basis of the fluorine tests:

> Eoanthropus [Piltdown man] had lived not much more than 50,000 years ago. Before the fluorine test was applied to the remains of Piltdown man, many authorities had suggested that

they were *about 500,000 years old and perhaps a million*! [Emphasis Added]

On page 353 she states:

[M]odern man, as a consequence, is pictured not as an ancient of a million years ago, but as a late-comer of the last fifty thousand years. And the difference matters mightily.

Yes, the difference matters *mightily* and above all it matters *eternally* when one considers that Piltdown man, very shortly after Ruth Moore wrote her book proved to be a *total hoax*. Yes, it matters *eternally* when one considers how many young children have been misled from their God and Savior by such damnable lies. This is nothing else than *the mental and spiritual rape* of little children, with taxpayers' money.

Then consider the tooth of *Hesperopithecus haroldcookii*, the Nebraska man, which was claimed to be *millions of years old* but which turned out to be just a recent pig's tooth. What a terrible evolutionary false claim. And what damnable damage this false claim did to William Jennings Bryan in the Scopes Monkey Trial, and what bad effect that trial had the past 60 years on our public schools.

8.   BILLIONS OF LIGHT YEARS

Regarding the billions of light years for the universe that the evolutionists assume, this no doubt is even wilder than the billions of years that they give for the existence of this earth and universe, which they derived from misreading the sedimentary rock and geology of this earth.

The wide expanse of the universe, which cannot be measured, give the evolutionists many more billions of years to play around with. The millions of light years are based on pure guessing. There is no way of measuring distances to outer space. (See pages 160, 169, 252 & 301)

XVII.   THE LAWS OF THERMODYNAMICS

1.   THE ORIGIN OF THE LAWS OF THERMODYNAMICS

Among the most powerful evidences against the idea of evolution are the scientific facts or laws of science called "the laws of thermodynamics." The two laws were discovered and proven to be true by science, about 140 years ago, in 1850. These laws are basic in every scientific field or system and are the two most basic, universal, and important laws of all science. Science has shown that they are universal in scope with no known exceptions.

The second of these two laws of thermodynamics was developed about 1850 by Carnot, Clausius and Kelvin. In its original form it was formulated about the time Darwin wrote the *Origins of Species*. Only by the end of the 19th century were its broader implications becoming gradually understood. Even to this day most evolutionists do not really understand the vast implication this second law has in proving wrong the theory of evolution.

2.   WHAT ARE THESE TWO LAWS OF THERMODYNAMICS IN GENERAL?

Thermo in Greek means *heat* and dynamis means *power* or energy. Thermodynamics is the science that deals with the energy or power that lies in heat. The first law deals with the conservation of energy. The second law deals with the disintegration or deterioration of energy or with degeneration in general. The first law deals with the total amount of energy remaining constant, never changing in quantity. The second law deals with energy deteriorating in quality. According to the first law, the amount of energy remains unchanged, but according to the second law the available usable energy continually decreases. According to the first law nothing has been either created or annihilated or totally destroyed since the beginning; but according to the second law everything that has been existing has deteriorated or degenerated and become less useful, and at some future time will end up with a condition of death or total uselessness. The first law states that energy can be converted from one form to another; but it can neither be created nor destroyed. The second law states that everything left to itself will constantly deteriorate and degenerate. In summary: the first law teaches that energy, which includes everything in the universe, is constant as far as quantity is concerned. The second law states that energy is constantly deteriorating as far as quality is concerned.

3.   THE THEORY OF BIOGENESIS

In this connection, a theory of science should be mentioned, which is almost as firmly confirmed as the two laws of thermodynamics. It is the theory of biogenesis or the origin of life, which states that *life comes from life*. Every living thing comes from some other living thing. No life has originated contrary to this theory. On the basis of this scientific finding, how can evolutionists explain how the first living being began to exist except from some other life! Certainly they have no scientific foundation for believing that the first living things went contrary to the theory of biogenesis which has not been falsified.

4.   MORE THOUGHTS REGARDING THE FIRST LAW OF THERMODYNAMICS

Princeton biologist Dr. Harold Blum states in *Time's Arrow and Evolution*: "Energy appears in various forms: heat, light, kinetic energy, mechanical work, chemical energy, and so forth. . .We know now that matter is another form of energy. . ." Other forms of energy are light, sound, pressure, electricity, nuclear energy in atoms, etc.

The first law is one of the most basic of all scientific laws and it has been tested and proven in many thousands of scientific experiments and no exception to this law has been found. This law teaches conclusively that the universe did not and could not create itself. For this reason science can know nothing about the origin of all things.

5.   SECOND LAW OF THERMODYNAMICS WHAT IS THE MEANING OF THIS LAW OF SCIENCE?

This is a universal law which scientists have called the "law of entropy." "Entropy" is a difficult term for many people to understand. It is from the ancient Greek word which basically means to turn in or to lose something such as heat. In physics it deals with heat as a form of energy. The *World Book* encyclopedia article "Entropy" says: "One way of stating the second law of thermodynamics is that mechanical energy can be converted completely into heat, but heat cannot be converted completely into mechanical energy. Entropy is this unavailable heat energy that cannot be put to work, or changed into mechanical energy. In the process of using energy, entropy will always increase. It never decreases."

In other words, everything is bound to wear out, run down, or grow old and die or go from order to disorder. Isaac Asimov said: "Another way of stating the Second Law is this:

The universe is constantly getting more disorderly! Viewed that way, we can see the Second Law all about us . . . In fact, all we have to do is nothing, and everything deteriorates, collapses, breaks down, wears out, all by itself — and that is what the Second Law is all about.

It is too bad Charles Darwin didn't know about or realize this before he went off in the opposite direction. According to the Second Law, everything runs off in a random way without any aim or plan or it falls into disorder, decay, degeneration or disarrangement.

Scientists say that the universe is dying a slow but certain "heat death." They say the entire universe is running down, the stars are dying out, the sun is slowly and surely burning out, throughout the entire universe heat is turning to a colder form, the atoms of matter are breaking down into radiation, and energy is being dispersed throughout space.

Hilbert Siegler in *Evolution or Degeneration — Which?* correctly states, p. 8:

The universe, in other words, is "running down." This means that it must have had a beginning when it was "wound up" that is, created, and that at that time its energy possessed its greatest potentiality. This is the inexorable conclusion forced upon us by the Second Law of Thermodynamics.

What happens to the energy that is not destroyed but is still in existence though it is no longer available or capable of performing any work? It has been dispersed in a useless form. For example the gas that was exploded in a car was dispersed in exhaust and is no longer useful. The heat that went into a hot bowl of soup will disperse as it cools, and the cold bowl of soup will not be able to disperse any heat back to a hot bowl of soup. Heat energy is radiated and dispersed into space.

6.   WHEN DEGENERATION CAN BE PREVENTED

Although according to the second law of thermodynamics, all things are bound to degenerate or decay, there are circumstances where it can be temporarily prevented. Decay and disorder can temporarily be prevented through the use of external energy and through the design and intelligence of a designer.

An example of the use of existing energy to go the opposite of the second law of thermodynamics is the temporary effect that the sun and water may have upon any tree or plant seed with the DNA program stored in the seed. Planted in the ground a seed with warmth from the sun and receiving water will temporarily sprout, grow and produce grain, fruits and food.

Another example of things going the opposite of the second law is through the design and intelligence of a designer. Men build homes and factories out of bricks, wood, metal and concrete; cars are being built, clothes are being fashioned; but in the end also these finally decay, deteriorate, grow old, weaken, wear out, and go back to dust and ashes.

7.   OPEN SYSTEMS

In contradiction to the second law of thermodynamics evolutionists like to use the power of the sun to say that the earth is not a closed system but an open system, in which the sun produces life upon this earth. But never in the history of the universe or of the earth has the sun ever produced any life by itself. The sun has shone on this earth from 6,000 to possibly 8,000 years or so, and it has never in the past or recent present produced life entirely by itself. The sun, however, can energize the earth, so that a seed with warmth from the sun and receiving water will temporarily sprout, grow, and produce grains, fruits, and food, because of the DNA program stored within itself. But the life that proceeds from the seed in the ground or the seed of a female or male living creature was due to the life that was placed into it by the Designer and Creator. Without that the sun could shine billions of years as the evolutionists falsely believe and never cause any life to spring forth from the lifeless elements of water, earth, sand or any mixture of chemicals.

If the evolutionists rely upon the heat of the sun to make this earth an open system in which decay can be prevented and entropy decreased, they should know that heat from the sun or any other source will increase the entropy and decay. Actually it will increase the degeneration all the faster, as was evident in the hot blistering sun of 1988 in the Midwest. Uncontrolled heat is not constructive but destructive! Rays from the sun do not help along any idea of evolution but instead increase and hasten the degeneration of that which already exists. Heat and light from the sun cannot evolve or generate life on earth any more than it has on the moon or Mars or any other planet or satellite. Furthermore life on this earth would be impossible without the ozone layer that shuts out most of the ultraviolet rays that come from the sun. See p.p. 222, 406.

8.   A PROVEN LAW

The second law of thermodynamics has been proven beyond question, with no known exceptions. Dr. Harold Blum, a biologist at the University of Princeton, states in his preface of *Times Arrow and Evolution*, p. V:

Wishful thinking to the contrary, the second law of thermodynamics remains with us . . . no wise scientists will, I think, deny its existence or impact.

Evolutionist Isaac Asimov agreed:

This law is considered the most powerful and most fundamental generalization about the universe that scientists have ever been able to make.

Another evolutionist, Jeremy Rifkin declared, 1980:

Albert Einstein said it is the premier law of all science; Sir Arthur Eddington referred to it as the supreme metaphysical law of the entire universe.

9.   RESULTS OF THE SECOND LAW — DEGENERACY IN GENERAL

Also in the social, political, economic and moral fields things very obviously are "going to pieces" and even "to the devil." Jeremy Rifkin, a social theorist, in *Entropy: A New World View*, maintains that all the problems of the world that seem to be unsolvable (such as bloated bureaucracies, inflation, unemployment, numerous new diseases, especially sexual ones, pollution of the atmosphere throughout the world, resources being depleted, plus many other problems) are due to the law of increasing entropy.

Also, all of mankind has degenerated in one way or another. When Charles Darwin was on his trip around the world to find evidence for evolution he did not realize that he found the exact opposite among the natives on the southern tip of South America, as I mention in Chapter XI, 3. The same degeneracy in mankind is evident today. The descendants of Adam and Eve and of Noah and his sons were not only handsome and beautiful and giants in stature, but were also giants mentally, far superior to mankind of today, in view of the structures that they erected in Egypt and other parts of the world of that time. Today, people as a whole, as we behold them on the streets and in gatherings, and as we look at ourselves, are actually deformed, crippled and degenerate copies in comparison to the original *masterpiece*, to the

258 XVII. THE LAWS OF THERMODYNAMICS

people that God created and who originally possessed this world. These early descendants have never been equalled or surpassed.

Only a few hundred years after the Flood, descendants of Noah at the very beginning of Egyptian history knew how to make saws and tubular crown drills with fixed teeth of corundum or gemstones for cutting huge granite and quartz rocks. Knowledge of this cutting tool disappeared completely so that by the time before Christ neither the Egyptian descendants nor Romans and Greeks knew about it. A device like this was not invented and used again until the tunnel through Mt. Cenis between France and Italy was nearing completion.

As the Egyptians, in the course of the centuries following the building of their pyramids and beautiful temples, degenerated, so also did other civilizations that had existed in those earliest years of history. Throughout history, nations and people throughout the world have degenerated and declined physically, mentally, morally and spiritually. The evolutionists, who see in the savage tribes the early stages of development from apelike animals to mankind, are making the same mistake that one would make if he believed that the decrepit, deformed and degenerate inmates of our asylums and poorhouses were the representatives of the lower stage of development from which the strong, healthy and skilled people of today evolved. Once people have sunk into barbarians or savages, they have never again come back by their own efforts to higher stages of civilization. Savages have never advanced and become civilized again, except by help from some outside civilized people.

After man rebelled against his Creator and fell into sin, the curse that God placed upon mankind and the universe put into effect the second law of thermodynamics. Man not only began to degenerate from his original glorious, beautiful, sinless, perfect, healthy, skilled and wise state, but also death set in gradually. Adam and Eve and their descendants began to die gradually, just as a weed in a garden or field begins to die gradually after herbicide has been instilled into it.

Not only did mankind degenerate, but also animals throughout the world. There are fossil records of giant sloths weighing tons. In the South Dakota Badlands fossils have been found of horses that could outrun modern race horses. Turtles have been found eleven feet long with heads over three feet long. The giant mammoths in Siberia no longer exist, and the immense dinosaurs are also long gone.

10.   THE LAWS OF THERMODYNAMICS AND EVOLUTION AND DEGENERATION IN GENERAL

These two laws stand *in direct contradiction and opposition* to the creed of evolution. The first law, which teaches that nothing is being created or destroyed, stands in opposition to the belief of evolution that the universe and things on this earth have come into existence by themselves and are still coming into existence today. The second law, which teaches that everything in the universe and on this earth is degenerating, deteriorating, decaying, dissipating, and going downhill, stands in direct opposition to the belief of evolution that the universe and things on this earth have evolved and progressed and are still doing so today. It is very evident that the second law and the creed of evolution contradict and stand in opposition to each other. The second law is based on science, while evolution is a creed or belief that stands contrary to proven facts of science. On the basis of the second law, it is obvious that evolution cannot be a fact. In fact, on the basis of the second law, evolution is impossible and could never have occurred.

Because of this, very few evolutionists have in the past paid any attention to the contradiction between this law of science and their beliefs, and they have ignored the contradiction. Dr. Henry Morris in his book *Scientific Creationism* says, p. 40:

Most books promoting evolution never mention it at all and many competent evolutionary scientists have been inclined to dismiss it as of no importance to the problem.

He also says in a footnote in another book, *The Troubled Waters of Evolution*, p. 121:

The writer and his creationist colleagues have participated in many formal debates with prominent evolutionists on university campuses. Never have any of them been able to deal effectively with the entropy question. Most of them ignore it, even when their opponents have made a major issue of it in the debate.

In recent years, when they have confronted this contradiction, they claimed the second law applies only to closed systems and not to open ones, in which the sun provides additional energy for the earth. They say that the energy bestowed upon the earth could counteract the degeneration resulting from the obvious effects of the second law. The sun's rays and heat by itself could never halt degeneration but only increase it. Only through outside force and use of an energy-conversion mechanism (such as chlorophyl) and a blueprint (such as DNA) can degeneration be halted or reversed *temporarily*. Examples have been given of a seed growing into a plant or tree, and of building materials being coverted into houses, structures, factories, cars and machinery. In all cases another force or a mechanism is needed to turn things around temporarily.

A seed, to turn into a plant or tree, needs not only the energy from the sun, but the growth force that is inherent or implanted in it when placed in the right condition for sprouting and growing. Certainly, no grain of sand has ever turned into a plant by the action of the sun. A plan of development, a code and a growth-force, has been placed into the seeds by the almighty Creator, which evolutionists just do not want to consider and recognize. Likewise building materials will never assemble themselves into buildings, cars, etc. by the rays of the sun, but it must be done by the planning of draftsmen and by the force used by workmen and machinery. Without proper planning and workmanship the structure or machinery will be slipshod. It takes planned force to produce anything constructive. You know what happens in the case of the proverbial bull in the china shop. He is applying force, but what a result! But even after all has been done properly, a plant or tree will die and structures will deteriorate and finally collapse and machinery will wear out and rust as every owner of a car well knows.

A pitiful attempt to prove that the second law is reversed at times was made by Dr. John Patterson of Iowa State University in a paper "Thermodynamics and Evolutions." He tried to contradict and ridicule what Dr. Henry Morris wrote in his book *The Troubled Waters of Evolution*. Patterson wrote in "The University of Minnesota Conference on Evolution and Public Education" (1981) p.p. 83-86:

> In this book *The Troubled Waters of Evolution*, Henry Morris develops an argument against evolution using a water flow analogy. His chapter entitled "Can Water Run Uphill?" alleges that evolution to higher forms is as impossible as water pumping itself uphill because both contradict the second law of thermodynamics (the "entropy principle"). Beneath a frontpiece photo of a picturesque waterfall appears the following caption (by Henry Morris):
>> Evolutionists have fostered the strange belief that everything is involved in a process of progress, from chaotic particles billions of years ago all the way up to complex people today. The fact is, the most certain laws of science state that the real processes of nature do not make things go uphill, but downhill. Evolution is scientifically impossible! [Morris 1973, page 110]

Dr. Patterson, after writing a number of paragraphs touching in an abstract way on the second law of thermodynamics, tries to show how living organisms can go counter to the second law. He quotes from Ira Levine, *Physical Chemistry* (1978) p.p. 123-124:

> Living organisms are open systems since they both take in and expel matter; further, they exchange heat with their surroundings. . .The organism takes in foodstuffs that contain highly ordered, low-entropy polymeric molecules such as proteins and starch and excretes waste products that contain smaller, less ordered molecules. Thus, the entropy of the food intake is less than the entropy of the excretion products returned to the surroundings . . . The organism discards matter with a greater entropy content than the matter it takes in, thereby losing entropy to the environment to compensate for the entropy produced in internal irreversible processes.

While it is true in actual plant growth that "the entropy of the food intake is less than the entropy of the excretion products," both Levine and Patterson ignore this: that living organisms have a built-in mechanism (code) and force to make them grow temporarily without which there would be no growth. They also ignore the fact that in the end the living organism dies, or that complete entropy sets in as the second law correctly declares.

In the next paragraph, the statement of another man C.R. Dawkins is given: "Morris' point about the second law of thermodynamics is pathetic." Actually Dr. Patterson's position is pathetic.

In addition Dr. Patterson gives another faulty example in which he tries to show *"how uphill processes occur."* He states p.p. 85-86:

> Consider the example of the self operating ram pump shown in Fig. 2 . . . By constructing a very simple arrangement of conduits, self-operating flap valves and such, any competent hydraulic engineer can get low lying water to pump part of itself uphill into storage tanks which may be well over a hundred feet in elevation. The pumping process in this simple but primitive system will run continuously. As long as there is an adequate supply in the low-lying reservoir, it proceeds without requiring any external source of power (electrical, chemical, etc.) nor are any types of rotary or displacement pumps used in the operation. Only a gentle sloped topography is required so that a downhill flow from the low-lying reservoir can be achieved. The conduit system taps energy from

this downhill flow in order to pump a small portion to very high elevations.

But again Dr. Patterson ignores the force of gravity in the "downhill flow" of water and he ignores "the ram pump" planned, devised and put into working operation by workmen. Without the force of gravity working together with a devised mechanism, water does not run uphill by itself. Using the same reasoning, a car also will not run uphill without the use of a motor as a mechanism and force. A car however will run uphill a certain distance without a motor, if it is given enough downhill gravity from another hill and a starting-force momentum.

11.   THE NASTINESS OF SOME EVOLUTIONISTS

Although numerous nasty remarks have been made by evolutionists in which scientists Dr. Henry Morris and Dr. Duane Gish have been ridiculed for not believing in the teaching of evolution, Dr. Patterson's attacks and nastiness have been some of the worst. In his concluding remarks he states: "In some cases Morris and his colleagues use *ad hominem* polemics" that is, he accuses them of attacking the man, one's opponent, rather than dealing with the subject under discussion. But Dr. Patterson is guilty of *ad hominem* polemics when, in referring to the ram pump, he stated:

> Because engineers are so prominent in the creation leadership, I have chosen examples which should be comprehensible to engineers, including creationist engineers.

He also attacked *the man* when he accuses them of using *obfuscation* to attack evolution. Obfuscation means to darken, to obscure, hence to confuse or bewilder. He continues:

> The creationists' second law arguments can only be taken as evidence of their willingness to bear false witness against science itself.

The correct statement would be: They bear witness against evolution, falsely called science.

Acts and Facts printed by the Institute for Creation Research (August 1982), p. 2 states:

> Patterson has repeatedly publicly accused creationists of ignorance and incompetence with reference to thermodynamics and evolution, maintaining that there is no contradiction between evolution and the laws of thermodynamics.

Dr. Duane Gish after a debate, June 22-23, 1982, with Dr. Patterson at the University of California, Santa Barbara (where he and Robert

Gentry debated eight evolutionists with doctoral degrees), challenged Patterson to use thermodynamics to answer three questions, each vital to the evolutionist's claim concerning origins. *Acts and Facts* (August 1982) p. 7 continues:

In answer to the challenge, Patterson merely repeated an imaginary scenario for the origin of the universe. Thrice, Gish challenged him to answer directly the three questions posed to him, using his expertise in thermodynamics. No answer whatsoever was forthcoming.

Two years later, February 20, 1985, Dr. Gish debated Dr. Patterson again at Iowa State University. *Acts and Facts* (April 1985) reported:

Since Patterson boasts of his expertise in thermodynamics and claims that creationists know nothing about thermodynamics and evolution . . . Gish challenged Patterson to answer three basic questions:

1. Since there is no doubt that the Second Law applies to an isolated system and states that the organization and information content of an isolated system can never increase with time but will inevitably decrease, and since Patterson believes the universe is an isolated system which started in a state of primordial chaos and simplicity which transformed itself into the present highly complex universe, how could that occur without violating the Second Law?

2. If the natural laws and processes governing the universe are now inexorably leading to its death and destruction, how could those very same natural laws and processes have created the universe in the first place?

3. If, as Patterson claims, order and complexity can be generated in one portion of the universe (as on the earth) at the expense of the order and complexity of another portion of the universe (as in the sun), where did the order and complexity in that other portion of the universe come from in the first place?

Patterson made no attempt to answer any of these questions, nor did he give any other scientific evidence for evolution. Yet he continued to claim that all creation scientists are incompetent.

Calling creationists incompetent, instead of answering the three basic questions, Patterson proved that he was guilty of arguing *ad hominem (the man)*, instead of facing the issue. Evolutionists have often ridiculed the person, the man, the creationists, calling them incompetent, because the creationists do not believe in evolution and because evolutionists falsely believe that evolution has scientific foundation and proof.

12.   HARMONY BETWEEN THE TWO LAWS OF THERMODYNAMICS AND THE BIBLE

The two laws of thermodynamics are nothing new. It is amazing that they were discovered and formulated only a little more than a century ago and not centuries earlier. They were evident from the accounts given in the Bible in the very first chapters of Genesis. Although the principles of these two laws were not stated in the Bible in the language of modern day scientists, yet the principles of these laws are clearly stated there. For this reason these two laws are not only scientific laws but also are laws instituted by God, or, in other words, science only formulated the laws that God instituted.

The first law is merely a scientific recognition of the fact that God's creation was complete, so that nothing has been created and nothing has been destroyed since creation. The second law is merely a recognition of the degeneration, decay, deterioration and death imposed upon creation at the time of the first rebellion of mankind against God in the Garden of Eden. The scientific facts stated in these two laws were stated in the Bible thousands of years before modern scientists discovered them and formulated them in scientific laws.

Let us behold the first law and the facts given in the Bible. The first law states that nothing is being *created* and nothing is being *destroyed* but is being *preserved or conserved*. This principle is clearly and strongly stated in Genesis 2:1-3: "Thus the heavens and the earth *were finished* . . . God *ended his work* which he had made . . . he had rested from *all his work which God created and made.*" Colossians 1:16-17: "[B]y Him all things *were created* that are *in heaven* and that are *on earth* . . . He is before all things, and in Him all things consist." NKJV Nowhere does the Bible state or science show that additional energy and matter are being created.

Not only did God create all things but He also *preserved* all things so that nothing is destroyed. The original creation is being preserved. II Peter 3:7: "[T]he heavens and the earth which now exist *are kept in store.*" Hebrews 1:3 states that He is *"upholding* all things by the word of His power." Colossians 1: 16-17: "[B]y Him all things were created . . . and in Him all things *consist.*" Psalm 148:5-6: "He commanded and they *were created.* He has also *Established them forever and ever.*" Nehemiah 9:6: "You have made heaven, *The heaven of heavens, with all their host, The earth and all things on it,* The seas and all that is in them, And You *preserve them all."* All NKJV

The second law is also clearly and emphatically stated in the Bible. When God originally created this earth and universe, He declared it to be *very good,* but when mankind through Adam and Eve rebelled against God, He *cursed the "ground"* and thus placed upon the entire universe as well as this earth the principle of degeneration, decay and death that was finally formally recognized by scientists a little more than 100 years ago in the second law of thermodynamics. God stated the curse of decay and degeneration and death in Genesis 3:17-19:

> *Cursed* is the ground for thy sake; in sorrow shall thou eat of it all the days of thy life . . . In the sweat of thy face thou shalt eat bread, *till thou return unto the ground*; for out of it wast thou taken: for dust thou art and *unto dust shalt thou return.*

How this curse affected the entire creation of God is stated in Romans 8:22-23: "For we know that the whole creation *groaneth and travaileth in pain* together until now . . . [E]ven we ourselves groan within ourselves, waiting for the . . . redemption of our body." Other parts of the Bible state, I Peter 1:24: "*For all flesh is as grass,* and all the glory of man as the flower of grass. *The grass withereth* and the *flower thereof falleth away."* Psalm 102:25-26: "Of old hast thou laid the foundation of the earth: and the heavens are the work of thy hands. They *shall perish,* but thou shalt endure: yea, all of them shall *wax old* like a garment; as a vesture *shalt thou change them,* and *they shall be changed."* Isaiah 51:6: " . . . the heavens *will vanish* away like smoke, The earth will *grow old* like a garment, and those who dwell in it *will die* in like manner; But My salvation will be forever, And My righteousness will not be abolished." NKJV Matthew 24:35: "Heaven and earth shall *pass away."* Ecclesiastes 3:20: "All go to one place: all are from the dust, and all *return to dust."* Romans 5:12: "[B]y one man sin entered the world, and *death* by sin."

Thus the Bible teaches the decaying of the universe, and especially of the earth, and of the life that exists upon it and all that is connected with it. Because of this, everything on earth runs down; plants, animals and humans grow old and die; societies and nations and governments deteriorate and everything becomes weaker than what existed when God first created the earth. The second law of thermodynamics merely formulates what the Bible states occurred over 6,000 or more years ago, but scientists do not know why things degenerate. They know that this is true and is a scientific fact, but they have no scientific explanation for it.

But from this second law true scientists should see that the creed or belief of evolution stands in *direct contradiction* to this second law. Evolution teaches that things are evolving upward, but the second law and the Bible say everything is moving downward. Evolution teaches that things are developing and growing better and more complex, but the second law and the Bible teach everything is deteriorating, decaying and dying. Very evidently, since evolution goes contrary to scientific facts, it is *not scientific* but merely an unproven creed or belief, held in rebellion against God.

13.   BUT THE SECOND LAW WILL SOME DAY BE ANNULLED BY GOD

The curse that God placed upon rebellious mankind will be removed at the end of this world when everything will be renewed, changed and restored. Revelation 22:3 states: "There shall be *no more curse.*" II Peter 3:13: "[W]e, according to His promise, look for *new heavens and a new earth in which righteousness dwells.*" And Romans 8:21: "[T]he creation itself also *will be delivered from the bondage of corruption* unto the glorious liberty of the children of God." NKJV

Thus God tells us in His Word not only what is the cause of the second law of thermodynamics, of the degeneration that is now taking place, but also that it will not continue until the universe finally reaches total heat death as the scientists predict. Instead God Himself will finally intervene and end the degeneration and final decay and restore a flawless new heaven and new earth.

XVIII.   THE HISTORY OF MODERN EVOLUTION

1.   EARLY HISTORY OF EVOLUTION

The idea of evolution has been in the minds of men ever since the *children of men* (Genesis 6:1-5) rejected and rebelled against their Creator:

> There were giants on the earth in those days, and also afterward, when the sons of God came in to the daughters *of men* and they bore children to them . . . Then the LORD saw that the *wickedness of man was great* in the earth, and that every intent of the thoughts of his heart was *only evil continually*. NKJV

Throughout the centuries ever since, there have been many cases of men rejecting God and developing ideas of evolution.

In ancient Greece, the philosopher Anaximanders, 600 years before Christ, fostered the idea that man was originally similiar to a fish. Four hundred years before Christ a Chinese, Chuantze, speculated with the idea that species developed through the process of variation. In 1589 the Frenchman Bernard Palissy died in the dungeons of the Bastille because, among other heresies, he played with the idea of evolution.

Although Carolus Linnaeus of Sweden (1707-1778) was no evolutionist and ardently opposed it, he gave biologists a framework by which they could analyze plants and animals according to species and kinds and thereby gave the evolutionists a framework from which they could develop their ideas. He developed a system by which plants and animals were classified and given Latin names. One name was given for the species and another for the genus, or main subdivision, of a family or kind.

Some of the first moderns since about 1750 to foster the idea of evolution were the French naturalist Comte Buffon (1707-1788) and an English physician, Erasmus Darwin, grandfather of Charles Darwin. Both wrote in the later part of the 1700s. They worked with the idea of acquired characteristics, such as camels acquiring thick knee pads because they kneeled when loads were placed upon them. Buffon was constantly groping for an evolutionary explanation of life.

Following these two men came Jean Lamarck (1744-1829), a French botanist and biologist. He reasoned that plants and animals changed their forms to adapt to their surroundings and that these changes have been passed on to their offspring. He fostered the false evolutionary idea that, for example, a giraffe's neck had become long just by stretching upward to feed on tree foliage. Thereby, he claimed, each generation acquired a slightly longer neck until we have the giraffe of today. This idea has been discredited by scientists of his day and also of ours. A German biologist, August Weissman (1834-1914), cut off the tails of several generations of rats without getting any tailless rats, and he showed that Lamarck's theory had no foundation. Yet Charles Darwin stated in regard to Lamarck's ideas: "The conclusions I am led to are not widely different from his."

Shortly after Lamarck, a British geologist, Sir Charles Lyell (1797-1875), developed the study of modern geology. He wrote three volumes of his *Principles of Geology*, in which he organized existing information about this science. He tried to show that the earth has changed *slowly and gradually* through the ages by means of actions that are still taking place today. (*Slowly* and *gradually* have been the key words for the evolutionists.) By his work, Lyell laid another false foundation for Charles Darwin and the theory of evolution. Darwin confessed that his ideas and books "came half out of Sir Charles Lyell's brain." Lyell's work provided the vast ages of time which Darwin's ideas of evolution needed to make evolution appear possible. Up to that time most people believed that the changes in geology that have taken place on this earth occurred in sudden world-wide catastrophes and upheavals.

Although Alfred Wallace (1823-1913) was about fourteen years younger than Charles Darwin, he developed the same ideas that Darwin did regarding the explanation for evolution.

2.   CHARLES DARWIN

This takes us to Charles Darwin (1809-1882), an English naturalist who has been credited with the idea of evolution more than any other man. The reason evolution took hold so easily in Darwin's day was that science was popular and fostered in England and that industrial progress was requiring more and more help from true science. The 1850s were also a time of great social and political upheaval. These were the times of Karl Marx; and socialism and communism were taking over much of Europe. Liberalism and rationalism were taking hold in many Christian denominations. The ground was ready for the ideas of evolution to flourish.

The spirit of rationalism, materialism and rejection of anything that could not be explained by nature and science also caused many of the intellectuals of those days to question the Bible and anything that was supernatural. Like the ancient pagan philosophers, they tried to find an explanation for the origin of the universe that appealed to reason. The philosophical and spiritual climate of that time set up an environment in which men like Darwin and other evolutionists could find a ready hearing and support.

In 1859, Darwin published his book, *The Origin of Species*, which made him the leader of the evolution movement, which is now often referred to as Darwinism. In 1832 Darwin, in a journey around the world, thought he had discovered the solution to the origin of species. Coming to the uninhabited Galapoagos islands off the coast of South America, he found that each island had its own peculiar and somewhat distinct animals and plants, even though the soil and climate were alike. This led him to two conclusions: 1) Variations exist so that no two living creatures or plants are exactly alike; 2) Living things increase in multitudes so great that the earth cannot provide room and food for all the untold abundant offspring. He saw that members of each species competed with each other and with members of other species to get the necessary food. He concluded that the superior varieties would finally crowd out the weaker ones, so that there would be a constant "struggle for existence" in nature. In this struggle inferior variations of the different kinds of plants and animals would eventually be eliminated, and superior variations would survive. And since all this happened gradually, small differences would gradually, over a long period of time, increase to major differences.

So gradually, by means of *natural selection* life on earth evolved to higher levels, so that from the simplest forms of life (single cells) more complex forms of life evolved, until finally from the lowest types of animals, higher types evolved and finally even man evolved from such animals. From the idea of *natural selection* developed the idea of *survival of the fittest*.

The influence that Darwin's thinking had upon the rest of the world during the last 125 years cannot be overestimated. His ideas of evolution have been carried over into every phase of life today. Astronomers began to speak of the evolution of the entire universe, starting out with the Big Bang and explaining the origin of all matter in the universe and the evolution of the earth and especially of the structure of its surface. Historians and anthropologists began to speculate on the prehistoric existence of man over millions of years. Psychologists began to look upon man as only a highly developed animal. And they tried to solve all of man's moral ills by changing his physical environments. Even theologians, either because they felt they could not harmonize the so-called scientific belief of evolution with the teachings of the Bible, or because they actually began to believe it, began to succumb to the teaching of evolution. They began to treat the Bible as a book which at best can only present highly developed religious ideals. I have seen and heard doctors of theology, trained in the most conservative religious denominations, speaking from the same platform on which rank evolutionists pronounced their beliefs, state that the Bible was no more than a myth and that the story of the fall of man was not factual. Dr. Otto of the University of Wisconsin stated correctly over 40 years ago that if anyone truly accepts the theory of evolution, he must also, to be consistent, be convinced that there is no God, that to harmonize evolution and belief in a God shows some flaw in clear logical thinking.

3.   WHERE DARWIN WENT WRONG

In spite of the title of his book, *The Origin of Species*, Darwin never really explained the *origin* of species. He could only refer to the *variation* within species, which is a fact recognized also by those who believe in creation. Or to put it in other words, natural selection may explain the *survival* of the fittest; but it cannot and does not explain the *arrival* of the fittest. Darwin himself stated:

> There are 2 or 3 million species on earth, sufficient field, one might think, for observation. But it must be said today that in spite of all the efforts of trained observers not one change of a species into another is on record.

Evolution means to produce not only new and different *kinds* or *families* of creatures, but the production of such different organs as the eyes, the brain, ears, heart, nervous system, lungs, stomach and many other extremely complex organs. Neither Darwin nor any evolutionist has been able to explain how these parts of the body came into existence and how all of these organs developed all at one time so that there would be an immediately functional body.

Darwin's entire idea of evolution was not based on scientific facts but on assumptions, guesses, imagination and speculation. In chapter IV of his book he uses phrases such as these:

> If . . . If assumed . . . It seems, therefore, extremely probably . . . if we suppose . . . if supposed to . . . may have been . . . perhaps . . . probably . . . we may suppose . . . it is probable . . . [etc.]

This is not the way a scientist speaks. A scientist works on the basis of tested, proven facts.

4.   DARWINISM REJECTED BY SCIENTISTS

Even so long ago as 1890 St. George Mivart wrote an exhaustive treatise entitled, *The Genesis of Species*, in which he gives the theories of Darwin a close examination, and he discards them as unproven in every part and as contradicted by the facts of nature. He called Darwin's hypothesis "a puerile [childish] hypothesis."

Dr. Theo. Graebner, in his book, *God and the Cosmos - A Critical Analysis of Atheism*, stated in 1932 that in the 1880s:

Darwin's influence was at its height, and exercised an absolute control over technical research. In the nineties, for the first time, a few timid expressions of doubt and opposition were heard; and these gradually swelled into a great chorus of voices, aiming at the overthrow of the Darwinian theory. In the first decade of the twentieth century it has become apparent that the days of Darwinism are numbered.

In that same time period, a professor of anatomy at Harvard University stated:

We have now the remarkable spectacle that just when many scientists are all agreed that there is no part of the Darwinian system that is of any great influence, and that, as a whole, the theory is not only unproved, but impossible, the ignorant, half-educated masses have acquired the idea that it is to be accepted as a fundamental fact.

In France, the *Dictionaire Encyclopedique des Sciences* stated:

Darwinism is a fiction, a poetical accumulation of probabilities without proof.

In connection with Darwin we must mention Thomas Huxley (1825-1895). He was an evolutionist before the days of Darwin's book, but that book gave Huxley additional reason for his beliefs. He became an ardent disciple of Darwin, and through his constant speaking and writing he did more than anyone else to spread Darwin's ideas of evolution. Because of that he become known as "Darwin's bulldog." He also opposed and lectured against the Bible account of creation, against Christianity, the resurrection of Christ and other Bible accounts.

While Darwin and Huxley were active, an Austrian monk and botanist Gregor Mendel (1822-1884), produced scientific evidence that raised serious questions regarding the theory of Darwin. Mendel, by his scientific and repeated experiments, proved that in both plants and animals no variation is possible outside of the limits that have been placed by the Designer into the species or kinds. It is now a simple law of biology that

> the factors which the individual receives and no other are those which he can transmit to his offspring. An organism cannot pass on to any offspring a factor which it did not itself receive. *Heredity and Environment*, p. 99.

This locked the door to Darwin's ideas of evolution by change of environment. The importance of Mendel's work was not realized, however, until 1900, fifty years after Darwin's theory was proposed.

Another man of that time who speculated as to the cause of evolution was a Dutch botanist, Hugo de Vries (1848-1935). He experimented with primroses. While working with them he thought he found new species of plants. He said, "New species rose suddenly, spontaneously, by steps, by jumps. They jumped out among the offspring." His theory was called the mutation (change) theory. This theory aroused great hopes among evolutionists for a few years. But this theory soon went the way of other evolutionary theories, when it was discovered that his supposed new species were merely different varieties within the same species. Professor Jeffrey of Harvard University stated in *Science* (April 3, 1914):

> The mutation theory of de Vries may now be relegated to the limbo of discarded hypotheses.

5. EVOLUTIONISTS OF THE 1900s

The most prominent evolutionists of the twentieth century have been the Leakeys: parents, Louis and Mary, and son, Richard. Louis began his search for and study of fossils in 1926. By the mid 1960s, Louis and Mary had found pieces of what they called *hominid* (manlike) fossils of man who could use tools. Louis believed they were some 2,000,000 years old without any truly scientific proof. He died in 1972, shortly after completing a trip to England.

Evolution stories by Mary and Richard Leakey are constantly being given in the *National Geographic, Reader's Digest, Family Weekly*, newspapers, television and radio reports. They have been digging in sedimentary layers of rock and soil near Lake Turkana in Kenya, Africa. Here among the ashes and mud from the erupting volcanos and floodwater sediments of the Flood in Noah's day many fossils have been found in those sedimentary rocks. But the *Reader's Digest* (February 1978) gives the evolutionary version for the fossils found there, in an article entitled:

Searching for Mankind's Roots. Clues that lead back almost four million years are revealing startling new evidence of the stirring saga of the family of man.

The *Reader's Digest*, p. 71, states:

that there was unearthed at Lake Turkana in Kenya the fragments of a shattered skull lying in a stratum dated at over two million years. It was labeled "1470" after its National Museum of Kenya catalogue number. When 1470 was reconstructed, an astoundingly modern-looking head emerged.

In fact the skull looks like it could be that of any highly intelligent man of today. But an artist's rendition of the skull made the original person look half like an ape. On page 72 the *Reader's Digest* continues:

Then in 1975, Mary Leakey unearthed from volcanic ash at Laetolil in Tanzania the teeth and jawbone of the oldest hominids yet discovered, dated at 3.75 million years.

Notice how lightly the millions of years are thrown around. Then notice the following account given in the *Minneapolis Tribune* (March 9, 1976):

Anthropologists Donald C. Johanson and Richard E. Leakey told a news conference in Washington Monday about a newly discovered skull of an early ancestor of man. This and other recent discoveries lead scientists [I would say *evolutionists*] to believe that man 3.75 million years ago was anatomically much more like modern man than was previously thought.

The evolutionists have three big strikes against them. First, their millions of years are based on dating methods that are an extrapolation backwards, which can never be proven scientifically because things were mature and had appearances of age when they were created. See my notes on dating methods. Secondly, if man was structurally or anatomically modern 3,750,000 years ago, why did it take only less than 10,000 years for man to learn to use fire and build homes and cities? With lightning starting fires by the thousands, it would not have taken modern looking man 3,750,000 years to learn how to use it! Thirdly, they have misread the *Sedimentary* rocks, which were laid down quickly from extremely muddy waters, see pages 86-91.

On page 73, February 1978, the *Reader's Digest* rehashes the old discredited theory of Jean Lamarck of about 1800 to 1829: the old fable of the giraffe's neck becoming long because in a few droughts it had to stretch its neck to eat tree leaves higher up. The *Reader's Digest* states regarding the imagined apelike forefather of mankind:

Some of Ramapithecus' descendants left the trees for grassy plains and clearings. Since they needed to see farther at ground level, they probably stood on two legs rather than four, thus freeing their hands for other uses.

Even in 1978 evolutionists still are clinging to old theories that were discredited 150 years ago. Anything just to make the evolution fable appear feasible or probable.

The [Mankato] *Free Press* (October 19, 1984) carried a story from Nairobi, Kenya given out by Richard Leakey again:

Scientists say the fossilized bones of a strapping 12-year-old boy who died 1.6 millions years ago indicate that early man was much larger than many scientists previously thought . . . The boy probably would have grown to a height of more than six feet, Leakey said . . . Scientists have generally assumed that early humans were smaller than we are today. This specimen confirms earlier hints that Homo erectus individuals were in fact fully as tall as modern people . . . Leakey said he did not know what caused the death of the Homo erectus boy, but he was near the edge of what was then a swamp, and the body was quickly submerged and preserved relatively intact.

No doubt he was buried quickly in the muddy sediments of the Flood in Noah's day. Also, this tall boy could be evidence that large people very likely existed before the Flood.

Then Mary Leakey has her human-foot-print story of modern-like people who, according to the evolution story, lived 3.6 million years ago. The *Family Weekly* (September 13, 1981) stated that:

a trail of footprints were found near Laetoli, which is a wooded area near a volcanic mountain some 25 miles south of Olduvai Gorge in Tanzania. When some ash from that volcanic mountain mixed with rain and then was dried by the sun, a chemical composition was produced that made it set like cement. Following the rain, various animals left their tracks in the deep volcanic ash; the footprints of a number of them can be clearly seen today, and among them are tracks of the three hominids, . . . they walked upright with a free striding gait just as we do today.

According to the *Minneapolis Tribune* (March 22, 1979):

Dr. Louis Robbins of the University of North Carolina, an anthropologist specializing in footprints, told the briefing the prints show the creatures feet were very similiar in shape and function to modern man's.

Why should they not have been those of people who lived before the Flood? Mary Leakey adds:

Because the prints show the creatures had a sophisticated walk much like modern man's, the scientists said this indicates man has to look further back from this date — perhaps another million years — for the beginning of upright walking.

See, how easily the evolutionists build up the millions of years for their fable! I also highly question their use of the word "scientist" for themselves to fortify their guessing and assuming. They have no scientific evidence; and why should it take such an imagined hominid millions of years to do some of the simple things we do today?

To build up the drama of the fable, Mary Leakey continues:

The smaller individual apparently stopped, turned to its left to observe something and then continued on, she said, "The motion, so intensely human, transcends time," she said. "Three million six hundred thousand years ago, a remote ancestor — just as you and I - experiences a moment of doubt."

The Los Angeles Times also of March 22, 1979, reported:

Mrs. Leakey said, "It was as if she saw or heard something to her left, possibly a threat, turned to see what it was, and then moved on."

Although the drama of the fable was exploited, the actual fact could have been more pathetic and fearful. The person, in fear, could have turned because the exploding volcanoes and flood water that took place at the time of the Flood were engulfing her and overwhelming her.

The trouble with the evolutionists is that they try so hard to somehow trace mankind back to apes, instead of trying to trace mankind back to the more highly advanced people who preceded the highly advanced Egyptians, Babylonians and their ancestors and who drowned in the Flood and were covered with the sediments the Leakeys and others are digging in. The apes (Australopithecus) they find are the apes that died in the Flood together with the other animals; and the humans they find are the humans that drowned and were covered with the sediments of that Flood.

To see how badly and wildly the story of evolution is expounded by the evolutionists (and the news media are just as gullible), at the end of that *Reader's Digest* account "Searching for Mankind's Roots"

(February 1978), a number of the classic errors of the evolutionists are revealed:

1. Somewhere between 1,500,000 to 200,000 years man or Homo erectus "had learned the use of the fire." Certainly man must have learned something immediately from the fires that lightning started.

2. "Out of the stock evolved the Neanderthals between 250,000 and 100,000 years ago. Their brains were fully as big as our own - even larger in some cases." These so-called Neanderthals could be the ones Genesis 6:4 refers to: "There were giants on the earth in those days . . . those were the mighty men who were of old, men of renown."

3. "Last actor in the evolutionary drama was our own species, *Homo sapiens*, who arrived seemingly from out of nowhere 40,000 B.C." Here again the evolutionists refuse to recognize the highly advanced Egyptians, Babylonians and others all around the world, who jumped out of nowhere, and their more highly advanced ancestors who were drowned and buried in the muddy sediments that the Leakeys and others are now digging in.

4. "Other experts believe . . . " I just shudder when men and women are referred to as *experts* as though they have all the answers to the past, present and future. There are billions of people who have been misled by the advice of so-called experts in many fields of human endeavor. How many people have lost thousands and hundreds of thousands and millions of dollars by listening to expert advice given in financial journals, in Wall Street Week, by stock advisors, and so on. How truly Psalm 118:81 declares: "It is better to trust in the LORD than to put confidence in man." In listening to the advice of experts, one must take it with a grain of salt; but in listening to the experts of evolution, *cups full of salt* are needed. There is a world of difference between the expertise of medical and surgical doctors and others skilled in other scientific fields and the attempts of financial and evolutionary experts. People misled by so-called financial experts lose only money; but people misled by evolutionary so-called experts lose a blessed eternity if they do not return to their Creator and Savior.

Throughout the world today, especially in the universities, there are many other modern-day evolutionists, such as Stephen Gould of Harvard University who received his Ph.D. from Columbia University in 1967. Then there are Carl Sagan and Isaac Asimov who have made a lot of commotion for evolution. To mention many other active modern day evolutionists would make this book still longer than I want it to be.

6.   PROMINENT SCIENTISTS WHO HAVE OPPOSED EVOLUTION

Up to the time of Darwin, almost all scientists believed the Bible account of the creation and the Flood. The great fathers of true science (Kepler, Newton, Faraday, Galileo, Brewster, Linnaeus, Pasteur, Kelvin and others) believed in creation. Yet such scientists today would be ridiculed by evolutionists, because they believed in a Designer and Creator of all things. Let us behold some of the opinions of former great scientists, which they expressed over against evolution.

Professor Rudolph Virchow (1821-1902) was a renowned Prussian anatomist, anthropologist and the father of human pathology. He was considered one of the highest authorities in physiology and a foremost chemist. He stated; (Evolution, Wm. Dallmann 1925, p. 73):

It is all nonsense. It cannot be proved by science that man descended from an ape, or from any other animal. Since the announcement of the theory, all real scientific knowledge has pointed in the opposite direction. [At a meeting of anthropologists in Vienna he said:] The attempt to find the transition from animal to man has ended in total failure. The middle link has not been found and never will be.

Louis Pasteur (1822-1895) was one of the greatest scientists in chemistry, medicine and bacteriology. He publicly refuted the idea of spontaneous generation or evolution and he gave an impassioned and widely publicized defense of creation.

Then Carolus Linnaeus (1707-1778), the Swedish taxonomist, whose system of classifying plants and animals is still followed today, was a strong opponent of evolution. Baron Cuvier (1729-1832) was the founder of comparative anatomy and paleontology. He defeated the evolutionists in private and public debate and was a strong defender of special creation.

Louis Agassiz, who worked in geological history, said that:

any man who accepted the doctrine of evolution ceased thereby to be a man of science.

Dr. William Bateson, professor of biology at Cambridge University, in his address for the Advancement of Science, in Toronto, December 1921, said that if Darwin had known the facts now proved regarding Mendel's law, Darwin would never have printed his books.

Dr. William Carruthers, botanist, stated, (Dallmann, p. 56):

The whole evidence is against evolution, and there is none in favor of it.

President Charles W. Eliot of Harvard; (Evolution, Dallmann, p. 23):

Evolution is a hypothesis and not a science at all.

Dr. Ethridge of the British Museum (Ev., Dallmann, p. 24):

In all this great museum there is not a particle of evidence of the transmutation of species. Nine-tenths of the talk of evolutionists is sheer nonsense, not founded on observation and wholly unsupported by facts. Men adopt a theory and then strain facts to support it.

Professor Fleischman, the zoologist at Erlangen, who at first believed in Darwin's theories, later said; (Ev., Dallmann, p. 26):

The Darwinian theory of descent has, in the realms of nature, not a single fact to confirm it. It is not the result of scientific research, but purely the product of the imagination.

Above all we must listen to men like Lord Kelvin, a famous physicist and discoverer of the second law of thermodynamics, who stated (1903), (Evolution, Dallmann, p. 42):

We are absolutely forced by science to believe with the perfect confidence in a Directive Power — in an influence other than physical or dynamical or electric forces.

In the *Journal of the Victorian Institute* No. 124, p. 267 he stated that the atheistic idea is so nonsensical that he did not see how he could put it in words.

President Lowell of Harvard University said the nebular hypothesis was (Dallmann, p. 46):

founded on a fundamental mistake.

Professor J. Clerk Maxwell, died 1879; (Dallmann, p. 48):

I have examined all [theories] that have come within reach, and have found that every one must have a God to make it work.

Dr. Robert Millikan, the Chicago physicist and winner of the Nobel prize; (Dallmann, p. 50):

The pathetic things is that we have scientists who are trying to prove evolution, which no scientist can ever prove, [because it is not testable and provable].

Sir R. I. Murchison, an eminent geologist, stated, (Dallmann, p. 52):

I know as much of nature in her geologic ages as any living man, and I fearlessly say that our geologic record does not afford one syllable of evidence in support of Darwin's theory.

Professor J. Reinke, a botanist in Kiel, Germany declared; (p. 60):

The only statement, consistent with her dignity, that science can make, is to say that she knows nothing about the origin of man.

John Ruskin in contempt of evolution, said, (Dallmann, p. 63):

I have never yet heard one logical argument in its favor. I have heard and read many that are beneath contempt.

George Wright, a prominent geologist of Oberlin, said that evolution,

is one-tenth bad science and nine-tenths bad philosophy.

Then we must listen to what Albert Einstein said, who was an atheist until shortly before his death when be became a firm believer in God; (From *The Free Press*, Mankato, MN 11-26-86):

I've come to realize that the universe is not a product of chance but is held together by formulated mathematical laws and principles. Only an intelligence could hold it together and where does intelligence reside but in a person?

A writer for the *Reader's Digest*, January 1968, p. 109 wrote:

Einstein once said to me, "Ideas come from God," and one could hear the capital "G" in the reverence with which he pronounced the word.

Svetlana Alliluyeva, daughter of the late Soviet dictator, Stalin, when she came to the United States in 1967 said:

I found it was impossible to exist without God in one's heart. I came to that conclusion myself, without anybody's help or preaching.

Alexander Kosygin, former second man in power in the Soviet who died in 1982, toward the end of his political career, occupied himself much with religion, and after suffering a heart attack intensified his study of God and religion. A similiar story was circulated after former President Khrushchev died. Throughout his political life Khrushchev made a number of references to God, indicating that he was not a total atheist. Whether all these people believe in the Savior, Jesus Christ, is not sure.

Today there are thousands of fully trained and qualified scientists holding important positions in scientific research and development who have become creationists and are opposing the idea of evolution. There are also thousands of students in colleges and universities who have rejected the evolutionary teachings of their professors and are holding to the Designer and creation point of view. Then there are many other scientists who just have not made a study and issue of origins because they cannot be tested and proven scientifically by experiment and they have simply ignored the issue of evolution.

Two very active present-day scientists who once were evolutionists are Dr. Henry Morris and Dr. Duane Gish. Henry Morris, in the preface, p. IV of *The Remarkable Birth of Planet Earth* stated:

> There are hundreds, perhaps thousands, of scientists today who once were evolutionists but have become creationists in recent years. I myself was one of these, having accepted the evolutionary theory all through college. Since that time, however, as a result of considerable reading in all the various sciences which bear on the evolution - creation question, as well as in the Bible, I personally have become thoroughly convinced that the Biblical record, accepted in its natural and literal sense, gives the only scientific and satisfying account of the origin of all things. Many other scientists today can give a similiar testimony.

Dr. Morris and his present co-worker, Dr. Duane Gish of the Institute for Creation Research, have in the last ten or more years debated against professors of the evolution belief in the most outstanding universities of our country, and in a number of cases no one of the opposite view was ready to debate them. More regarding these men and others of today will be presented a little further on.

However there are scientists who are not Christians but who reject evolution. For example, British astronomer Sir Fred Hoyle and his colleague, astronomer Chandra Wickramasinghe, have given up their atheistic evolutionary views and now believe that the origin of the universe, of life and all forms of life were the result of a supernatural Designer and Creator. Although neither one claims to have become a Christian, or literally accepts the Bible account of creation, their present views are due entirely to scientific evidence and facts. Sir Fred Hoyle is the originator of the steady state theory of the origin of the universe and was an outspoken atheist for many years. Today they endure much rejection and ridicule from their former colleagues who still hold to the evolutionary view.

Then there is also Dr. Michael Denton, author of *Evolution: A Theory in Crisis*. He does not claim to be a creationist but says that the creationists stick closer to actual scientific evidence while the evolutionists resort to flights of fancy.

Evolution is ignored not only by many scientists who do not want to become involved in questions of origins that cannot be proven scientifically, but many high school teachers also ignore the subject entirely. Norman Macbeth, a lawyer, made a thorough study of the Darwinian theory. His conclusion was that the theory (and he insists it is only a theory) is totally unproven and goes contrary to scientific evidence. Using the keen logic of an attorney, he investigated and proved worthless all evidence that has been presented for the Darwinian theory. Besides all his arguments against evolution, what struck and surprised me was this statement in *Darwin Retried*, p. 146:

> . . . [W]hen evolutionists address gatherings of high school teachers; they learn that the teachers have no questions and want no answers. Simpson reports: "As regards my subject, evolution, a significant minority of them simply do not believe a word of it and automatically close their mind when the subject is named."

And yet there are always some teachers in high school and professors in college and universities who like to parade their unproven theories before gullible children and young adults. Trying to appear highly learned, in disdainful conceit they become intolerant and dogmatic in fostering their evolutionary beliefs. I have heard of many instances where this has happened, including the experiences of my own grandchildren. Many children have been ridiculed for refusing to believe in evolution. In many books used in public school the fable of evolution is brought to the children, if not brazenly so, then by being slyly slipped in. And how many children have been led away from their Creator and Savior by the teachings of evolution in schools supported by public taxes?

Yes, how many theologians have been misled by the fable, believing that evolution has a scientific foundation and is a proven fact? They try to reconcile the account of creation with the evolutionary theory and they try to convert the lion into a lamb by calling it theistic evolution. So when an evolutionist hears of a theologian attempting to explain that evolution is God's method of creation, calling it *theistic* evolution, the evolutionist grins to himself, knowing that the theologian has given up the miraculous and supernatural of the Bible. He has thereby given up the God of the Bible. *Christian* evolution is a contradiction (an oxymoron). There is and can be nothing but complete antagonism between Christianity and evolution. It takes us back to Genesis 6:1: the children of God and the children of men.

7.   MANY EVOLUTIONISTS ADMIT THEY ARE WRONG

Although Darwin and his co-evolutionist, Wallace, fostered and furthered evolution, they could not explain the origin of life and it remained an unsolved problem for them. Darwin was compelled to accept a Creator somewhere in the beginning. He said:

> There is grandeur in this way of life, with its several powers, having been originally breathed by the Creator into the first forms or into one.

If life had to be created, why shouldn't everything else be created? Darwin here showed his entire theory of evolution by chance to be wrong.

The advance of life from the vegetable kingdom to the animal kingdom was, according to Wallace:

> completely beyond all possibility of explanation by matter, its laws and forces.

Again, an original evolutionist admitted that his theory had no foundation and was wrong.

Thomas Huxley, the "bulldog" for Darwin, who did more than any man of his time to spread the acceptance of Darwin's ideas, said:

> Creation in the ordinary sense of the word, is perfectly conceivable. I find no difficulty in conceiving that, at some former period, this universe was not in existence and that it made its appearance in six days . . . in consequence of the volition of some pre-existing Being." (*Life and letters of Thomas Huxley*, p. 429, by Leonard Huxley.)

Errol White, who was foremost in the study of fish:

> I have often thought how little I should like to have to prove organic evolution in a court of law.

8.   EVOLUTIONISTS ARE REFUSING TO DEBATE

Debates in a number of university cities throughout much of the United States and the world have been going on for sixteen years, since October 1972, between creationists Dr. Henry Morris and Dr. Duane Gish of the Institute for Creation Research and evolutionist professors and doctors who are involved with origins in various subjects. Dr. Henry Morris in *A History of Modern Creationism*, p. 263-265 wrote:

The first formally structured ICR debate, however, was one between Dr. Robert Gentile, Professor of Geology at the University of Missouri at Kansas City and myself in October 1972. I was in Kansas City for other meetings and a student Christian organization asked me, since I would be in the area anyway, if I would be willing to debate on campus.

I rather reluctantly agreed, not having any idea what might be involved, since I had never taken a course in debate, or even in public speaking . . . I did not know what new evidences and arguments a supposed expert in evolution would be able to present in a debate. My fears proved groundless. Dr. Gentile's case was extremely weak and largely irrelevant to the issue. He made only a very feeble attempt to answer my own arguments. I am sure he could have done better, but he evidently didn't take it seriously and was badly unprepared. In any case it was a clear victory for creationism, according to the student newspaper, and the word began to spread.

Soon Dr. Gish and I were getting many other invitations to participate in similiar debates on other university campuses . . . Even the campus and community newspapers all seemed to agree that the creationists were winning the debates . . . The first of the four-man debates was at the University of Oklahoma in January 1973. The two evolutionists were geologist David Kitts and biologist Hubert Frings, both outstanding scientists and well respected in their own fields . . . Again, it was a clear victory for creationism, as far as the audience and newspapers were concerned . . . I quickly learned that there was nothing much to fear from these encounters, at least not in the scientific evidence, but I have never learned to enjoy them . . . I still try to avoid them if possible, but I have by now participated in at least three dozen of these debates.

Dr. Gish is really in his element in a debate. He . . . has a great store of knowledge, and a tremendous memory. He is a fearsome debater. He has participated by now in well over a hundred . . . We are always careful to stick strictly to scientific arguments, especially using the fossil record to show that macro-evolution has not occurred in the past . . . The evolutionists, however, more often than not, do *not* stick to scientific arguments. They will attack the Bible, show that creationists have religious motivations, argue that one can be religious and still believe in evolution, contend that creationism is not scientific, or attack our personal character or credentials.

But one thing they will *not* do is give any real scientific evidence for macro-evolution. This is because there isn't any real scientific evidence for macro-evolution! This is why creationists almost always win the debates. We win, not because we are better debaters, but because creation is true, evolution is false, and real science confirms this.

"Macro" means "large"; and by macro-evolution is meant a large change from one "kind" of animal or plant into another "kind," like fish turning into land animals or cats turning into dogs.

In *The Troubled Waters of Evolution* Dr. Henry Morris states, p. 121, in a footnote:

The writer and his creationist colleagues have participated in many formal debates with prominent evolutionists on university campuses. Never have any of them been able to deal effectively with the entropy question. Most of them ignore it, even when their opponents have made a major issue of it in the debate.

See my section on the second law of thermodynamics, p. 257ff.

In February 1975, Dr. Duane Gish was scheduled in the University of New Orleans by sponsoring students to debate but the other scheduled debater withdrew. The students could find no biologist to defend evolution even among those teaching formal courses on the subject of evolution and biology in the various colleges and universities of New Orleans. (*Battle for Creation*, p. 54)

In October and November 1974, Dr. Gish lectured at thirteen universities in Canada, all the way from the west coast to the east coast. At Queen's University in Kingston, Ontario, one professor had challenged Gish to debate, but he finally refused to do so on the grounds that Gish's published material was dishonest and even diabolical. Gish, however, did lecture there and received prolonged applause. The professor who had refused to debate was there but he did not challenge Gish in any way or ask any question, although others had asked questions.

In 1985 and 1986 refusal to debate was still occurring regularly. On February 6, 1986, at the University of Georgia, students had asked evolutionist professors of the University to debate Dr. Gish. All who had been asked refused. Finally Dr. Schwimmer, an associate professor of Columbus College who has a doctoral degree in paleontology, agreed to debate, although he stated at the beginning he would not speak regarding the origin of the universe. He tried to show that the fossils proved direct evidence of evolution. Gish pointed out that the missing links are still missing among the fossils. And so the propagators and defenders of evolution are showing that they have no scientific foundation for their belief or creed (*Acts and Facts*, April 1986, p. 2). On November 9, 1987 a debate between Dr. Henry Morris and a University of Houston professor was cancelled at the last minute by a university official who said he did not want scientific creationism discussed on his campus. Ordinarily evolutionists will take every opportunity to propagate their belief.

In his book, *Creation and the Modern Christian*, Dr. Morris stated, p. 102:

Evolutionists are especially afraid of participating in scientific debates on evolution versus creation. "All but one voice at the N.A.S. (Nation Academy of Sciences) gathering agreed that debating with creationists should be avoided."

The quotation by Dr. Morris is from *Science*, November 6, 1981, p. 635.

Niles Eldredge in *The Monkey Business* (1982) stated p.p. 17-18 in regard to all this:

Creationists travel all over the United States, visiting college campuses and staging "debates" with biologists, geologists, and anthropologists. The creationists nearly always win. The audience is frequently loaded with the already converted and the faithful. And scientists, until recently, have been showing up at the debates ill-prepared for what awaits them. Thinking the creationists are uneducated, Bible-thumping clods, they are soon routed by a steady onslaught of direct attacks on a wide variety of scientific topics. No scientist has an expert's grasp of all the relevant points of astronomy, physics, chemistry, biology, geology, and anthropology. Creationists today — at least the majority of their spokesmen — are highly educated, intelligent people. Skilled debaters, they have always done their homework. And they nearly always seem better informed than their opponents, who are reduced too often to a bewildered state of incoherence. As will be all too evident when we examine the creationist position in detail, their arguments are devoid of any real intellectual content. Creationists win debates because of their canny stage presence, and not through clarity of logic or force of evidence. The debates are shows rather than serious consideration of evolution.

The last statement is due especially to the evolutionists not having any scientific proofs and falsely attacking the men on the creationist side. Then the argument that not all evolutionist debaters are educated in all the different sciences is extremely weak. In the debates, different evolutionists educated in special fields have not been able to provide scientific proof for evolution from their own specific field of biology or geology.

The March 1987 *Acts and Facts* pamphlet, p. 2, mentions that three of the most outstanding insistent evolutionists in the United States have refused to debate. They are Dr. Carl Sagan of Cornell University, Dr. Isaac Asimov, president of the American Humanist Association, and Dr. Stephen Gould of Harvard University:

> Constitution Hall was reserved for the night of March 23 and Dr. Gish immediately agreed to participate. Then began the major effort by Dr. LaHaye and others to induce Dr. Sagan to represent evolution. Since he is extremely positive in his devotion to total evolution and frequently berates creationism as pseudo-science, one would think this would have been an ideal forum in which he could demonstrate the scientific validity of evolution and be well paid for doing so. Not so! After several weeks of being vigorously urged to defend his evolutionary world view, Carl Sagan said, no, he would not! Probably the next best-known evolutionary scientist is Dr. Isaac Asimov . . . an even more sarcastic anti-creationist than Dr. Sagan. Therefore he also was invited to debate Dr. Gish, but in a curt note, he said he would not do so for the same reasons as those of Dr. Sagan (whatever they might have been) . . . Dr. Stephen Jay Gould has been approached for a possible future debate, but early indications are that he also will refuse.

All this was summed up clearly by Paul Ackerman in *It's a Young World After All*, p. 12:

> . . . the past decade of intense activity by scientific creationists has left most evolutionist professors unwilling to debate the creationist professors. Too many of the evolutionists have been publicly humiliated in such debates by their own lack of erudition and by the weaknesses of their theory.

9.   EVOLUTIONISTS ARE INTOLERANT

Yet in spite of all that was mentioned in previous sections, evolutionists are very intolerant and try to ridicule the creationists as being ignorant people, unscientific and unscholarly. In criticizing creationists, ridiculing remarks like the following by the evolutionists are common. Niles Eldredge in *The Monkey Business* (1982), p. 83 referring to creationists said:

> The literature is all written in extremely simple terms, to convince the uninitiated rather than to enter into sophisticated dialogue in science. Moreover, creationists are sloppy; they make simple spelling errors when quoting scientists.

Words with ancient Latin and Greek derivation do not make a writing scientific. Why not use the more common terminology of the English language? Using words like flora and fauna instead of plants and animals does not make a treatise more sophisticated. And in debating creationists why don't they delve into scientific proof for their ideas? Yet on p. 130 Eldredge makes the nasty remark:

Earlier I said that creationists are poor scholars.

January 1984 the *Los Angeles Times* printed an article by Robert Solomon entitled:

In the beginning . . . Evolution — A battle of ignorance against intelligence.

The story of evolution definitely is not based on scientific intelligence.

Dr. Alfred Rehwinkel in *The Wonders of Creation* (1974) summed up this entire attitude extremely well in stating, p. 31:

Meanwhile, their unproven theories will continue to be accepted by the learned and the illiterate alike as absolute truth, and will be defended with a fanatic intolerance that has a parallel only in the bigotry of the darkest Middle Ages. If one does not accept evolution as an infallible dogma, implicitly and without question, one is regarded as an unenlightened ignoramus or is merely ignored as an obscurantist or a naive, uncritical fundamentalist. Such a man will have difficulties finding a publisher for a manuscript presenting a view contrary to this theory, and if published his book will not be recommended for a textbook in schools or colleges. It will not be easy for him to secure a position in the science department of one of our leading universities. Anyone who does not join in the modern "Baal worship" is a heretic and is treated accordingly.

Evolutionists are indeed very intolerant of creation views. Dr. Henry Morris in *The Troubled Waters of Evolution*, p. 81, asked in a footnote:

Why is it that whenever scientific questions are raised concerning the validity of evolution, evolutionists respond angrily or sarcastically? Is there a "religious" commitment to evolution?

Attorney Turner for the Creation Science Research Center in the Sacramento evolution case in early 1981 said regarding the evolutionists:

They're pompous and arrogant, just the kind of people that the First Amendment was written to protect us against.

Dr. W. Scot Morrow, Associate Professor of Chemistry, Wofford College wrote (1986) in a Foreword for *Creation's Tiny Mystery* by Robert Gentry:

If I were to follow the unwritten, but commonly understood guidelines laid down by my fellow evolutionists, many of whom are agnostics like myself, when presented with a book written by a fundamentalist Christian on the topic of "creation," I would ignore the work. Of course, I might kick over the traces a bit, skim through the thing quickly — one *MUST* be fair, you know — and then give the document a decent quiet burial in the nearest wastebasket. After all, those among us who have brains in our head instead of rocks . . . know that (1) science and religion are immiscible, (2) true scientists cannot be creationists, (3) creationists cannot be scientific, let alone scientists, (4) the last factor is doubled and redoubled — in spades — for fundamentalists . . . The preceding six commandments . . . may be referred to as the A & S Doctrine, in honor of the guiding cosmic luminaries, Isaac Asimov and Carl Sagan.

Robert Gentry himself in that book stated, p. 95:

The second thing we have to gain is our decency and humanity. I have myself sat in class after class in the sciences and humanities in which any idea remotely religious was belittled, attacked, and shouted down in the most unscientific and emotionally cruel way. I have seen young students raised according to fundamentalist doctrine treated like loathsome alley cats, emotionally torn apart, and I never thought that this sort of treatment was any better than the treatment that religious prelates, who held authority, gave Galileo. Why scream about the inhumanity of nuclear war if you are also willing to force people of fundamentalist faiths to attend public schools in which their most cherished beliefs will be systematically held up to ridicule and the young children with it?

Hilbert Siegler in *Evolution or Degeneration - Which?* wrote in the last two sentences of his book that evolution:

has made brilliant professors of science who under other circumstances would insist that their students approach all subjects with a questioning mind, bully and badger students who attempt to question phases of this theory which many scientists consider utter nonsense. Our hope lies in the youth of today and tomorrow who will have the intellectual honesty to ask searching questions.

XIX.   EVOLUTION VERSUS SCIENCE

1.   UNIFORMITARIANISM

To understand how the ideas of evolution increased the past 120 to 150 years, it is necessary that we look at how uniformitarianism got started, and at its authors. Uniformitarianism is the belief that all things evolved gradually, uniformily, over millions and billions of years and that "the present is the key to the past." In other words they used the idea of "extrapolation" to assume that all things happened in the past as they are known to be happening now; that is, changes in the geology of the earth have always taken place slowly and gradually. Extrapolation is used in business statistics to determine what the future business may be on the basis of present statistical figures for the business. But we know that extrapolation into the future in business statistics is often way off course and does not work out as computed.

One key blunder is committed by the evolutionists in using the idea of extrapolation in geology. They totally ignore evidences that at some time in the recent past there was an immense worldwide Flood and upheaval of the earth's surface, a catastrophe that runs counter to the uniformitarian creed.

The idea of uniformitarianism originated more or less with James Hutton (1726-1797) who was a farmer and doctor. In 1785 he wrote a paper entitled "The Theory of the Earth" in which he stated his belief that the forces in the weather, wind and rain now taking place on the earth would have been able, *if given enough time*, of producing every feature of the earth's crust that now exists. He believed that the Genesis account of creation was a figment of man's imagination. He concluded his essay by stating:

> It is vain to look for anything higher in the origin of the Earth . . . we find no vestige of a beginning — no prospect of an end.

This idea was accepted by Charles Lyell (1797-1875), a Scot who lived in London. Lyell's three volumes, *Principles of Geology*, were published between 1830 and 1833. In them he told how rains and rivers wear down hills and mountains, how waves destroy rocky seashores and build up beaches, and how eruptions build lava plains and mountains. Lyell claimed that the earth is changing now as it has changed throughout the centuries, and that it has changed at the same rate it is changing now. He claimed that to find out what happened in ancient times we must go by what is happening at the present time. He believed that the mountains, hills, valleys and plains and the strata of the earth with their many fossils were the result of slow gradual erosion in past ages.

These ideas blended in perfectly for Charles Darwin (1809-1882) when he wrote his book, *The Origin of Species* (1859), in which he tried to promulgate his idea of the gradual evolution of plants and animals. Both Lyell (for his gradual development of the geology of the earth) and Darwin (for his gradual evolution of plants and animals) needed millions of years, so Darwin eagerly adopted the idea of uniformitarianism. Truly, whether to explain the origin of the universe, or the geology and make-up of the earth, or the evolution of plants and animals, evolution needs uniformitarianism with its billions of years, and it assumes these ages to be a fact. With this background one can easily see why George Wald in *The Origin of Life* wrote in 1955:

> Time is in fact the hero of the plot . . . Given so much time, the impossible becomes possible, the possible becomes probable, and the probable virtually certain. One has only to wait; time itself performs miracles.

But along came Lord Kelvin, (1824-1907) a physicist, who threw a monkey wrench into the vast ages for uniformitarianism. Applying physics to the study of the earth's ages, he figured the earth was only 30 million years old. Later this was reduced to 20 and then 15 million years. To make the idea of evolution work, Thomas Huxley, Darwin's bulldog, stated that maybe evolution took place in a shorter space of time. Darwin was upset at such a short space of time for evolution to develop and stated:

> I am greatly troubled at the short duration of the world according to Lord Kelvin, for I require for my theoretical views a very long period.

Hilbert Siegler, in his book *Evolution or Degeneration — Which?* p. 76, stated:

> This principle — this belief — is labelled "uniformitarianism." It is easy to see how this assumption should have led to the belief that the earth is tremendously old. It is also easy to see that the evolutionist is very much in need of such an explanation. After all, if the vast complex of today's organisms gradually evolved out of a mere spark of life in some chemical brew, an almost incomprehensible number of years is needed to allow time for these organisms to develop.

Evolutionists claim that uniformitarianism "has now gained universal acceptance among intelligent and informed people." This belief is usually *assumed* to be a fact and is presented as such in the textbooks and in the news media. In fact, it is cited as a positive proof for evolution. And yet, today there are thousands of truly intelligent and informed scientists and individuals who reject the belief of uniformitarianism.

In fact, up to the time of Darwin, and up to the time when many were hoodwinked into believing that evolution and science were one and the same, most scientists believed that the catastrophe of the Flood was the cause of the earth's present surface and of the fossils being buried in these rocky sediments. Also in recent years many famous scientists and leaders of universities have rejected both evolution and its faulty premise of uniformitarianism.

The principle of uniformitarianism, with its slow, gradual processes as causes of the present geology of the earth, has created many problems for men who are truly scientists, who work with testable, proven experiments and evidences. This is especially so with geologists. In studying the upheavals that have taken place on the earth and the strata of the earth, geologists can readily see that these things did not take place slowly, but extreme violence and catastrophe took place in the structure of the earth's surface. The idea of uniformitarianism married to the idea of evolution has gotten modern geology into many absurdities, and has gotten geology all messed up. More and more the geologists are listening to the evidences of catastrophe, such as the Bible relates regarding the Flood.

The book *The Genesis Flood*, p. 149, by Whitcomb/Morris, states that:

> [In the Columbia Plateau] vast and intricate dug canyons or coulees, hanging valleys, dry waterfalls, rock-rimmed basins and other bizarre features are found in profusion. These things are obviously not being formed anywhere at the present time, so there is much disagreement among geologists as to their explanation. The man who has made the most thorough study of the area is Harlan Bretz, whose theory envisaged a sudden vast flood as being the only agency capable of creating these forms.

W. D. Thornbury in *Principles of Geomorphology* (1954) wrote that Harlan Bretz:

> has been unable to account for such a flood but maintained that field evidence indicated its reality. This theory represents a return to catastrophism which many geologists have been reluctant to accept.

But the evolutionists are fighting for the uniformitarian idea with all their might, because if the uniformitarian ideas with its billions of years is wrong, the whole structure of evolution crumbles. For that reason evolutionists have turned to radioactive dating methods to provide them with billions of years. But these dating methods are based on the false assumptions that the decay rates of radioactivity have been constant and that the earth originally was not created a mature earth. And so here also the uniformitarian idea and its accompanying evolution idea is crumbling.

2.   UNIFORMITARIANISM AND EXTRAPOLATION

Although I referred to extrapolation *a few pages previous* to this (Chapter XIX, part 1), it is well to make additional remarks regarding it. Evolutionists with their belief in constant, slow and gradual processes of uniformitarianism have hoped that the processes taking place now on earth can be extrapolated or extended into the distant past and also into the distant future to explain everything that happened evolution-wise in the past and to predict, like prophets, all that will ever happen in the future billions of years. Richard Alexander in *Evolution, Creation and Biology Teaching*, (February 1978) stated:

> To argue that the past cannot be reconstructed is even less reasonable than to argue that the future cannot be predicted.

But the evolutionists ignore totally the supernatural in their materialistic principle (that something supernatural messed up all the natural when this whole earth was at the time of the Flood torn all to pieces), and they ignore the thought that the supernatural may or rather will some day tear up the natural again. The book *The Genesis Flood* p. xxvi correctly states:

> Thus, extrapolation of present processes into the prehistoric past or into the eschatalogical future is not really science. Such extrapolation necessarily involves assumptions and pre-suppositions and is therefore basically a philosophy, or even a faith.

It is faulty extrapolation to assume that because there have been only local floods in the recent past there could not have been a world-wide flood in the more distant past. Also it is faulty reasoning to assume that because there have been only local isolated volcanos and earthquakes in the recent past there could not have been volcanos exploding and earthquakes taking place all over the earth at one time in the past, or that there might not be worldwide calamities and catastrophes in the future.

3.   EVIDENCES AGAINST UNIFORMITARIANISM

There are all kinds of evidences that the earth's major geological features were formed catastrophically, not gradually: 1) The sedimentary rocks were laid down one upon another rapidly with each layer laid upon the other without any sign of a time gap. The evidence in these sedimentary rocks is powerful. No floods like we have today could begin to lay down sedimentary deposits to the depths they are found in the earth today. Sediments thousands of feet thick have been found in many parts of the earth including the Mankato, MN area. One outstanding example is the Grand Canyon of Arizona. Such vast layers are not being laid down today.

2) Fossils of plants and animals are heaped and entwined with each other *in masses* showing that they did not die gradually. All of these animals must have died suddenly and have been buried quickly and deeply or otherwise they would not have been preserved as fossils. Nowhere on earth are any fossils being formed today, gradually and in masses.

3) Some 150,000 square miles in Idaho and eastern Washington and Oregon are covered with lava, some places a mile deep. All the volcanos today acting in unison at one place could not produce that amount of lava. Also a figurine of baked clay was found some 300 feet down, showing that that lava must have been hardened there in recent centuries.

4) The recent age in which the mountains have been formed confounds the evolutionists. Evolutionist Ruth Moore in *The Earth We Live On* (1956), p. 243 stated:

The bewildering old question of what has elevated the mountains and the continents still has not been answered.

5) The layers of coal could not have been formed by vegetation hardening into coal unless buried quickly and deeply and in vastly larger amounts than is grown today.

6) All those huge animals that froze suddenly in Siberia and Alaska could not have died gradually. This could not have been a local event, because those thousands and thousands of frozen carcasses are found over an area of several thousand square miles. If the evolutionists cannot read these facts in Siberia correctly, how would they be able to tell the origin of the stars, the moons, planets and the rest of the universe, plus the origin of life, of plants and animals?

4.   UNIFORMITARIANISM VERSUS CATASTROPHE

The trouble with evolution is that it just simply ignores geological evidences of the Flood and rules them out as being nonexistent and nonscientific. Such prejudices against the Flood evidences did not exist until some time after Lyell's idea of uniformitarianism and Darwin's idea of both evolution and uniformitarianism were being accepted. *The Genesis Flood* p. 137, correctly stated the case:

> *Uniformitarianism, in other words, has simply been assumed, not proved. Catastrophism has simply been denied, not refuted.*

5. GEOLOGISTS TODAY ARE ABANDONING UNIFORMITARIANISM

The old uniformitarian theory has been called a dangerous doctrine by Paul Krynine of Pennsylvania State; and the idea of "the present is the key to the past" has been called "a maxim without much credit" by J. Valentine of the University of California, Davis. Professor Stephen Gould of Harvard, an evolutionist, attacked uniformitarianism and has stated that "The fossil record with its abrupt transitions offers no support for gradual change." Natural History, June-July 1977.

Although they do not want to return to the Bible account of the Flood for an explanation, they are realizing more and more that the earth's surface was changed very suddenly with catastrophes of various kinds taking place, even if not worldwide then at least here and there on earth. Dr. Niles Eldredge of the American Museum of Natural History, in his book, *The Monkey Business* (1982) p.p. 96-97 refers to this change to catastrophism. He calls it:

> The *other* meaning of uniformitarianism . . . For well over a century now, we have spoken of the Ice Ages in the recent geological past . . . Volcanoes and earthquakes are truly sudden in their action, and many wreak huge changes. And the recent invocation of an asteroid impact as the trigger to the ecological collapse that ended the Cretaceous world and wiped out perhaps as many as ninety percent of all living species is a catastrophe *par excellence* (and even if there was no asteroid, the extinction "event" itself was a disaster). [The parenthesis are his.]

And so the evolutionists have been turning from old uniformitarianism to neouniformitarianism with a new, catastrophic explanation.

The newspapers, the radios and TV are constantly blaring out how the dinosaurs were killed by catastrophic volcanic explosions, asteroids, comets or meteors hitting the earth, plunging it into prolonged darkness and destroying the vegetation, cooling the air, creating acid rain, increasing ultraviolet radiation. All these events are claimed to have created local, regional, even worldwide catastrophes. *But* the Flood, because it is considered a religious Biblical event, is just simply ignored or denied as a nonevent. Anything in the Bible just cannot be considered, even if it agrees exactly with historical events and explains many geological features of the crust of the earth. (See Chapter XI, Part 7)

This entire evolutionary mess has been well summed up by Dr. Henry Morris in *Acts and Facts,* January 1986, p. 3:

> A fascinating controversy is dividing the camp of modern evolutionary scientists. The traditional "gradualists" still maintain that evolution takes place very slowly, but the problem is that there are no intermediate transitional forms between species, either in living organisms or in the fossil record. Therefore modern revolutionary evolutionists, or "punctuationists," now insist that real evolution (as distinct from small horizontal variations) takes place in quantum evolutionary leaps. The problem is that no one has ever seen such a thing happen or has any knowledge of how it could be accomplished genetically.

> And so the battle rages. However, both gradualists and punctuationists close ranks whenever they confront the creationists, insisting that evolution is true even though they don't know how it works.

Morris refers to Dr. Niles Eldredge as representing the punctuationists, and to Dr. Richard Dawkins, professor of zoology of Oxford University, as defending the gradualists, with Dawkins complaining that punctuationism aids the creationists. He says:

> If you throw out gradualness, you throw out the very thing that makes evolution more plausible than creation.

Yet both of these men argue that the only alternative to either gradual or sudden evolution is special creation and an intelligent Designer.

Thus, as a clumsy clod or oaf stumbles over himself physically, so evolutionists with gradual and sudden evolutionary ideas are stumbling over themselves logically, contradicting past and present guesses, assumptions and theories.

Without uniformitarianism evolution does not have one bit of basis or evidence for their billions of years for the formation of the universe and the solar system. The false explanation of how and when the sedimentary rocks were supposedly laid down over millions and billions of years as it was propagated by Charles Lyell is out of date, antiquated and obsolete. The entire false idea is enough to blow the whole idea of evolution and the billions of years to smithereens.

XX.   SCIENCE

1.   SCIENCE IN GENERAL

This leads us to science with the question: *What is science?* The word "science" is derived from the Latin word "scientia" meaning knowledge. Science deals with a fact which has been observed, first through hypotheses, then through theories, until it becomes a scientific law that has been tested, demonstrated and proven. In other words, science is knowledge of facts, behavior of things, phenomena, experiences that can be tested, described or appraised. Scientific knowledge of natural things can be obtained either through direct experiences or through indirect experiences of others by means of books or written or spoken records of others. Man can test only the things that now exist, such as material things, life, and the laws of nature that now govern inorganic matter and organic plant, animal, and human life.

Knowledge of supernatural things such as the origin of matter and of life, and the Originator of matter and life cannot be obtained by testing, observing, probing or proving. Origins came before all material things that now exist, and knowledge of them can only be obtained through revelation from the Originator. The book of Hebrews expounds not only a theological truth but also a profound philosophical truth.

> Through faith we understand that the worlds were framed by the word of God, so that things which are seen were not made of things which do appear. Hebrews 11:3.

Only He who existed before the origin of matter and life can reveal the mystery of the origin of all things.

Let us first consider the scientific knowledge of natural things. True science can be applied only to *presently* existing processes and phenomena, for we have no scientific way of knowing whether the same facts held in the past or will hold in the future. Therefore the facts of present scientific knowledge cannot be extrapolated backwards and forwards, as far as origins are concerned.

Natural science begins with trying to understand a certain problem, process or phenomenon. Phenomenon is a Greek word meaning to appear or something that appears so and so to us. A scientific explanation or solution of a problem usually begins with a *hypothesis*. Hypothesis is a Greek word meaning to place under or beneath. It is an idea which is set forth to try to explain certain observations, processes or phenomena. Therefore a hypothesis is a foundation for the development of certain scientific ideas. It is a starting point, a premise, a foundation, a guess on which the probable theory will stand, which the experimentor is trying to prove. Therefore the scientist must collect evidences directly by himself or indirectly through books and others to see if the problem is solvable. The hypothesis must be tested by observation, experiment, measurement and other means to see if the hypothesis is correct and provable. If one's ideas hold true, then his hypothesis may be verified and he will have a foundation for the theory he is trying to test and prove.

One more requirement is necessary in order for a hypothesis to act as a foundation for a theory. The hypothesis must be tested not only to see if it is verifiable, but also to see if it can be disproven or refuted or is falsifiable. Sir Karl Popper is an Austrian-born philosopher, who was a professor of logic and scientific methods at the London School of Economics. He has been testing scientists and others for many years to see if their scientific logic is holding up.

He has formulated a number of statements by which theories can be tested to see if they are good or bad. One of his statements is: "A theory which is not refutable by any conceivable event is nonscientific. Irrefutability is not a virtue of a theory (as people often think) but is a vice." A case has been given where a young professor presented a paper trying to prove a theory. It appeared that he had gained fame for himself. But only a few hours later another professor produced evidence that the theory was wrong and the young scientist went home in disgrace, because he had not checked his data and work carefully to see if his ideas could be proven false.

After a hypothesis has become a theory and that theory with time and through many tests has been verified and not proven false and irrefutable, it will finally become a scientific law like the two laws of thermodynamics and other scientific natural laws. Yet it must remain falsifiable, according to Popper.

2.   HOW DOES A TRUE SCIENTIST WORK?

1) A scientist observes certain things or phenomena happening.

2) He wonders why this thing happens as it does.

3) He begins to guess and assume why this thing happens so and so, and he forms or dreams up a hypothesis about it.

4) He tests and experiments with the problem or phenomenon to see if the hypothesis could be the basis or foundation of a theory.

5) He conducts many tests and experiments to check the hypothesis.

6) Then he discards the nonscientific ones that do not check out with the observable facts, and he works to test the provable ones.

A true scientist accepts only what is backed by acceptable evidence and has proven not to be false. After a theory has been proven with much testing and after considerable time, it may become probable or even become a scientific law.

3.   YET EVOLUTIONISTS ARE SEEKING FOR FACTS AND TRUTH REGARDING ORIGINS THAT INVOLVE PRENATURAL AND SUPERNATURAL THINGS THAT CANNOT BE PROVEN

True scientists state that origins belong to philosophy and religion, so for origins the supernatural must be considered. How stupid it is to think and believe that material can arise out of nothing without some prenatural, nonmaterial Force or Being creating the material. Scientists have stated, "Out of nothing comes nothing." that is, no material can come out of a nonexisting material. There must be something greater than material elements. True science must consider every possible cause for the source of all things. Evolutionists have found no first cause for the universe, for gravity, for electricity, for why the solar system moves about so clocklike. Ruling the supernatural (a Creator and Designer) out of the natural is like ruling the inner nonmaterial part of man out of all the material things men have made and devised. It is not the material body of man but the non-material mind, will, spirit and wisdom of man that has devised and designed all the inventions and things we have. So also there must be some non-material cause behind all the things that exist — from hydrogen to life on earth.

4.   MATERIAL SCIENCE IS NOT CONCERNED ABOUT ORIGINS

There is one field that material science cannot enter into and that is the origin of all materials because before there were materials there was nothing to experiment with and to test. For this reason scientists as a rule do not want to enter into the origin of matter and materials. When it is suggested to a true scientist that any theory of origins should also account for the *very first origin,* to the beginning of all things, he will say that there we must turn to religion and philosophy. He will say in effect: Science is not concerned with the origin of matter; it takes matter for granted as it is. The origin of matter is not a scientific problem but a philosophical or theological one.

Evolution, however, not being a science but only an idea that is *anti-supernatural*, tries to explain origins scientifically and claim that its hypotheses and theories are facts of science. But the supernatural cannot be explained by provable hypotheses and theories.

Yet man wants to know also about the prenatural (what existed before materials) and the supernatural. To obtain knowledge, science or the truth about this, man must go beyond the natural, material things that his senses can behold. Man must seek the truth about the prenatural and the supernatural wherever it may be revealed, not only in the things that exist naturally but also in things that have been revealed supernaturally. Supernatural revelation cannot be ignored in seeking knowledge and the truth regarding origins. Call it supernatural science if you wish. When a Christian refers to God as the origin of all things, the evolutionists, in cocky pride, ask, "But then, who made God?" — as though that will stop the Christian cold in his belief. But the Christian in turn asks, "But who then made matter?" Since according to scientific law, nothing (material) comes out of nothing, there must be a supernatural Force or Being that created the natural, the material. There must be a Force, a Designer, a God, who was before and beyond the material things that now exist.

Science (tested knowledge) and the truths of Scripture (about both natural and supernatural things) do not conflict. The truths of the Bible have been confirmed by science again and again. The supernatural truths of the Bible have also been confirmed in the created things that exist. "For the invisible things of him, from the creation of the world, are clearly seen, being understood *by the things that are made,* even *his eternal power and Godhead,* so that they are without excuse" (Romans 1:20).

Complete and truthful science requires knowledge of the supernatural, not only of the Originator but also of the laws of nature that the Originator installed in the force of material things and nature. Scientists in the past have proclaimed this. Professor Lamarck stated:

Nature is the wonderful produce of His Almighty will . . . Thus the will of God is everywhere expressed by the laws of Nature, since these laws originated from Him.

Maedler, in *Astronomy,* has the motto:

The heavens declare the glory of God. [He states:] A true naturalist cannot be an atheist; the laws of nature and the law of God are one and the same.

Edward Maunder, founder and president of the Royal Astronomical Society, stated:

> In the beginning God created the heavens and the earth, is the foundation of all science, as well as all religion.

Professor J. Clerk Maxwell, a great scientist at Cambridge University (died 1879) said:

> I have examined all (theories) that have come within my reach, and I have found that every one must have a God to make it work.

5.   AND SCIENCE, EVEN IN DEALING WITH NATURAL LAW, IS NOT CERTAIN OF ITS WORK AND REPORTS

Science reports often use phrases such as: "Science believes . . . or science has shown . . . or science has proved . . . " One man said that phrases like this are often used as a kind of insurance against any kind of criticism that people might raise. And many people falsely believe that if *science* says so, it must be true. So *science* has become a sort of a Sacred Cow.

But a commentary given in the *Minneapolis Tribune*, October 7, 1982, presents quite an eye opener on this matter. The commentary states in regard to a symposium held in a small auditorium at Catholic University in Washington, D.C.:

> The same fissure between faith and knowledge that troubled Galileo opened up . . . Owen Gingerich, a small gray-haired astronomer from Harvard, was speaking toward the end of the symposium about Galileo's trouble as a man of faith who had found some evidence that his church and scripture were wrong.

The account continues:

> Today in science, Gingerich said in a rather offhand way, there is no "belief" as such, only probability. A man in the audience, visibly emotional, stood up. "I cannot credit it. I cannot believe you would say" that scientists do not really "believe" in the objects they study, and that astronomical science might be wrong about what stars are and how they move. "Do you really think it's possible that it's all wrong?" he demanded.
>
> "Yes," said Gingerich. As an example, physicists if pressed will say that atoms, as real objects in the form we imagine them, cannot be proved. The most you can say, Gingerich explained, "is that the universe acts as if its made of atoms." With the stars too, the

distinguished astronomer said, we know stars only as grains of light exposed on photographic plates. Proof of what they are is absent.

But, intoned a tall, gray-haired Domincan priest, Rev. William Wallace of Catholic University, "Do you take (astronomical knowledge) as only highly probable? Or do you really believe it as something that is true?

For the most part, scientists don't think about it, Gingerich said.

But when pressed, scientists cannot fail to remember that absolute reality collapsed just after the turn of the century, with Einstein, Gingerich said. Time itself was proved to be elastic, a matter of perception. Matter proved to be fluid and quirky. It became apparent that no measurement is absolute.

"So much of the absolute reality of space and time had to be abondoned," Gingerich said. Since then one simply cannot speak of certainties.

"I can't believe it," muttered the man in the audience as he sat down

So far from the commentary.

Yes, there are things that scientists, and especially evolutionists who claim to be scientists, *cannot do and know nothing about definitely.* Immanuel Velikovsky in his *Worlds in Collision* 1950 stated, p. 21: "Here comes *Homo ignoramus.*" I like that expression *Homo ignoramus* (Ignorant Man) because it deflates proud, arrogant *Homo sapiens, sapiens* who delights in his imagined wisdom, answers and progress, but whom God on the day of judgment will most likely before all mankind address as "smart wise guy" in his verdict before all humanity.

Velikovsky continues:

He [Homo ignoramus] does not know what life is or how it came to be and whether it originated from inorganic matter . . although he has built up a few hypotheses about it . . . He does not know what this mysterious force of gravitation is that holds him and his fellow man on the other side of the planet with their feet on the ground, although he regards the phenomenon itself as "the law of laws." He does not know what the earth looks like five miles under his feet. He does not know how mountains came into existence or what caused the emergence of the continents, although he builds hypotheses about these, nor does he know from where oil came — again hypotheses [and so on].

Yes, there are many things, not only regarding origins but also regarding the workings of the laws of nature that God created, that science cannot explain: electricity, gravity and magnetism. He can predict and measure their effects, but their ultimate nature is not known any more than Thales of Miletus knew, who speculated about electricity, amber and lightning already 585 before Christ.

Science can describe the world as it now exists, but it cannot tell us how it came into existence, because this is a problem that cannot be tested and proven. In regard to things on earth, evolutionists cannot tell how the inorganic is supposed to have given birth to the organic and caused life to appear, how the plants turned into animals, and the animals into man. When they try to delve into these things and explain them, they are not even acting as philosophers, but are merely letting their imaginations run wild. They do not even begin to have a hypothesis on which to build a foundation and a theory.

6.   HOWEVER THERE ARE THINGS THAT TRUE SCIENTISTS CAN TEST AND PROVE

There are branches of science such as geology, physics, chemistry, biology, zoology, archeology, medicine, etc., that can be tested and proven. The science of geology deals with present geological processes and the features of the earth; the science of chemistry works with chemical properties and actions of matter and the elements; the science of physics deals with phenomena of the physical world; and the science of biology analyzes life in plants, animals and mankind. As long as science does not try to explain scientifically the origin and destiny of things that cannot be explained scientifically there will be no conflict between science and the facts and truths of the Bible. Science can prove experimentally that the earth revolves around the sun, that gravity, electricity and magnetism exist, and it can prove that hydrogen and oxygen can be turned into water, but it cannot prove origins and destinies.

7.   SCIENCE AND TECHNOLOGY

Science is the mother of technology. Science is the study and discovery of natural processes, whereas technology applies the discoveries of science to practical purposes. In other words, technology takes what science has discovered and applies it in usable forms. Science is the mother of many of the inventions we see all around us, such as television, radios, airplanes, cars, telephones, light fixtures, refrigerators, boats, atomic machinery, household appliances of all kinds, modern farm machinery, above all advances in medical care, etc. Also scientific knowledge of gravity, magnetism and electricity has been put abundantly to use in technology.

8.   THE HYPOTHESES OF EVOLUTION ARE NOT SCIENTIFIC

In fact evolution as such is not recognized as a science in itself. A student cannot take a graduate course in the subject and receive a degree. Although evolutionary ideas are brought into scientific fields or disciplines such as geology, physics, botany, zoology, chemistry, paleontology, etc.; many scientists working in these fields do not use the theory of evolution in their work or deal directly with it. The speculations of the evolutionists that are proclaimed through the news media as "proven facts" would get nowhere in the investigations and examinations of reputable scientific journals.

The prestige of science is being falsely used to give commendation, trust and credibility to the assumptions of evolution. Students and others are constantly being misled into believing in evolution, not because it has any scientific foundation, but because it is being falsely associated with true science. And this is so even though, for example, the scientific second law of thermodynamics, which teaches that things are constantly degenerating or changing downwards, squarely confronts and rejects the evolutionary assumption that all things are evolving into higher and better states and moving and changing upward. Both of these teachings cannot be correct.

9.   EVOLUTION A PSEUDOSCIENCE

From all this it is evident that evolution is a false science, a science so-called, a pseudoscience, a counterfeit, a sham.

There is nothing wrong in speculation with hypotheses and theories, in order to discover the truth about some phenomenon. The trouble with evolution is that its claimed hypotheses and theories are proclaimed directly and indirectly by implication as though they were established, proven facts. Because this is being done openly and insistently by evolutionists and others, it has become a pseudo or false science; and it is harmful in the search for the truth and pure scientific facts and it has misled many sciences. See p.p. 415-417.

But evolution does serve as a foundation for beliefs which reject God such as atheism, communism and humanism, and therefore is a hand-maiden for those three ideologies.

Norman Macbeth, in *Darwin Retried* p. 147 stated correctly:

Unfortunately, in the field of evolution most explanations are not good. As a matter of fact, they hardly qualify as explanations at all; they are suggestions, hunches, pipe dreams, hardly worthy of being called hypotheses. A man who was careful and precise in his language would never have used the word *theory* for classical Darwinism. [Macbeth has a footnote:] The elder Huxley expressly called it a hypothesis and recommended that it be held "with a light hand" and only provisionally: T. H. Huxley (1893), 468-469.

But Sir Julian Huxley, grandson of T. H. Huxley, told a television audience:

The first point to make about Darwin's theory is that it is no longer a theory, but a fact.

It is declared to be a fact although there is no way of testing the theory, because the imagined events of evolution would need millions of years of experiments before positive scientific conclusions could be reached.

10.   THE IDEA OF EVOLUTION IS ALSO LUDICROUS AND PATHETIC

Evolutionists believe that the original element of this universe was hydrogen, and they believe that all things evolved from hydrogen. They also believe that all this evolution happened by chance. Following through with this, people evolved from the odorless, colorless gas of hydrogen in the course of millions and billions of years. How did they arrive at this fantastic, unbelievable conclusion? Where else, they claim, could man have come from? On the one hand the simplest element is hydrogen; on the other, the most advanced life is in man. Believing that man evolved from hydrogen is ludicrous, ridiculous and would be absurd enough to create laughter, if the idea were not so dangerous in misleading little children eternally.

The idea of evolution appears pathetic, when one sees that men who claim to be intelligent believe in things that are contrary to all evidence and science. John A. Moore, an evolutionist, who is not to be confused with John N. Moore, a creationist, stated in regard to Darwin and his critics:

Furthermore, it was recognized that the stratified rocks of the earth's crust represent materials deposited long ago, usually under water. The materials were slowly changed into rock and in some instances contemporaneous remains of animals and plants were included in the deposits.

But animals and plants must be buried suddenly and deeply or they will decay. To believe otherwise is pathetic reasoning.

Another case of false science or pathetic reasoning is believing that because certain animals have similiar features or biological forms they have common origins and are interrelated. Evolutionist Niles Eldredge, in his book *The Monkey Business* (1982), p. 36 and 37 tried to foster such reasoning by comparing the origin of different plants and animals to different copies of ancient manuscripts resulting from two or more monks in ancient history making mistakes in copying manuscripts. As a result there arose manuscripts that were slightly different. Using the same reasoning regarding the origin of plants and animals, he tries to use the same argument: that different plants and animals could have arisen from one original source of life. Then also, an animal all by itself by chance without having any sexual mate would have had to propagate life.

Eldredge states, p. 36:

Here is another way of putting the prediction: the very idea of evolution implies that each species will tend to have some features unique to itself, but each species *must* share some similarities in structure or behavior with some other species. Furthermore, each group of similar species will share further features with other groups of species (the two-monk analogy again), and this common group *must* share features with still other groups. This pattern of sharing similarities with an ever-widening array of biological forms *must* continue until all of life is linked up by sharing at least one similarity in common. *This* is evolution's grand prediction: that the patterns of similarities in the organic world are arrayed like a complex set of nested Chinese boxes. [Emphasis his.]

From this he turns to doglike animals. He continues, p. 37:

The kinship of dogdom widens as we see that some creatures, including all dogs, carnivores, mammals, and tetrapods, share backbones and other features with various sorts of animals we call fish. These collectively are the vertebrates. The circle widens to embrace progressively more groups: dogs, fungi, rosebushes, and amoebas have fundamentally similar (eukaryotic) cells.

Finally even man and roses had a common origin, according to his belief.

Eldredge and other evolutionists like him ignore entirely the possibility that all the different plants and animals did not start from one cell or tree but from a forest of trees each different from the other, even though many may have vertebrae or other similar bodily features.

11. NEITHER EVOLUTION NOR CREATION IS SCIENTIFICALLY PROVABLE

Many leading evolutionists admit that evolution is not a scientific theory, which can be proved or disproved on the basis of observation and experiment, and that therefore it lies outside testable science. No one can go into a laboratory and make appropriate experiments to explain historical events like the origin of elements and material, the origin of life or the evolution of different kinds of plants and animals. Because these events are not repeatable, observable, testable, and above all not factual, the idea of evolution regarding these things is not scientific.

And what is true of evolution is also true of the account of creation. It is also not repeatable, observable and testable, and therefore it cannot be proven scientifically. No one can see and test events that took place in the distant past. Karl Popper, an evolutionist and outstanding philosopher of science, declared that in essence evolution is not testable and provable.

The entire subject of origins lies beyond the field of scientific proof or disproof. Therefore both evolution and creation require faith or belief, because they are based on prehistorical events that have no secular history behind them. However, the Bible does have a history that goes back farther than the Egyptians, Babylonians and other peoples. The histories of the world begin with what is given to us in the tenth chapter of Genesis; *but* they lack the history given us in the first nine chapters of Genesis, covering a period of 1700 or more years. This is a time span nearly as long as that from the days of Christ to our time, when billions of people could have been born and could have covered the earth with immense progress and a highly advanced civilization, which could have been greater than mankind has accomplished since the days of Christ.

12. EVOLUTION IS NOT FALSIFIABLE IN THE BROAD SENSE

Evolution is not observable, repeatable and testable and it is also *not falsifiable* in the broad sense, as formulated by the present day evolutionists. The idea of evolution is not falsifiable because, according to the evolutionists, the critical events of evolution are assumed to have taken place millions and billions of years ago, or they would need tens of thousands of years into the future before scientific experiments could be completed and scientific conclusions could be reached. Murray

Eden, an evolutionist at the Massachusetts Institute of Technology, stated in regard to falsifying the evolutionary theory:

> This cannot be done in evolution, taking it in its broad sense, and this is all I meant when I called it tautologous in the first place. It can, indeed, explain anything . . . but it is still an unfalsifiable theory.

Paul Ehrlich of Stanford University and L. C. Birch of the University of Sidney stated *Scientific Creationism,* H. Morris, p.p. 6 & 7:

> Our theory of evolution . . . cannot be refuted by any possible observation. Every conceivable observation can be fitted into it. It is thus "outside of empirical science" but not necessarily false.

13.   BUT YET DIFFERENT EVOLUTIONARY IDEAS HAVE BEEN FALSIFIED

And yet evolutionists are continually finding fault with each others ideas and arguments and are constantly finding fault with each others reasoning and presentation of evidence. When the evolutionists get through with each other, most of their ideas have been falsified.

Most important, recent evolution is falsified by the general prehistory that precedes the written history of mankind, which shows that prehistoric people were not descendants of apes and savages but of highly advanced, intelligent people. Evolution has also been falsified by the history given in the first nine chapters of Genesis which precedes the history given from the tenth chapter onward. The history given from the tenth chapter of Genesis onward runs parallel to the general history books of the world, so why ignore and reject the first eleven chapters of Genesis and go contrary to the rules of science?

Recent evolution is falsified also by *archeology,* which reveals that advanced civilizations existed in the prehistoric past. Evolution is also falsified by *geology* which shows not merely fossils scattered here and there but multitudes of fossils heaped and mixed together in piles showing that they were not buried gradually here and there but in masses as a result of some world-wide calamity like Noah's Flood. Then the *rock strata of sediments,* placed layer upon layer, do not prove evolution but falsify its ideas of gradual sedimentation. *Zoology* falsifies evolution with no evidence that different kinds of animals and plants have *ever* evolved one from another. *Biology* falsifies evolution with its scientific theory that: Life can only come from life. Therefore the evolutionary theory that organic life evolved from inorganic material is falsified.

There is also the *scientific second law of thermodynamics* which falsifies the idea that all things evolved upward.

Finally, scientist Robert Gentry's book, *Creation's Tiny Mystery*, which is a result of his working with the *pleochroic* (many colored) halos of polonium, gives evidence that the earth and its granite must have been created in a very few minutes, since the half-life of 218 Po is just three minutes. This falsifies the theory that the earth and the universe evolved over billions of years. Robert Gentry, in the preface of his book, p. xii, states:

> The central thesis of this book is that the Creator left decisive evidence enabling us to identify the Genesis rocks of our planet. But genuine evidence for creation falsifies the evolution model of origins, irrespective of how many pieces of the evolutionary puzzle seem to fit together.

14.   CREATION IS ALSO NON-FALSIFIABLE

On the other hand, creation is non-falsifiable because it was not witnessed by human observation and it cannot be tested through experiments. According to the rules of science it cannot be considered a scientific theory or law. Yet, creation has never been proven false.

Professor Stephen Gould, in *Discovery*, May 1981, in an article entitled "Evolution as Fact and Theory," stated;

> Philosopher Karl Popper has argued for decades that the primary criterion of science is the falsifiability of its theories. We can never prove absolutely, but we can falsify. A set of ideas that cannot, in principle, be falsified is not science. [A little further on:] "Scientific creationism" is a self-contradictory, nonsense-phrase precisely because it cannot be falsified. I can envision observations and experiments that would disprove any evolutionary theory I know, but I cannot imagine what potential data would lead creationists to abandon their beliefs. Unbeatable systems are dogma, not science.

Yes, creation is a dogma, a doctrine of the Bible. But creation is logical and reasonable on the basis of a non-material First Cause. Everything must have a first cause including the existence of materials and life. Listen again to the logic and reasoning of Romans 1:20:

> For *the invisible things of him* from the creation of the world are clearly seen, being understood *by the things that are made,* even his *eternal power* and *Godhead [a non-material being];* so that they are without excuse.

Yes, creation is logical and reasonable also on the basis of archeology, geology, the permanent *kinds* in zoology and botany, written history and above all the first nine chapters of Genesis which evolutionists purposely ignore for some anti-God, anti-supernatural reasons.

15.   TRUE SCIENCE DOES NOT SUPPRESS CRITICS

Evolutionists constantly try to suppress and ridicule creationists as not being intelligent and scientific. True science in search of the facts and the truth seek critics to verify or disprove its ideas and hypotheses. Therefore, when evolutionists try to suppress critics because of their beliefs, their status as scientists is extremely questionable. However, since creation is a dogma and belief that affects the eternal welfare of its adherents and others, creationists must therefore of necessity be critical of all contrary beliefs.

16.   SCIENTISM — WORSHIP OF FALSE SCIENCE

Science means "to know" or "to understand." As such it is extremely valuable to all of us in our daily life. All this was part of God's original command to Adam: "Subdue the earth and *have dominion over*" all things on earth. Psalm 8:6 declares: "You have made [man] to have dominion over the works of Your hands. You have put all things under his feet." But the worship of science and scientific achievements become scientism, an idol, and can become dangerous in a number of different ways, like any other idolatrous belief and action. NKJV

1) When science and its achievements are glorified with the purpose of ruling God out of our lives and thinking, science then has become scientism.

2) When science is looked upon as being able to solve all of earth's and man's problems without God, scientism has set in.

3) Above all, when evolution has become a foundational principle in many other fields such as geology, zoology, botany, astronomy, history, and even theology; and when evolution's falsehood is proclaimed, taught and indoctrinated as a scientific fact (as it is almost everywhere today throughout the world), then scientism has become the idolatrous handmaiden of evolution.

As a result of this scientism, evolution has become an idolatrous religion no better than the idols of ancient peoples.

17.   THE BIBLE AND TRUE SCIENCE DO NOT CONFLICT

At times people have made statements such as this: "Science contradicts the Bible" without having any proof for such statements. This is very evidently true of the evolutionists. There is no conflict between true science and the Bible. False science may contradict statements of the Bible or it may make a false interpretation of the original intent of the Bible. Ancient people may have made statements of the Bible appear contrary to what science has established, such as the earth moving around the sun; but there just is no conflict between the Bible and true science. The Bible merely states what the sun appears to be doing, the sun going around the earth, instead of the earth merely turning on its axis. If anyone claims the Bible contains scientific mistakes, he should state and prove just one of them.

Some of the greatest scientists have never had any problem harmonizing science and the Bible. In fact, it was the other way around: science convinced them of the truths of the Bible. Isaac Newton stated that:

Belief in God rested for him chiefly in the admirable order of the universe.

Sir James Jeans stated:

Behind the universe there is a great mathematical Something.

In the book on *Science and Religion,* p. 149, we read:

The science of physics has made it increasingly impossible to accept the idea of chance to explain the origin of the universe. Physics has found design in the origin of life which proclaims the necessity of a Designer . . . So it is with chemistry, biology, anthropology, medicine, astronomy, physiology, psychology and the other sciences. Each one demonstrates the futility of an explanation of life without recourse to a Supreme Being.

True science works with the observed and proven facts and functions of the universe, earth and life. None of these have ever been shown to conflict with the teaching of the Bible. Science has never discovered a single fact that contradicts the Bible.

18.   THE BIBLE'S ANSWER TO FALSE SCIENCE

The answer is given 2000 years ago in the Apostle Paul's advice to young Timothy, I Timothy 6:20-21:

O Timothy, keep that which is committed to thy trust, avoid profane and vain babblings and opposition of *science falsely so called:* which some professing have erred concerning the faith.

XXI.   EVOLUTION IS NOT SCIENTIFIC

Although this chapter appears to be a repetition of the previous chapter, it approaches evolution and science from a different angle. It stresses an important fact: that evolution is *not a fact.*

1.   NO EVIDENCE FOR EVOLUTION

Although evolution is believed by many, if not by most intellectuals, throughout the world to be a fact, there is no real scientific evidence for it anywhere. There is no scientific evidence that evolution took place in the distant, intermediate or recent past, or that it is taking place now, or even that it is possible at all. No theory regarding evolution has ever been proven by observation or by scientific tests. Although evolutionists again and again emphatically declare that evolution is a proven scientific *fact,* based on many scientific proofs, they are unable to provide even one such proof.

No one has ever seen evidence of life beginning to form from non-living elements: of chemical molecules turning into the extremely complex cells of plants and animals that can reproduce, of fish turning into part sea and part land animals, or of such amphibians turning into birds and animals, or of apes changing into people. There is not one bit of evidence that reptiles, birds and mammals evolved from creatures of the sea. Evolutionists have tried for years to find evidence that winged reptiles evolved into birds, but their search has been in vain.

There is no evidence of vertical evolution — of a lower kind of animal developing into a higher kind. If evolutionists could provide such evidence, creationists would be stopped cold. Different kinds of animals are found in the same layers of the earth's sedimentary strata. Evolution cannot explain the extremely wide gulf that exists between life and nonlife, between plant and animal life, nor can evolution explain the origin of the many different kinds of living creatures and why the different kinds of animals and plants are fixed and cannot be crossed. They also cannot explain why no new kinds of creatures are evolving today, or why none have appeared in the past thousand years.

Dr. Ethridge of the British Museum said:

In all this great museum there is not a particle of evidence of transmutation of species. Nine-tenths of the talk of the evolutionists is sheer nonsense, not founded on observation and wholly unsupported by facts.

Dr. Austin Clark of the Smithsonian Institute stated:

> There is not the slightest evidence that any of the major groups [of animals] arose from any other.

One of the most remarkable statements in this regard comes from the mouths of two outstanding evolutionists of today. The *Minneapolis Tribune* of March 9, 1976, printed a picture of anthropologists Richard Leakey and Donald Johanson, and it stated beneath their picture:

> Recent discoveries lead scientists to believe that man 3.75 million years ago was anatomically much more like modern man than was previously thought.

What a confession for evolutionists to make, even though they are off millions of years.

2.   EVOLUTION IS BASED ON MERE ASSUMPTIONS

The entire claim of evolutionists is based on assumptions, including its millions and billions of years. Dr. E. H. Andrews, professor in the University of London stated that even the time-scale and radiometric dating used by the evolutionists is questioned. He stated that such dating which gives hundreds of millions of years to fossil bearing rocks is based on *assumptions* and that these assumptions cannot be justified scientifically.

Because evolution has no scientific evidence for its beliefs and because it cannot give scientific answers to origins and is based merely on assumptions, *it is not scientific*. When evolutionists assume something to be a fact without positive proof, they are resorting to nonscientific methods to establish something as a scientific fact. Evolution is an assumption, a speculation, a belief. Stretching the imagination it might be called a philosophy, but it is not science. It has rightly been referred to as a new kind of mythology, or religion.

Hilbert Siegler summed all this up correctly in stating in *Evolution or Degeneration — Which?*, p. 88:

> No other so-called science on earth is so thoroughly based on a totally unproved assumption; continues to flourish in the face of so many unanswered questions; has so many devotees who do not even understand the theory but insist on calling it a proven fact; and has so many who worship at its materialistic altar, while calling it a science.

3.   EVOLUTIONISTS FALSELY CLAIM THAT THE SCIENCES NEED THE THEORY OF EVOLUTION

One evolutionist, Preston Cloud, JKN. Pub 1977, states:

Any student of morphology, systematics, paleontology, molecular biology, molecular genetics, populations, genetics, population biology, biogeography and a host of other disciplines cannot comprehend them [these sciences or disciplines] without the theory of evolution as a unifying principle. Conversely, each of these disciplines, in turn, provides data in support of the theory of evolution. See p.p. 415-416.

But the data they provide for evolution is not based on tested, proven scientific experiments. Moreover, all these sciences listed could get along nicely and very likely advance more accurately if they were not influenced by the non-scientific principles and methods of evolution.

4.   EVOLUTION IS UNREASONABLE

There are many people today, including many who are true scientists, who, after examining the evolutionary belief, are amazed how unreasonable and illogical the entire idea is in the light of what archeology, geology and earliest recorded history teach and in the light of many evolutionary frauds and evolutionary fallacies. One man wrote:

There is nothing more unreasonable than the creed of the unbeliever, not withstanding all his prattle about the excellence of reason.

Unbelief makes a man illogical and unreasonable, in spite of his assumed wisdom and scientific knowledge.

How could millions of different kinds of plants, fish, birds, animals and man come from one spark of life that has been assumed to have started from chance? Above all how could all these different forms of life evolve when not one kind of life today can be changed into another kind of life or ever has changed in the past thousands of years. How could an ape develop into a man when nothing like it has happened in the history of fossils? How could the mind of man, which is more complex than the most sophisticated computer, have developed by chance, and be reproduced in one human being after another? In the cerebral cortex, there are ten billion neurons, processing ten trillion bits every second. And the cortex is only a small part of the brain. Although the computer, which the mind of man developed, is complicated, the mind of man is still much more complicated. To believe that the unbelievably complex brain of man is merely the result of chance is totally unreasonable.

A prominent scientist referred to by newspaper columnist George Will declared:

If all the banging and sloshing of the universe produced, through sheer randomness, mankind, that was an improbability comparable to a typhoon blowing through a junkyard and producing a computer.

Claiming that a single cell can develop all by itself into a human body or even into an animal with all its complex organs without an Originator behind it, is more ridiculous than claiming that a piece of iron or plastic or wood or cloth can develop all by itself into a car or a watch or a computer or a house or a factory or a dress, together with all their complexities. To make such claims is not scientific, much less rational, reasonable or logical.

On November 24, 1985, I took time out to watch one of the evolutionary TV programs on the Public TV station regarding the "Creation of the Universe." It was a most pitiful attempt to explain the origin of atoms in the universe, galaxies and especially the Big Bang. Evidently their creator god is the little atom that blew up in the Big Bang in a tiny fraction of a second to create all the matter of the universe without any design behind it. The entire theory of evolution is filled with more miraculous events than God presents in the Bible. Evidently miracles are acceptable to the evolutionists no matter how unreasonable and ridiculous they may be, just as long as they are not performed by some prematerial, spiritual being, and above all not by the God of the Bible.

5.   EVOLUTIONISTS DISAGREE AMONG THEMSELVES

It is natural for evolutionists to disagree among themselves since their assumptions are merely the concoctions of fallible, erring men, having theories without any scientific foundation. This disagreement among evolutionists goes back to the days of their arch-evolutionist Charles Darwin. *The New York Times Literary Supplement* (June 9, 1903) under the caption of "The Riddle of Evolutionists," stated:

No one possessed of a sense of humor can contemplate without amusement the battle of evolution, encrimsoned with the gore of innumerable combatants, encumbered with the corpses of the slain. [Then follows a long list of the various aspects of evolutionists. Then it continues:] Never was seen such a melee. The humor of it is that they all claim to represent "Science."

Today evolution is attacked also by reputable scientists.

A *London Times* writer, Christopher Booker, who is an evolutionist, said:

> It was a beautifully simple and attractive theory. The only trouble was that, as Darwin was himself at least partly aware, it was full of colossal holes . . . A century after Darwin's death . . . A state of almost open war exists among evolutionists themselves.

Evolutionists are repeatedly contradicting each other. What one teaches with definite certainty, another disagrees with, with equally emphatic certainty. Britian's *New Scientist* stated:

> An increasing number of scientists, most particularly a growing number of evolutionists . . . argue that Darwinian evolutionary theory is no genuine scientific theory at all . . . many of the critics have the highest intellectual credentials.

6.   EVOLUTION — A FRAUD

Yes, evolution is not only unreasonable but also a fraud and misrepresentation. Skulls and skeletons have been manipulated and pictures have been made and touched up to bring out the desired effect as occurred in the *National Geographic,* November 1985. (See Chapter XI, Part 5.) Then there are the infamous Piltdown man and, above all, the Nebraska man that falsely turned the tables in favor of the evolutionists in the famous Scopes "monkey trial" in Dayton, Tennessee in 1925. In 1926, a Viennese zoologist, Paul Kamerer, claimed he had caused two completely different species of salamanders to inherit each others characteristics. But when his work was examined, it was found that the "acquired characteristics" were faked, probably with India ink. Shortly thereafter he committed suicide.

Again evolutionists are guilty of fraud when they speak of certain birds and animals being 100 million, 200 million or more years old, without any scientific proof for such claimed ages. Immense ages are assumed from radioactivity by extrapolating backwards. They proclaim these fantastic ages to impress the naive and simple-minded and to make themselves appear as though they were the super-intelligent, the intelligentsia, the enlightened — thus they try to get people to fall down and worship the new Baal of evolution. Here they followed the example of Hitler's famous statement:

> If you must lie, lie boldly and make your lies big enough if you want people to believe them.

The past 125 years will go down in history as the most gullible of all times when men believed the fables of evolution and the lies of Satan;

and educated men propagated them with public tax money. Evolution is guilty of fraud, hoaxes and misrepresentation more harmful than all the financial and other frauds in the world, for which governments have punished the perpetrators.

The teaching of *creation* does not harm anyone either on earth or for eternity. *But* what condemnation awaits those who went out of their way to mislead the little ones:

It would be better for him if a millstone were hung around his neck, and he were thrown into the sea than that he should offend (mislead) one of these little ones. (Luke 17:2)

7.   EVOLUTION IS DECLARED TO BE A FACT, WITHOUT ANY SCIENTIFIC PROOF

In spite of the fact that evolution is not scientific, is unreasonable and a fraud, evolutionists continually blare forth that evolution is a fact without giving any scientific proof. In an article in the *Reader's Digest* (September 1982), p. 9, an introductory statement is made:

[E]vidence gathered during the last two centuries - from geology, paleontology, molecular biology and many other scientific disciplines - makes evolution a virtual certainty.

But no evidence of any kind is provided. On February 2, 1984, Dr. Steven Shore, associate professor of Astronomy, in a debate with Dr. Duane Gish, began by asserting that evolution is a fact. In another debate on February 20, 1985, Dr. John Patterson at Iowa State University stated flatly that evolution was a fact doubted by no competent scientist, with only the mechanism in doubt. Again no scientific evidences are provided.

On February 17, 1987, Richard Leakey, who digs for fossils in Africa, speaking to a large crowd at Mankato State University, Minnesota, compared evolution to gravity:

It astounds me today that people still consider evolution to be a *mere* theory . . . Do you know that gravity is also covered by a theory . . . Similarly, there is no question about the fact of evolution.

What illogical reasoning this is! Gravity is not a *mere* theory. It is a proven fact, proven in countless experiments. But evolution has never been proven. It is not even a theory. At most it is a guess, an assumption or presumption.

In 1961, a *Life* nature library proclaimed evolution to be a fact when it wrote:

The theory of evolution was substantiated and proved by the undisputable remains of the animals that lived and died during the long climb from the first organized forms to the intermediate predecessors of man; only the capping evidence of man's emergence remained to be found.

But again no evidence is provided except the huge imagined jumps from invertebrates to fish to amphibians to reptiles to mammals to primates to apes to man, with immense unproven gaps between the creatures. To make evolution even slightly plausible, intermediate animals should have existed.

In this regard, Richard Carrington in his book, *The Story of our Earth* (1956) wrote, p. 187:

[W]hat is undeniably true is that at some time in the past a group of animals existed from which men, apes, monkeys, tarsiers and the lemurs all derived.

No proof — just another guess or assumption. In stupid illogicality he declares on page 185:

Today it is no longer necessary, as it was even fifty years ago, to defend the simple fact that men, apes and monkeys belong to the same great family.

But where is the evidence for such unfounded beliefs?

In the March 1965 issue of the *American Scientist,* Dr. Rene Dubos wrote in an article, "Humanistic Biology":

Most enlightened persons now accept as a fact that everything in the cosmos — from heavenly bodies to human beings — has developed and continues to develop through evolutionary processes.

See how the claim that evolution is a fact is referred to as something that enlightened people accept. But that is no proof. Many highly enlightened people have been severely misled and harmed by people who claim to be experts. I will refer to *experts* a little further on.

But I must refer now to at least a few prominent evolutionary so-called experts of *recent* years. Sir Julian Huxley, a world famous evolutionary biologist and grandson of Thomas Huxley, stated at the time of the Darwinian Centennial Celebration at the University of Chicago (1960):

The first point to make about Darwin's theory is that it is no longer a theory, but a fact. No serious scientist would deny the fact that evolution has occurred, just as he would not deny the fact that the earth goes around the sun.

What miserable logic! That the earth goes around the sun has been proven in many exacting ways, but evolution has no proven evidence to give it even the rating of a theory. It is outright stupidity and arrogance to even compare the idea of evolution to the fact that the earth is going around the sun.

Another example of a poor attempt to prove evolution to be a fact was given by Professor Stephen Gould of Harvard University in *Discovery* (May 1981):

> Our confidence that evolution occurred centers upon three general arguments. First, we have abundant, direct, observational evidence of evolution in action, from both the field and the laboratory. It ranges from countless experiments on change in nearly everything about fruit flies subjected to artificial selection in the laboratory to the famous British moths that turned black when industrial soot darkened the trees upon which they rested. The moths gain protection from sharp-sighted bird predators by blending into the background.

I did not think that such a supposedly intellectual man as Dr. Gould would refer to the experiments with fruit flies and the increase in black moth as evidence for evolution being a fact. The fact is that after endless experiments with generations of fruit flies, they still were only fruit flies; and the increase in black moths was not due to evolution but to the fact that the *poor*-sighted birds could find the light moths more easily on the soot-darkened trees than the dark colored moths, and if some moths would have turned black, they still would be only moths.

Another example regarding evolution being a fact has to do with the Big Bang and the universe. Joseph Silk in his book, *The Big Bang* (October 1979), stated in his Preface, p. XIV:

> The bulk of the Big Bang theory, however, rests more on fact than on speculation. In addition the relative simplicity of the Big Bang theory favors it over more exotic cosmologies.

But the Big Bang could hardly be a scientific fact. The Big Bang could not create order, any more than any explosion has ever created order. The Big Bang, such as the evolutionists concocted could only create the greatest of all explosions and disorder. The universe is a closed system and according to the scientific second law of thermodynamics, a Big Bang could only create more discord and decay as time went on, instead of the imagined assumption of evolution, that an orderly universe evolved out of a Big Bang.

Another poor attempt to prove that evolution is a fact was a statement made by Niles Eldredge in *The Monkey Business* (1982):

Evolution is a fact as much as the idea that the earth is shaped like a ball. But both facts remain ideas — falsifiable scientific ideas.

This again is extremely poor logic. The earth has been proven to be round, in many different ways, so it is not merely an idea but a proven scientific fact. But evolution has never been proven. However much of evolution has been falsified, as I have shown. To put a guess, an assumption, or an idea on the same level with a proven fact is not only extremely poor logic but an extremely poor attempt at trying to claim to be scientific.

The folly of declaring evolution to be a fact has been effectively and clearly summarized by Dr. Robert Gentry in his *Creation's Tiny Mystery* (October 1986), p. 85:

But evolution is neither a confirmed theory nor a fact. If life actually originated by chance, as evolution requires, evolutionary biologists should be able to reproduce that process in laboratory experiments. Still, despite decades of intensive efforts and generous government funding, all attempts to produce life from inert matter have proved fruitless. Likewise, if life evolved by the transformation of one major group into another, where are the numerous transitional forms expected on the basis of evolution? Biologists could long ago have put to rest embarrassing questions about the general absence of transitional forms in the fossil record, if they had produced examples of missing links under laboratory conditions. All attempts to create new forms in the laboratory, such as inducing mutations through nuclear irradiation, have produced only variations of existing types.

The reason I discussed the claim that evolution is a fact at such length is that, as you have seen, it is the evolutionist's only hope of gaining the confidence of hoped-for followers. It is the old story that if you repeat a lie frequently enough people might believe you, without you providing evidence or proof.

8.   EXPERTS

Many times claims are bolstered and propped up to be facts by claiming that they have the backing of experts, or that the experts say so. This is especially so with the claims of the evolutionists. In many cases they claim that experts in the scientific field back up their claims. While there have been true scientists who have added their names to evolutionist's claims, in most cases the experts were only fellow evolutionists. I have already cited the statements of many true scientists who have rejected the claims of the evolutionists. There also have been many cases where one evolutionist contradicted and rejected the claim of another evolutionist. So, appealing to the testimony and statements of experts proves nothing. In most of these cases the so-called experts are only guessing.

One outstanding case among expert psychiatrists is the case of John W. Hinckley, Jr, who shot President Reagan. In response to a letter from the *Boston Herald American,* he wrote:

> I found it a little absurd that four doctors could find me delusional and psychotic while four other doctors said I was only a loner with a couple of minor personality problems. In my case, not one of the doctors that examined me learned what is really going on inside my head. Some of them were way off base in certain areas.

Professional economists are many times far off in their economic forecasts. George Meany, who had headed the AFL-CIO, said that economics was the only profession where a man could have a lifelong reputation as an expert without ever being right.

The *Claremont Letter* of 1985 states:

> How many times has Henry Kaufman caused the market to plummet by making one of his dire interest-rate predictions? In the last three years, Henry Kaufman and most other "top" analysts have been repeatedly wrong. They make a prediction, and then within a few weeks the market is doing precisely what they said it would not.

Stock experts have already predicted 28 of the last eight recessions. (Yes, 28 out of the 8 is correct).

In 1985, Dr. Morton Shuman, a self-made investment millionaire, wrote:

> I have found that most "experts" are unfortunately wrong. I used to host a weekly TV show in Canada. Once a year I did a program on investing. After one such show, I walked away in utter amazement at the foolishness of what the "experts" had to say . . . They were unabashed in making pronouncements and

recommendations that, in many cases, would lead their clients to slaughter.

But the worst experts have been in the field of forecasting the trend of the stock market. The *Hulbert Financial Digest,* which checks out the investment newsletters with their expert's advice, stated in the fall of 1985 that many investors who heeded the advice of these "experts" have been butchered. One outstanding case was Joe "I'm the Greatest" Granville. Granville has led thousands of people to the slaughter in spite of his claim of giving expert advice. In October 1985, he predicted a severe market decline between then and Thanksgiving, with the Dow tumbling to 1,200 or below. Instead it went up to 1,500.

But the worst case of leading people to the slaughter was when the stock market turned extremely bullish in August of 1982 and yet Joe Granville kept preaching bear-market advice and worst of all had people, including widows, shorting the market. Many people lost *hundreds of thousands* of dollars on such "expert's?" advice. And the amazing thing is that this expert gave bear market advice for five years through *the wildest raging bull market* in the history of the New York Stock Exchange. Finally, in September of 1987, when the market had already turned "south" on the way to one of the steepest declines in history, he turned bullish, declaring that the Dow Jones Industrials will no doubt get to around 3,000 by the end of 1987 and probably will go still higher in 1988. On October 19, 1987, as we all know, the market plunged over 500 points. And all this took place in spite of his expert claim that he would infallibly "get you in at the bottom and out at the top," and in spite of the fact that the stock market had already gone too high without a major adjustment and correction.

The same kind of "expert" advice, with all kinds of wild figures that you have among the stock market advisors, exists also among the so-called experts in the field of evolution. The evolutionary experts throw around the millions and billions of years without any positive proof. How many children and also adults have been misled for eternity by such so-called expert advice and information! They are being misled into *eternal slaughter.* See p. 276

The mere fact that many of the stars, galaxies and quasars are millions of light years away from the earth (and it is questioned that they are), does not prove that the universe is billions of years old. The same God who created the earth, the solar system, the stars and the galaxies could also in creating a *mature* universe place the light rays in place instantly when he created a mature universe. It is *not* as the *Minneapolis Tribune,* August 27, 1984, stated:

[This] could mean that we are seeing light that originated billions of years ago, at the beginning of time, from material that was part of the original expansion of matter which created the universe.

9.   CHANCE

In the final analysis, the evolutionists ascribe their entire idea of evolution to chance. To claim that our entire universe and the intricate and precisely designed rotation and movement of our earth happened by chance, is about as reasonable as to claim that the world's greatest literature was composed by a group of wild monkeys running wild in a print shop. Evolutionists have never been able to explain scientifically how the universe came into existence. The Big Bang idea is only a wild assumption, a desperate attempt, which runs counter to the existing laws of science and nature. And where did the original matter of the universe come from? Why did the explosion take place? What force caused the original explosion? Dr. M. W. Smart, an English astronomer, in 1951 declared that the universe cannot be the product of blind, evolving chance. He wrote:

When we study the universe and appreciate its grandeur and orderliness; it seems to me that we are led to the recognition of a Creative Power and Cosmic Purpose that transcends all that our limited minds can comprehend.

When we consider our earth, how it day after day, month after month, year after year, and century after century revolves on its axis at just the right speed, so that our days and nights are just at the right and varying length of days; and our earth goes around the sun at the right distance away and at the same uniform speed century after century and is tilted just the right tilt, so that we have the right and varying length of seasons — all this certainly is not due to mere chance. At the time I am writing this, December 22, 1987, we have reached the shortest day of the year again. We know that now we can look forward to lengthening days, and before long to another delightful spring and summer with all their fruits and vegetables to enjoy. Thank God that unreliable chance is not in control of all this!

In 1946, A. Cressy Morrison, a former president of the New York Academy of Sciences, wrote an article for the *Reader's Digest,* December 1946, entitled "Seven Reasons Why a Scientist Believes in God." He pointed out many facts known to science which he says:

prove that our universe was designed and erected by a great engineering intelligence. [He also wrote:] Because of these and a host of other examples, there is one chance in a million that life on our planet was an accident.

This takes us again to the origin of life. It too is a great mystery that could never have happened or developed by chance. If life happened and was activated by a chance stroke of lightning hitting a pool of amino acids, why hasn't this process happened again and again throughout the recent centuries? Sir Fred Hoyle, a well-known astronomer, stated, (Impact, Dec. 1984, p. 1):

. . . as biochemists discover more and more about the awesome complexity of life, it is apparent that its chances of originating by accident are so minute they they can be completely ruled out. Life cannot have risen by chance.

Although Hoyle does not claim to be a Christian, he believes that there must have been some "Intelligence" behind the emergence of life on earth. Hoyle points out that the chances of the simplest forms of life developing themselves are about as hopeless as a blindfolded man ever solving Rubik's Cube. He gave another example of life happening by itself. It has about as much chance as a tornado blowing through a junkyard containing all the parts of a 747 and the tornado accidentally assembling the parts of the 747 so that it would be ready after the tornado for an immediate commercial flight.

Plain common sense demands that a designing supreme Intelligence is needed to explain the origin of everything in the universe. Looking at all the superb, excellent, majestic and supreme engineering achievements that are present in this universe and on this earth and solar system, one following logical reasoning must declare that only a supreme, intelligent Masterbuilder and Engineer could have done this. James Maxwell declared:

There never was a theory of the origin of the universe that did not need a God to make it go.

Even ancient Roman Cicero, who had no knowledge of Scripture, declared in, *De Natura Deorum* (of the Nature of God):

The most potent cause of the belief was the uniform motion and revolution of the heavens, and the varied groupings and ordered beauty of the sun, moon and stars, the very sight of which was in itself enough to prove that these things are not the mere effect of chance. When a man goes into a house, or a wrestling-school, or a public assembly and observes in all that goes on —

arrangement, regularity and system — he cannot possibly suppose that these things come about without a cause; he realizes that there is someone who presides and controls. Therefore, with the vast movements and phases of the heavenly bodies, and these ordered processes of a multitude of enormous masses of matter, which throughout the countless ages of the past have never in the smallest degree played false, he is compelled to infer that these mighty world motions are regulated by some Mind . . . Yet what better name is there for this than "god."

Yes, of all the creeds and beliefs existing in the world today, both religious and nonreligious, deistic or man-worshiping humanistic, none is more unreasonable, absurd, non-scientific and ridiculous than the creed of the evolutionists. Their beliefs require far greater faith than any religious creed of the present or of the past.

IN SUMMARY

On the basis of:

1. The known facts of sound geology, that the surface of this earth was not formed gradually.
2. The known facts of archeology, that the first people in history were highly intelligent and advanced.
3. The known facts regarding plants (botany) and animals (zoology), that they cannot be changed one into another.
4. The complexity of the many different organs of mankind and animals, that they could not have developed functionally all at one time.
5. The impossibility of all things developing by chance.
6. The impossibility of one kind of creature changing into a different kind or species.
7. Cause and effect.
8. The perfect operation of the earth, of the solar system, and of the universe.
9. The continual PERPETUAL MOTION of the earth and solar system in precise order. They just keep going on and on at about the same speed.
10. The factual, known history of mankind.
11. The factual history given in the Bible, that the evolutionists ignore and reject.
12. The proven laws of science.
13. And ordinary common sense and logic.

On the basis of all of the above:

EVOLUTION IS TOTALLY AND SCIENTIFICALLY IMPOSSIBLE
and
The IDEA of evolution is the most ridiculous absurd, foolish, illogical, non-scientific, impossible idea ever conceived by the minds of educated people.

See the more than 32 reasons why evolution is not scientific, p. 404ff.

XXII. EVOLUTION IS AN ANTI-RELIGIOUS BELIEF AND AT THE SAME TIME A RELIGION IN ITSELF

This takes us to the antireligious nature of evolution and the fact that it is at the same time a religion in itself.

1. EVOLUTION IS GUESSING, STORYTELLING, FICTION

First we must consider that evolution is mere guessing, assuming, storytelling, and fiction. We must give Isaac Asimov credit for at least calling much of his writings "science fiction." Correctly, they should be called "evolution fiction." True science is never fiction. You ask evolutionists about their hypotheses and theories and they will say that they are "scientific guesses." But a guess in science may be false. A scientific worker may guess in setting up a hypothesis, but he should not try to pass on such guessing as a scientific theory.

Good examples of mere guessing are the ideas that many men had regarding the moon. Before Apollo 11 returned, all kinds of guesses were prevalent, as I showed before. Some believed that the astronauts might sink in the depths of moon dust. Other faulty guesses were that the moon dust could be poisonous, filled with moon germs, or other hazards and plagues.

Isaac Asimov in *The Collapsing Universe* (1977), p. 90, stated:

In 1927 the Belgian Astronomer George Lemaître (1894-1966) suggested . . . that a certain number of billions of years ago the matter of the universe was all in one place and formed a structure he called the *primeval atom.* Others have called it the *cosmic egg.* How long the cosmic egg existed, or how it was formed, Lemaître did not venture to guess, but at some moment, it must have exploded.

Lemaître could not guess how long that primeval atom existed or how it was formed, but he definitely did guess that it existed just as many other evolutionary ideas are mere guesses. This is well stated by Ruth Moore in her *The Earth We Live One* (1956), p. 292:

But with the conclusion that the earth, its moon, the sun, and the planets evolved from a primordial cloud of dust, agreement ends. Beyond this point the uncertainties, the unknowns, the conflicts are limitless.

On page 400 she continues with guesses fellow evolutionists have made regarding lead and the resulting guess as to the age of the earth:

Arthur Holmes assumed that when the earth began it contained no lead 207 and that all the lead 207 present in the modern crust had therefore been generated from uranium 235. Calculating the time it would have taken the lead to form, he arrived at an age of 3.3 billion years for the earth.

On such false assumptions and guesses the billions of years for the age of this earth have been arrived at.

Jacob Dell in *I Still Believe in God,* stated correctly on p. 17:

Where did it [matter and the universe, etc.] come from? Where is it going? Science has no answer to these questions, for to answer them one must either guess or believe, and neither guessing nor believing is science. The moment one attempts to answer them one steps out of the field of science into that of philosophical speculations or that of faith . . . A true scientist must deal with facts.

Yes, proven, verifiable and falsifiable facts.

All that the evolutionists try to pass off as science through the news media is not only guessing but also plain *storytelling.* A good example was given in the *Life* nature library (1964), On p. 111 it stated:

If life began as a molecule with the miraculous capacity to reproduce itself, developing later as a simple cell, and then into a cluster of a few soft cells, it could not possibly leave even the shadowiest imprint behind. Yet somewhere on earth, somehow life indeed began, possibly more than two billion years ago. [Page 112 continues:] The bony jaw . . . spread throughout the fish population . . . Even so, these early jawed fishes were themselves replaced by different and overwhelmingly successful descendants. Mutations and selection produced better fins for better swimming. ventured out on the land. It is a plausible guess that they lived in streams which dried in the drought of summer into a few scattered pools. Did the fish struggle and flop from one drying pool to another with more water? No one knows, but those fish that were able to stay out of the water for a longer time certainly would have been the survivors and would have left behind progeny with their own greater ability to breathe in the air.

The storytelling continues, p. 113:

The ichtyostega combined a fish tail with lungs and well-developed legs and feet. With their lungs and "walking feet," these early fish-out-of-water had a whole new source of food open to them. They could crawl along the banks of streams and snap up the insects which were beginning to swarm there. The earth lay open before them — for no other vertebrates were there to contest it.

Just like that it happened! And where did the insects come from? The account continues:

In the fullness of time [a Bible expression] mutations and selection again performed their wonders. Some of the amphibians developed an egg . . . With their new found freedom from the water, the reptiles literally took over the earth, and the "age of reptiles" began . . . As time went on . . . some of the reptiles returned to the water whence their ancestors had come, though they never went back to their ancestral structures. Those which returned continued to breathe with their lungs, while their reptilian legs became modified into paddles and fins. Some of these marine reptiles looked strikingly like the modern whales and porpoises.

How fantastic. In this story the evolutionists provide us with even *reverse* evolution: land animals becoming whales. Even more amazing:

Still other reptiles ventured into the air.

Richard Carrington in *The Story of Our Earth* (1956) provides us good examples of other evolutionary stories, p. 24:

At that time the Earth had no atmosphere . . . But gradually . . . clouds began to form . . . rain began to fall.

All this is *supposed to have happened* all by itself. Where did the clouds come from? Where did the rain come from? The moon also has had no atmosphere all these claimed billions of years, but no clouds or rain have shown up there. On page 73 he states that:

we can reasonably assume, This guess [p. 75] aids us in our speculations, [p. 121] for the purpose of our story, [p. 198] we can only guess at.

On pages 203 and 204 he admits the evolutionists guessed very wrongly in regard to the age of the Piltdown man which turned out to be a total hoax.

One of the most famous of the evolutionary stories is how the giraffes got such long necks. It has been supposed that as the giraffes stretched their necks more and more to reach leaves on higher branches, the necks grew longer and longer. It is a clever little fable, and even primitive people have developed fables like this. *But* in all the fossils ever found of giraffes there never has been found one with a shorter neck during the assumed evolution of giraffes.

The difference between children reading Aesop's fables and older people reading the fantasies of the evolutionists is that children know that Aesop's fables are just make-believe, fables and not facts.

2.   EVOLUTION IS AN ANTI-RELIGIOUS PHILOSOPHY

If evolutionary fables were only guessing and storytelling, they would not be so dangerous, not only to children but also to some adults; but they are an anti-religion and at the same time a religion unto itself. To make matters still more deceptive and dangerous, evolutionists try to hide their beliefs under the guise of being scientific and factual.

Evolution has made God unnecessary and nonexisting. Dr. Alfred Rehwinkel in his book *The Wonders of Creation,* p.p. 140f, correctly stated that evolutionists:

have deified a vague, impersonal, irrational, nonexisting force called evolution. This force operates solely on the principle of chance and accident, completely ignoring the law of cause and effect; it does not have even a semblance of reason or experience to support it. Yet they regard this "something", which is "nothing", as the creator of the universe with all its wonders. This new form of idolatry, compared with even the most extravagant and naive mythology of darkest heathenism, is more irrational and absurd.

Dr. E. H. Andrews in *Is Evolution Scientific?* stated, p. 3:

We must therefore recognize evolutionary theory for what it is, a philosophy (indeed for some, a religion) and not basically a scientific discipline at all . . . In the thinking of most people evolution has achieved its initial objective of making redundant a belief in God. If man, along with all animate nature, is the product of this "blind" process of evolution, then God is either nonexistent or at best the manufactured product of our own social consciousness.

At the Nobel Conference XVIII, St. Peter, Minnesota (October 5-6, 1982), the antireligious attitude of the evolutionary speakers was very evident. Vernon Harley, member of the Board of Directors of Bible-Science Association, stated in a letter to *The [Mankato] Free Press:*

The various speakers did not hesitate to express their disdain and actual animosity toward religious creationists, many of whom are top-ranking scientists. Various essayists bitterly denounced the creationist position as anti-intellectual, anti-scientific . . . Many of these remarks were actually slanderous, yet the conference made no provision for those being attacked to respond.

And how many times have children been ridiculed by evolutionary teachers for their religious beliefs and for not accepting the "millions and billions of years" ideas of the evolutionists?

The book, *The Battle for Creation,* by Dr. Henry Morris and Dr. Duane Gish, p. 9, mentions in regard to debating evolutionists:

> The remainder of Dr. Kuijt's prepared statement consisted of a diatribe against the Bible, Christianity, and Christians! Thus Dr. Kuijt, although specifically demanding that no Christian testimony be given, spent the bulk of his time giving his own atheistic religious testimony. He did not present any scientific argument in support of evolution, nor did he attempt to refute any of the scientific evidence presented by Dr. Gish . . . His presentation thus uniquely illustrated Dr. Gish's claim . . . that evolution was as religious as creation.

Drs. Morris and Gish encountered the same attitudes and lack of scientific evidence in numerous other debates with evolutionists in the universities of our country and Canada. *Acts and Facts* (December 1985), p. 4, reports:

> Dr. Patterson repeatedly attacked the Bible, Christian theology and creationists, while limiting his scientific material primarily to evidence for minor variations. His continued emphasis on religion rather than science finally provoked the moderator's intervention.

If belief in God (theism) is a religious belief, dogma or teaching, so is the denial or rejection of God, or a belief that there is no God (a-theism — without God) a religious dogma, teaching or belief. Evolution and atheism go hand in hand. Because evolution is constantly being taught in many public schools and the students are being indoctrinated in it, evolutionary beliefs and atheism have become the established religion of these schools, contrary to the First Amendment of the U.S. Constitution. This shall be treated more fully further on.

The evolutionists are very clever. One of the best methods of defense is to take the offensive. Evolutionists cleverly take the offensive by denying that their beliefs have a religious or antireligious connotation or connection. Niles Eldredge in *The Monkey Business* (1982), p.p. 145-6, declares:

But if evolution has served as the basis of the peculiar ethics of some individuals, does that make evolution a "religion," as some creationists claim? Certainly not — though this is precisely what Nell Segraves & Company argued in their "Scopes II" case in California early in 1981. To the Segraves, creationism isn't science so much as evolution is religion — an aspect, if you will, of the more general religion of "secular humanism". But no practicing scientists invoke the supernatural in their work — a cardinal rule of the trade — whereas all religions worthy of the name *do* embrace a concept of the supernatural. [Emphasis his]

To be religious and antireligious does not merely mean one has to "invoke the supernatural." It means and includes any system of beliefs, ethics and conduct over against others. Webster's dictionary defines religion in these words:

Any system of beliefs, practices, ethical values, etc. resembling, suggestive of, or likened to such a system; as humanism is his *religion*. (See p. 349 for a fuller definition.)

The evolutionists definitely do have a system of beliefs in rejecting creation and denying the existence of a creator; and they do have a system of religious and ethical values, in that they believe mankind does not need a God and that it can take care of itself without God.

To be religious, one does not need to make reference to the supernatural. Although the idea of evolution does not "embrace the concept of the supernatural," yet the evolutionists in promulgating their ideas are teaching and promoting the religious idea that there is no God and at the same time a religious belief that opposes the religious belief in creation. So they are promoting an antireligious idea that opposes religion.

Eldredge continues, p. 146:

That biologists these days continue to see no alternative to evolution as an explanation of how we got here is far from sufficient grounds for labeling the practice of evolutionary biology a "religion."

The mere fact (that evolutionary biologists can see no "alternative to evolution" but oppose the conflicting alternatives given in the Bible) makes evolutionary biology an antireligious belief or creed. It makes it an antireligion.

Niles Eldredge tries to deny the religious side of the evolutionary idea by ignoring its anti-religious and its anti-supernatural teachings.

Evolution just cannot tolerate a higher, nonmaterial, supernatural, creating Cause or Being, no matter how logical and reasonable such a creating Being or Force may be for the explanation of all material things, both inanimate and animate.

Eldredge says: "But no practicing scientists invoke the supernatural in their work." Yes, it is correct that no true scientists do this, but the evolutionists do invoke the supernatural with all their evolutionary fables in regard to origins. The supernatural in their religion is that they give credit to natural material things doing supernatural things, by trying to make material things go contrary to the natural course and laws of material things. They say that the inanimate things of this earth finally developed into animate things, even though true science has stated that life can only come from life. The evolutionists claim the supernatural for the inanimate, and that has become their religious belief.

The statement, "But no practicing scientists invoke the supernatural in their work," is another clever, deceitful attempt to mislead people, by trying to make people believe that evolutionists are scientists.

Evolutionists with their accompanying "no-God" and "no-creation" ideas are fostering anti-creation, anti-religious and religious ideas. They see that there is a universe that could not come out of nothing or create itself according to the first law of thermodynamics, and yet they will not admit that there is a nonmaterial power that could have made it. Religiously, they are *a*-theists, *without* God and *against* God. Napoleon stated it correctly:

It is strange what men can believe, as long as it is not in the Bible.

Yes, how can the evolutionists begin their history that corresponds with Genesis chapter twelve onward, and then totally ignore and fight against chapters one to eleven, that give the prehistory they are searching for in vain? The foolishness of evolutionists was well stated by Isaac Asimov, evolution fiction writer, who wrote many books:

Emotionally I am an atheist. I don't have the evidence to prove that God doesn't exist, but I so strongly suspect he doesn't that I don't want to waste my time.

3.   HOWEVER EVOLUTION AT THE SAME TIME IS *A RELIGION IN ITSELF*

Comparing creation and evolution, one can rightly state that *creation in essence and on the basis of logic and reason is truly scientific.* On the other hand *evolution* requires greater faith and therefore *is just as religious,* or more so, than creationism. Science is based on definite knowledge which has been observed, tested repeatedly and proven. Science therefore is not something one merely believes to be true. However, evolution, which has been assumed to have taken place in the past, cannot be proven and tested. It can only be believed. It is therefore a matter of faith, of something that one believes just as the creationists believe the exact opposite. Christians accept the fact of creation by faith and evolutionists accept the idea of evolution by faith. However, Christian faith is not based on the changing opinions of men, but upon the eternal never-changing truth of the Creator's Word.

Some people have the mistaken idea that faith and religion belong only in connection with faith in and worship of a Supreme Being. However, many have put their trust and faith in themselves, in their knowledge and wisdom, in their skills and abilities, in "I am the greatest;" and thus they worship themselves and other human beings. How many people idolize and worship musicians, athletes and others as though they were gods! How many ancient people practiced idolatrous religion by worshiping themselves, their forefathers or mere inanimate objects! The belief, the faith, the religion of evolutionists is not one bit better. As far as religion is concerned evolutionists believe one thing, creationists another, and they stand in opposition to each other. It is as George Herscher put it in *Letters To Church and State* magazine, September 1987: "If creationism is considered a religion, then evolution, its antithesis, is also a religion."

The entire idea of evolution is based on belief and faith in its suppositions. Professor L. T. Moore in *The Dogma of Evolution,* p. 160, wrote:

> The more one studies paleontology, the more certain one becomes that evolution is based on faith alone; exactly the same sort of faith which it is necessary for one to have when he encounters the great mysteries of religion.

Because evolution cannot be tested and proven scientifically, it must be accepted by faith, on the basis of the opinions and mere assertions of evolutionists. Dr. N. Heribert-Nilsson, Director of the Botanical Institute in Lund University, Sweden, stated:

> My attempt to demonstrate evolution by an experiment carried on for more than 40 years has completely failed . . . The idea of an evolution rests on pure belief.

Paul Ehrlich and L. C. Birch in *Evolutionary History and Population Biology* (1967) stated:

Our theory of evolution . . . is thus outside of empirical science
. . . no one can think of ways in which to test it. Evolutionary ideas
. . . have become part of an evolutionary dogma accepted by most
of us as part of our training.

Yes, just as children in church catechetical classes are taught the dogmas
or beliefs of the Bible, so the students in public schools are taught the
dogmas or beliefs of evolution. Since evolution cannot be proven by
observations and tests, it must be accepted in faith. The origin of the
universe is a matter of faith and belief and all other evolutionary ideas
on origins are also a matter of faith and belief. In the hands of
evolutionists, these ideas have become dogma and not proven scientific
laws.

Even after evolutionists have been shown that evolution has no
scientific foundation, some continue to say: "I still believe in evolution."
Therefore their belief is a matter of faith and not of science. So many
evolutionary ideas and so-called theories have fallen by the wayside
during the past 100 years, that one would think the whole idea would
have been discredited, discarded, disavowed and repudiated by now.
Yet it is surprising how strong the hold is on the minds of many men,
even on highly educated men. They cling to it with a religious fervor
stronger than that of Christians. Yes, they many times cling to their faith
and belief even though they are not able to find any convincing evidences
to support their beliefs.

It seems as though evolutionists will believe anything, no matter how
incredible the fable might be, even that life evolved from the simplest
cells to highly developed mankind. To believe all the evolutionary tales
that are told in regard to the origin of the universe and all that is in it;
— (small cells developed from dead matter; the cells turned into fish;
some fish turned into sea animals and some into land creatures; these,
in turn changed into reptiles, and some of the reptiles into mammals,
apes, and finally man) — all this requires an astounding faith and belief.
To say that all life evolved from one cell, even though no one has ever
seen one kind of creature evolving into a higher kind, requires greater
faith than to believe a nonmaterial power created all material things and
life itself. The faith and belief required by a believer in the Bible is very
small compared to the faith required of an evolutionist. The believer in
the Bible at least has a nonmaterial Cause. Science requires a cause for
every resulting effect. Evolutionists do not have even a first cause for
what they believe.

The faith of an evolutionist has to be greater because it goes counter to the laws of established, proven science. Professor L. Harrison Matthews, a leading British evolutionary biologist, wrote in the introduction to the 1971 edition of Darwin's *Origin of Species*, p. x:

The fact of evolution is the backbone of biology and biology is thus in the peculiar position of being a science founded upon an unproved theory — is it then a science or a faith? Belief in the theory of evolution is parallel to belief in special creation — both are concepts which believers know to be true, but neither, up to the present, has been capable of proof.

For the evolutionist there is no *sovereign God* to whom he must be responsible and to whom he might have to give an accounting at some future day of judgment. For the evolutionist man is his own superior being, who is responsible to no one but himself and who can control his own destiny. *Life* nature library (1964) in its story of the evolution of man and the emergence of Homo sapiens, summed up the belief of the evolutionists, p. 172:

Only today is man recognizing that as he reshapes the world and replaces the relentless but stabilizing action of physical selection with a new, cultural evolution and inheritance, he is taking control of the future. Therein lies the climax of all the eons, the epochs and the years.

Thus man in his self-glorification and self-deification is trying to "take control of the future" without God. That is the religious belief that our children are being subjected to in the evolutionary creed taught to them in textbooks and by teachers in public schools.

Dr. Duane Gish in his 1981 book *Evolution - The Fossils Say NO!* p. 26, summed it all up very correctly by stating:

They have then combined this evolution theory with humanistic philosophy and have clothed the whole with the term, "science." The product, a nontheistic religion, with evolutionary philosophy as its creed under the guise of "science", is being taught in most public schools, colleges and universities of the United States. It has become our unofficial state-sanctioned religion.

Norman Macbeth stated in *Darwin Retried*, p.p. 126-129:

Darwinism itself has become a religion . . . I have compiled a list of five traits that seem to me to be earmarks of religious attitude among the evolutionists:

All who are not with me are Against Me

Reproof of the Fainthearted

Missionary Zeal

Perfect Faith

Millenarianism

In number three they believe that evolution should be taught at taxpayer's expense in every high school. In number five, they claim that man has the power to control the future. They have the religious idea of heaven on earth. Evolutionists worship their evolutionary ideas — falsely called "science," and thus their worship of this science (scientism) has become a form of religion, a faith in the material progress that *Homo sapiens, sapiens* has made for the welfare of mankind now and forever on earth.

The evolutionists' belief that there is no creator, that man evolved all by himself and has risen to the heights of *Homo sapiens, sapiens* without a Creator-God is just as religious as that of a Christian who believes in the Creator. The anti-religion of *a-theism* is just as religious a that of *theism*. The evolutionists, in trying to explain the origin of things, are delving into the field of religious and antireligious beliefs, faiths, creeds, dogmas and opinions, teaching the exact opposite of what Christian parents teach their children at home and in the schools of their church.

In short, evolution is a fable which has become a religion in itself and at the same time it stands in opposition to and opposes the Christian religion and some other religions. Edwin Conklin said:

The religion of evolution deals with this world rather than the next.

A number of evolutionists have made statements in which evolution is referred to as a religion. Maynard Metcalfe during the 1925 Scopes Trial stated:

God's growing revelation of Himself to the human soul cannot be realized without recognition of the evolutionary method He has chosen.

For him evolution and God go hand in hand as it does for other theistic evolutionists. So both theistic evolution and atheistic evolution consider evolution a form of religion. See end of this book: Strike 3, Reason 11: Why Evolution Is Not Scientific.

4. HUMANISM

Closely allied with evolution is humanism. The humanists believe that the universe, earth and man had an evolutionary origin. Like evolutionists they do not believe in a Creator and Designer who is above the natural things. The typical belief or creed of the humanists is expressed in the statement of the British Humanist Association:

I believe in no god and no hereafter. It is immoral to indoctrinate children with such beliefs. Schools have no right to do so, nor indeed, have parents. I believe that religious education . . . should be abolished . . . I believe that children should be taught religion as a matter of historical interest, but should be taught about all religions including Humanism, Marxism, Maoism, Communism, and other attitudes of life. They must be taught the objections of religion. I believe in a nonreligious social morality . . . Unborn babies are not people. I am as yet unsure whether the grossly handicapped are people in the real sense . . . I believe in no sin to be forgiven, no life beyond the grave but death everlasting.

From all this it is obvious that the teachings of humanists are antireligious and at the same time a religion unto themselves, just as are the teachings of the evolutionists. Yet there are people who claim that neither evolution nor humanism is a religion. Professor Frank Rhodes, president of Cornell University, Ithaca, New York, in an editorial in the *Minneapolis Tribune* (April 30, 1983), claimed that:

Evolution, as such, is neutral, it is neither theistic nor atheistic.

Yet both evolution and humanism are the handmaidens for atheists, just as creation science is a handmaiden for the creationists.

James Kilpatrick, in an editorial in the *Universal Press*, wrote very correctly under the title "Humanism in the Schools?" (February 20, 1986):

Under the Constitution, as we know, the states may not in any way foster an "establishment of religion." There can be no official prayers, no reading of Bible verses, no recitation of the Lord's Prayer, no posting of the Ten Commandments in a classroom. This is well understood. A teacher who sought to convince pupils that God exists, and that a divine power created our solar system would be in deep trouble. But what if the thrust of public school instruction is in the opposite direction — that God does not exist, and that our universe came into being by accident? Is it "religion" to teach that God is, but not religion to teach that God is not? . . . Humanists describe themselves as "non-theists." They hold that man has no "soul," that man is only a complex animal, that God is a "myth." . . . To the humanist, science and reason are the be-all and end-all. There is no life after death. Orthodox religious teachings are "sham" . . . There are no absolute moral or ethical values. These are "situational." The trouble, from a constitutional standpoint, is that these convictions amount to articles of faith.

Naturally they do not believe in a life after death. Gerald Larue in *The Humanist,* September/October 1948, pp. 20-23, stated in the "Way of Ethical Humanism."

We have no belief in an afterlife — no resurrection, no immortality, no reincarnation, no heaven, no hell, no nothing in between . . . We believe that this life is all that we have.

Naturally the great purpose of humanistic teaching is to contradict and oppose the Bible, to turn people away from a belief in God and to focus upon life on this earth only.

In regard to the Bible, John Dunphy in the *Humanist* (January/ February 1983), p. 25, stated:

The Bible is not merely another book, an outmoded and archaic book, or even an extremely influential book; it has been and remains an incredibly dangerous book.

In the teachings and beliefs of humanism man worships himself. Man not only evolved, but as a product of evolution man can now also control his own future evolution. A promotional brochure, by the American Humanist Association, says that:

Humanism is the belief that man shapes his own destiny. It is a constructive philosophy, a non-theistic *religion,* a way of life.

In a promotional brochure, evolutionist Julian Huxley, one of the founders of the Humanist Association, declared:

I use the word humanist to mean someone who believes that man is just as much a natural phenomenon as an animal or plant, that his body, mind and soul were not supernaturally created but are the products of evolution, and that he is not under the control or guidance of any supernatural being or beings, but has to rely on himself and his own powers.

The 1974 Humanist Association declared very bluntly:

No deity will save us; we must save ourselves.

In substance humanism and evolution, hand in hand, want to dethrone God and enthrone man. It is nothing less than the deification of man. Humanists who worship the achievements of man are no different from the ancients who worshiped themselves, their rulers and ancestors. In fact the first humanists in this world were *the children of men* (Genesis 6:1) who, in contrast to the *children of God*, denied God and elevated and deified themselves.

Humanism, on the basis of their own teachings, is very evidently an antireligious belief and at the same time a religion in itself. Also the Supreme Court of the United States declared secular humanism to be one of the nontheistic religions in our country. In the case of *Torcaso vs the State of Maryland* in 1961, Justice Black wrote:

> Among religions in this country which do not teach what would generally be considered a belief in the existence of God are Buddhism, Taoism, Ethical Culture, Secular Humanism and others.

On the basis of this Supreme Court decision, James Kilpatrick in his editorial February 20, 1986, "Humanism in the School?" stated:

> As a matter of law, Secular Humanism is as clearly a religion as Christianity or Judaism.

In fact, a humanist membership brochure (San Jose, California) *What is Humanism?* stated:

> The American Humanist Association is a non-profit, tax-exempt organization incorporated in the early 1940s in Illinois for educational and religious purposes.

Notice their word *religious*.

But, like evolution, the pitiful and dangerous thing about humanism is that it is also using the public schools for its antireligious and religious teachings. John Dunphy in "A Religion For A New Age" declared in *The Humanist* (January/February 1983) p. 26:

> I am convinced that the battle for humankind's future must be waged and won in the public school classroom by teachers who correctly perceive their role as the proselytizers of a new faith; a religion of humanity that recognizes and respects the spark of what theologians call divinity in every human being. These teachers must embody the same selfless dedication as the most rabid fundamentalist preachers, for they will be ministers of another sort, utilizing a classroom instead of a pulpit to convey humanist values in whatever subject they teach, regardless of the educational level — preschool day care or large state university. The classroom must and will become an arena of conflict between the old and the new — the rotting corpse of Christianity, . . .

Another proponent for humanism declared:

If we can have the children for 16 years, we can drive all that religious superstition out of them.

5. THEISTIC EVOLUTION AND PROGRESSIVE CREATION

In essence there is very little or no difference between atheistic evolution and theistic evolution. The only difference is that theistic evolution allows a god along the way here and there to get things started and then leaves all the rest of origins to evolution with its millions and billions of years of evolvement. Both use the present processes going on in the world to try to explain the origin of things. But those theologians and others who believe that theistic evolution is different from atheistic evolution are only fooling themselves and others. J. M. Stanfield, in *Modernism*, p. 96, wrote:

Christian evolution is a logical impossibility. No matter how we try to qualify or modify evolution, its basic principles of natural ascent, natural improvement, are always there.

Yet, in spite of all this, many theologians and others have fallen for the idea of theistic evolution. Some timid theologians, including doctors of theology, believing or fearing that science has succeeded in proving that evolution is a fact and a proven scientific law, have accepted evolution, with God taking part in it somehow and somewhere along the way. These men have not studied all the facts to see if evolution is a proven idea. They have tried to reconcile evolution with Christian theology, and thus they tried to change the lion into a lamb by calling it *theistic* evolution.

A professor in one of the schools of a formerly conservative Lutheran church body wrote:

To call himself reasonably well educated and informed, a Christian can hardly afford not to believe in evolution. Evolution, including human evolution, is no longer in contention . . . And to announce that you do not believe in evolution is as irrational as to announce that you do not believe in electricity.

However, evolution is an unproven idea. Electricity is a proven fact.

With theistic evolution these theologians seek to straddle the evolutionary fence by trying to appear as theologians among Christians and as supposedly scientific evolutionists among the *children of men*. This position is common in numerous seminaries and liberal arts religious colleges and especially among professors who teach science and biology. The reason for all this was well summarized by Dr. Henry Morris in A *History of Modern Creationism*, p.p. 328-29:

> The factor of peer pressure seems to be more intimidating among Christian academics than any other group. The wistful desire for acceptance by their professional colleagues in the secular universities, the supposed necessity to earn advanced degrees in such secular universities, . . . and the rush to attain institutional accreditation from secular accrediting agencies have all been tremendously powerful and effective compromise-generators!

To make their ideas of Christian evolution appear more acceptable to their Christian associates, some have given the idea a new name: *progressive creation*. Dr. Henry Morris in *The Remarkable Birth of Planet Earth*, p. 75, says:

> They prefer it merely because it sounds better, especially to alumni and boards of trustees who have become alarmed over reports of evolutionary teachings in their Christian colleges and church literature.

To give theistic evolution and progressive creation the appearance of having Biblical support they have reinterpreted Genesis chapter one so that a very long period of time (millions and billions of years) existed between verse one and the rest of the chapter. And the days in Genesis one are stretched out as covering long periods of time, although Genesis clearly states: "So the evening and morning were the first day," etc.

Theistic evolution fabricates a God who is not the God of the Bible.

Harvey A. Wegner in *Christian News,* April 19, 1993, p. 19 summarized it correctly:

> Theistic evolution, endemic [prevalent] among liberal Christian clergy and theologians, is beyond any reasonable doubt the least logical and coherent of all approaches to the problem of origins. It really deserves the contempt of the atheistic materialists and Christian creationists.
>
> Although the hodge-podge is filled with incompatible elements and is logically nonsense, the contrivers are quite pleased with themselves. They like to have the best of both worlds. They aspire to be Christians and unbelievers at the same time.

XXIII.   THE EFFECTS OF TEACHING EVOLUTION

1.   THE TEACHING OF EVOLUTION IS FORCE-FED IN PUBLIC SCHOOLS

Richard Culp in *Remember Thy Creator* (1975), p. 13:

Although I was at one time an evolutionist myself, for many years I have had the conviction that the teaching of evolution has been a powerful force in unsettling young people and in destroying their faith in the Word of God, turning them away from the message of redemption through the sacrifice of Christ. [He continues, p. 45:] The need to examine the doctrine of evolution is obvious. It is being presented in popular magazines, scientific journals and newspapers. It is being force-fed to millions of children in the public schools, beginning in the lower grades. Many states now require the subject to be taught in their curricula. [Page 129:] Evolution has become so popular, however, that geologists, biologists and anthropologists with extensive training at the graduate level now accept it without question, as we have already noted, and for the most part without knowing its crude origins and history. It scarcely need be said that those who sit at their feet and the vast numbers who never attended college are likewise uninformed but thoroughly persuaded, trusting the word of the "great men of science." [Page 148:] How does this view gain a foothold? Put yourself in the place of an incoming freshman in a large university. The order of the day is change: a new rooming house, new classmates, new roommate, new subjects. Above all, the student is "on his own." If he has not been pressured to believe the evolutionist teaching in elementary or high school, he will be in college. It appears in one course after another, sometimes very subtly, sometimes rudely, but always with the assumption that it has been proven thoroughly by scientific research. He usually hears *nothing* to the contrary. After awhile this daily indoctrination begins to make a dent. The student's head begins to swim in confusion.

Those students who question the idea of evolution are ridiculed or their faith in the Bible is questioned. Robert Gentry in *Creation's Tiny Mystery* (October 1986), p. 11, stated:

I was one of many Americans brought up in a conservative religious environment which conflicted with the evolutionary concepts taught at the university. However, my convictions were not strong enough to raise questions about the inconsistencies between Genesis and evolution. Students who did were not always treated with respect.

Numerous students have told me of the same sad attitude shown by their teachers.

2.   FAITH IN THE BIBLE IS DESTROYED FOR MANY STUDENTS

A child's faith comes under severe attack when it is confronted by materials and teachers who promote evolution as the only answer to the origin of things. A child does not have the scientific background to face this attack on its faith in the Bible. The teaching of evolutionary belief and dogma in the public schools has caused many a young Christian to waver. These young Christians must decide how to respond to teachings which oppose and contradict the Christian teachings they learned at home and in church.

Behind this attack on the Word of God stands Satan himself. His attack and challenge to the Word of God has been his greatest and most successful maneuver and action down through the ages. It worked so well for him, in the Garden of Eden and within a few generations after Adam and Eve, that he has practiced it to the fullest extent ever since. Through the teaching of evolution Satan also challenges the Word of God, and he has used evolution effectively on millions of people and on the entire world, as Revelation 12:9 declares: that Satan is the one "which deceiveth the whole world." II Corinthians 4:4 says that he "hath blinded the minds of them which believe not." Evolution definitely is a worldwide view by which the whole world has been deceived and misled. Satan knows full well that if the first chapters of Genesis are doubted and fall, then the entire Bible falls with it. Then there is no God, no creation, no Adam and Eve, no original sin, no need for a Savior; and Satan has won the battle.

To show how effective the teaching of evolution has been in their public, anti-Bible schools, Richard Culp stated in *Remember Thy Creator* (1975), p. 160:

> [T]hat in 1914, 80 percent of incoming freshman in College A were believers in God and in immortality, . . . and that in 1933, after the teaching of evolution had become widespread in high schools, this had dropped to 42 percent.

No doubt the bungling that took place in the Scopes Trial in 1925 had much to do with the increase in evolutionary teaching. The Scopes Trial is treated further on.

3.   MORAL AND SOCIAL STANDARDS HAVE BEEN DESTROYED THROUGH THE TEACHING AND PROMULGATION OF EVOLUTION

Richard Culp, in *Remember Thy Creator*, stated correctly, p. 161:

When the Bible is attacked, even indirectly and subtly, it is felt in the very fibers of the fabric of our society. The evolutionist has not considered that, when faith in the Bible is taken away by false teaching, the platform of moral and social standards that have guided our youth in past generations is also removed. Without the Bible as a standard, each individual is left to his own discretion and is in reality plunged into a sea of unbelief without helm or compass. If he can no longer go to God's Word for his principles of right and wrong, where can he go?

Rev. Steven Briel in an article "Man's Origin and Destiny" printed in *Christian News* (November 14, 1977) stated:

If ultimate extinction is our only destiny, then ought we not "eat, drink and be merry for tomorrow we die?" If there is no God and we are responsible to no one for what we do in this life, then how can there really be any reason for morality? To be sure, we are seeing the fruits of the evolutionary doctrine in our world today as violent crime is on the increase, homosexuality is becoming an "alternate life-style," divorce is becoming the rule, and the ruthless butchery of helpless babies continues mercilessly.

Already in 1932, Professor McDougall of Harvard said that this spirit is making America the most lawless country on the planet. Also in 1932 Professor August Zich stated:

Are you aware of the fact that these materialistic and godless teachings are begun in the public grade schools, continue in the public high schools, and logically receive the full cap-sheaf at the universities? Are you alive to the danger threatening your children and those of your neighbor, and thus the whole youth of the land to the moral disintegration of our coming citizens? If so, what are you doing about it?"

And how true was this analysis of the future by Professor Zich! Today on moral issues 80 percent say homosexuality, such as practiced in Sodom and Gomorrah and in the United States, is not wrong, 51 percent believe that adultery is not wrong, and pro-choice abortion is favored by a large percentage. If we are just another animal why not live like animals?

In its January 1970 issue, the *Reader's Digest* printed what they called "a provocative inquiry into our present confused state of belief" by David Klein. The article was entitled "Is There a Substitute for God?" A few quotes from that article are eye-openers:

How can he teach a child to do right if he cannot justify the right? . . . If a parent must tell a youngster that his life has no meaning, how can he tell him that he should not take drugs? In fact, how can he convince him that he should not commit suicide outright? . . . There are still other consequences of man's portentous leap into materialism. In freeing himself of the terror of hell, he gave up his hope in heaven: you live, you die, that's the end of it . . . The idea that man is *morally* responsible only to himself has been behind the creation of whole new societies: communist, fascist, socialist and shades between — while the older societies are being shaken, changing in nature even as they retain the old names and forms.

The evolutionists try to defend themselves from the charge that evolutionary ideas have increased immorality. Niles Eldredge in *The Monkey Business* (1982), p. 144, stated:

Now it is surely irony that the Old Testament amply documents the presence of many of the same social ills (and plenty more) plaguing Jewish society thousands of years ago, yet nothing is said of their teaching evolution to their children.

But Eldredge fails to realize that the children of Israel turned their backs on God many times and thus rejected God, and could have not only practiced the idolatry of their heathen neighbors but also many of their "social ills" and also have taught evolution to their children. Above all, Eldredge fails to realize that children very easily go off on a wrong tangent, even without encouraging them, by teaching them humanistic man-worshipping idolatry which could lead to accepting evolution. The danger, the harm, and the punishment for such beliefs and practices are clearly stated for mankind in Romans 1:18-32:

For the wrath of God is revealed from heaven against all ungodliness and unrighteousness of men, who suppress the truth in unrighteousness, because what may be known of God is manifest in them, for God has shown it to them. For since the creation of the world His invisible attributes are clearly seen, being understood by the things that are made, even His eternal power and Godhead, so that they are without excuse, because, although they knew God, they did not glorify Him as God, nor were thankful, but became futile in their thoughts, and their foolish hearts were darkened.

Professing to be wise, they became fools, and changed the glory of the incorruptible God into an image made like corruptible man — and birds and four-footed beasts and creeping things. Therefore God also gave them up to uncleanness, in the lusts of their hearts, to dishonor their bodies among themselves, who exchanged the truth of God for the lie, and worshiped and served the creature rather than the Creator, who is blessed forever. Amen.

For this reason God gave them up to vile passions. For even their women exchanged the natural use for what is against nature. Likewise also the men, leaving the natural use of the woman, burned in their lust for one another, men with men committing what is shameful, and receiving in themselves the penalty of their error which was due.

[Yet a woman minister who is a lesbian stated October 1988 on TV to a woman reporter that the Bible does not say anything against homosexuality. She needs to study her Bible. Romans chapter one continues:]

And even as they did not like to retain God in their knowledge, God gave them over to a debased mind, to do those things which are not fitting; being filled with all unrighteousness, sexual immorality, wickedness, covetousness, maliciousness; full of envy, murder, strife, deceit, evil-mindedness; they are whisperers, backbiters, haters of God, violent, proud, boasters, inventors of evil things, disobedient to parents, undiscerning, untrustworthy, unloving, unforgiving, unmerciful; who, knowing the righteous judgment of God, that those who practice such things are worthy of death, not only do the same but also approve of those who practice them.

What an indictment these words of God are to our generation today, as well as to the Romans and other ancient people, above all to the people who lived just before the Flood.

December 15, 1982, the *Minneapolis Tribune* carried a lengthy article entitled "Sex is beginning to take a back seat for many people." It referred back to the 1960s and 1970s when the pill and loose and wild living were the rage. But God in his grace and mercy sometimes provides severe punishments as well as warnings, as God warned in the previous passage from Romans, chapter one. The article stated:

Herpes and *AIDS* may have stopped it [the sexual revolution] dead in its tracks. Overnight herpes has sobered a generation that oral contraceptives freed from second thoughts, and AIDS has traumatized gay people . . . Among its sublimest effects, herpes has returned to sex its former shadings of corruption and sin. The virus has come to symbolize massive guilt, it's viewed as the mark of an angry God punishing people for the sins of the sexual revolution. The irony is that it's just those who pioneered the revolution who are most likely afflicted with the disease. They are between 20 and 30, college educated, and middle-to-upper-class. There are no jokes about *AIDS*, only sad stories about friends who have died and friends who have seen on their bodies the telltale purplish lesions. No one quite knows how *AIDS* is contracted, but promiscuity is common in the histories of its victims.

Very likely evolution and humanistic teachings have helped destroy the morality and social standards of much of mankind. As a result many innocent people live in fear of contracting sexual diseases. See p.p. 413f.

In addition, *evolution,* falsely claiming to be scientific and a fact, *has even harmed science itself.* The continued acceptance of the false premise that evolution is a scientific fact has actually become a stumbling block to true science. Evolution has misled and adversely affected sciences such as paleontology, taxonomy, astronomy, biology, archeology, geology and other sciences. These sciences could be more advanced and accurate if they had not been misled by the false premise that evolution is a fact. See a fuller treatment of the effect of evolution on sciences at end of book. See p.p. 451ff.

4.   CREATIONIST STUDENTS HAVE BEEN DENIED COLLEGE DEGREES

Henry Hiebert in *Evolution: Its Collapse in View* wrote, p. 138:

In addition there are at least many scientists who reject the evolutionary theory of origins, but, for reasons of their own, remain silent. Apparently there are instances in which graduate students have been prevented from obtaining their Ph.D.'s because they were creationists, and professors have been dismissed and have not been given tenure because of expressed creationists views.

Acts and Facts, August 1982, reports, p. 2, that Dr. John Patterson of Iowa State University:

[G]ave a speech before the Iowa Academy of Sciences in which he recommended that faculty contracts held by creationists should be cancelled and their degrees should be taken away from them.

Dr. Henry Morris in *The Battle for Creation* stated, p. 83:

> I have known students who have failed courses, and some who have been denied admission to graduate school or have been hindered from obtaining their degrees, largely for this very reason. When I was on the faculty of Virginia Tech, a professor who was on the graduate faculty there in the Biology Department told me that he would never approve a Ph.D. degree for any student known to be a creationist in his department, even if that student made straight A's in all his courses, turned in an outstanding research dissertation for his Ph.D., and was thoroughly familiar with all the evidence for evolution.

I.L. Cohen in *Darwin Was Wrong* stated, p.p. 213-14:

> There are certainly a good number of scientists who now reject the concepts of evolution — not on religious grounds, but on strictly scientific grounds. Most of them are keeping their own council. Outwardly they support evolution (so as to be in step with their peers) but inwardly they have second thoughts on the subject. It is not easy to take a stand against the beliefs of the majority, and expose oneself to ridicule, especially when one's job and academic and professional prospects are on the line. It is only the very brave and those highly placed scientists whose standings are universally acknowledged (and thus secure) that can afford to contradict the general trend.

The sad thing about evolutionists is that they are not only intolerant but also very stubborn in their belief. They cling to their belief even though they cannot find the first cause of all things. It is as Robert Jastrow stated in the *Reader's Digest* (July 1980), p. 53:

> Science has proved [?] that the universe exploded into being at a certain moment. It asks, What cause produced this effect? Who or what put the matter and energy into the universe? Was the universe created out of nothing, or was it gathered together out of pre-existing materials? And science cannot answer these questions.

5.   YET A LARGE PERCENTAGE OF PUBLIC SCHOOL GRADUATES BELIEVE IN CREATION

Although evolutionists have turned the public school into their own antireligious and nontheistic schools, yet a very large percent of the people believe in God. According to a *Reader's Digest* Gallup Survey in 1986:

95 percent profess belief in God or a universal spirit. 66 percent perceive God as a being who watches over and judges them personally, and to whom they are answerable. 87 percent of those polled say they pray sometime during their everyday lives.

According to a Gallup poll in 1982, 44 percent of Americans agreed with this statement: "God created man pretty much in his present form at one time within the last 10,000 years." Only 9 percent believed that: "Man has developed over millions of years from less advanced forms of life. God had no part in the process."

That 44 percent still believe in creation after many decades of evolutionary preaching and indoctrination in public schools from the grades through universities is shocking to humanists, atheistic and theistic evolutionists. What is still more shocking to them is that one-fourth of the 44 percent who believe in the creation of mankind were college educated.

Niles Eldredge again in *The Monkey Business*, p. 147, reported:

Here are the results of a recent reader survey conducted by *Glamour* magazine: "Do you believe in Darwin's theory of evolution?" No - 53 percent; Yes - 47 percent . . . Now it may be supposed that the respondents were mainly people with strong opinions on the subject - and there are far more people passionately committed to creationism than there are devotees to evolution . . . . Nonetheless, the results of this poll are disconcerting. Creationists have been making truly great inroads. How can they be thwarted?

The evolutionists, after controlling the public schools for many decades and having turned the public schools into their own religious and antireligious schools and above all after teaching evolution as a scientific fact and having evolution force-fed through the news media, should have almost all people believing in evolution by now. But this is not the case. Evolution is losing among the people because it has no scientific foundation. Many if not most people laugh at evolution as being illogical and unreasonable.

See the six evil effects that evolution has on mankind, p.p. 413ff.

XXIV.   EVOLUTION IN THE PUBLIC SCHOOLS IS CONTRARY TO THE SEPARATION OF RELIGION AND ANTI-RELIGION AND STATE

1.   THE USE OF THE TERM "SEPARATION OF CHURCH AND STATE," OR SHOULD IT BE "RELIGION AND STATE?"

The use of the term "Separation of Church and State" is a misnomer on the basis of the First Amendment of the United States Constitution. Professor Paul Kauper of the University of Michigan Law School wrote regarding the terminology of these words:

> Separation of Church and State is the symbolic language so often used as a beginning point of discussion. Actually this precise language does not have much relevancy to the American scene. It is borrowed from European history and tradition where the problem could be identified in terms of a single church and a single state and in later years of a single state and two churches, named Catholic and Protestant.

The First Amendment reads:

> Congress shall make no law respecting an establishment of religion or prohibiting the free exercise thereof . . .

On the basis of this amendment the proper words should be "Separation of Religion and State" or "Religion and Government." The word religion covers a wide field; it covers nonreligion and antireligion as well as religious beliefs.

Webster's New World Dictionary defines religion:

> 1. a belief in a divine or supernatural power or powers to be obeyed and worshipped as the creator(s) and ruler(s) of the universe. 2. expression of this belief in conduct and ritual. 3. a) any specific system of belief, worship, conduct, etc., often involving a code of ethics and a philosophy; as the Christian *religion*, the Buddist *religion*, etc., b) loosely any system of beliefs, practices, ethical values, etc. resembling, suggestive of, or likened to such a system, as humanism is his *religion*.

The United States Supreme Court in Everson vs Board of Education 1947 declared:

> We have staked the very existence of our country on the faith that complete separation between state and religion is best for the state and best for religion.

The Americans United for the Separation of Church and State declared correctly in their *amicus* brief regarding the 1987 Alabama school case:

> We are a nation of diverse religious believers and non-believers. Government neutrality toward religion is essential to preserve the richness and variety of religious life. The Establishment Clause of the First Amendment to the constitution guarantees this neutrality and assures that the government shall not favor any single religion, all religions or non-religion.

To be more exact they should also have mentioned anti-religion.

Establishment and fostering of religion covers anything that might disturb and upset the religious conviction of any other citizen or group of citizens. Thus while the term separation of church and state might be appropriate for some European countries, it does not cover what is stated in the First Amendment of the U.S. Constitution. Our government should not help, foster or promote any kind of religious belief, any nontheistic belief, or above all any antireligious beliefs that go counter to the religious beliefs of others, that might disturb and upset other citizens, or that are repulsive to them.

2.   EVOLUTION IS PROTECTED FROM CRITICISM IN SCHOOL

The most disturbing element in our schools today in regard to religion is the teaching and fostering of the ideas of evolution. Not only is evolution presented as a fact, but it is also protected from any criticism. Evolution is taught as something that cannot be questioned. A doctor wrote regarding the education of children in the magazine *American Laboratory* (October 1980):

> Evolution is presented as reality, not as a concept that can be questioned. The authority of the educational system then compels belief. A student is not permitted to hold personal *beliefs* or to state them; if the student does so, he or she is subjected to ridicule and criticism by the instructor. Often the student risks academic loss because his or her views are not "correct" and the grade is lowered.

In June 1987, Chief Justice Rehnquist and Justice Scalia in a dissenting opinion denounced strongly the majority opinion:

> In this case, however, it seems to me the Court's position is the repressive one. The people of Louisiana, including those who are Christian fundamentalists, are quite entitled, as a secular

matter, to have whatever scientific evidence there may be against evolution presented in their schools.

But evolution should not be taught in the first place both because it has no scientific foundation and also because of its religious and antireligious nature and because it contradicts the religious conviction of most children and parents.

3. EVOLUTION IS ANTI-CREATION, ANTI-BIBLE, ANTI-GOD, ANTI-CHRISTIAN

Although the Arkansas Law of 1966 was wrong in requiring a balanced treatment of evolution and creation, it was very correct in stating:

> The public school presentation of only evolution . . . abridges the Constitution's prohibition against establishment of religion, because it produces hostility toward many theistic religions and gives preference to Theological Liberalism, Humanism, Non-theistic religions, and atheism, in that these religious faiths generally include a religious belief in evolution.

William Jennings Bryan also was correct in the Tennessee Court trial (1925) in stating:

> I cannot believe that any court will deny to the majority of the people of Tennessee . . . the right to protect their religions from what they regard as an assault upon it by a minority that is trying to force its views upon the children . . .

On the other hand, Frederick Edwords in a paper on creation and evolution stated in 1980:

> If it's because evolution is itself supposedly a religion, they will have to prove it using scientific means . . . and actually showing that evolution is untestable and nonscientific in nature.

In previous sections of this book evidences have been given showing that evolution is a religion in itself and also that scientifically it is untestable and nonscientific in nature.

4. FOSTERING ANTI-RELIGIOUS BELIEFS IN PUBLIC SCHOOL IS THE SAME AS TEACHING RELIGION

By teaching and fostering evolution in school, creation is rejected, ridiculed and denounced. This is the same as teaching anti-religion and in essence it is religion in itself. As a nonscientific belief regarding origins it opposes the religion of origins given in the Bible and it excessively entangles religion and the state.

Dr. Gould Wickey in 1936 correctly stated:

I believe that denouncements of religion by professors of tax-supported schools are unconstitutional by the same barrier which prevents the teaching of religion at public expense.

Under the guarantee of religious freedom, neither Christianity nor any other forms of religion may be taught in public schools. On the same basis any teaching or doctrine that denies and denounces any teaching of Christianity or any other religion should also not be allowed. A preamble to a resolution passed by the legislature of the state of Florida in 1923 correctly stated:

Whereas the public schools and colleges of the state, supported in whole or in part by public funds, should be kept free from any teachings designed to set up and promulgate sectarian views, and should also be equally free from teachings designed to attack the religious beliefs of the public . . .

The public schools are set up by the states for purely secular purposes. Their function is not to make or unmake Christians, or to educate children in any religious or anti-religious beliefs. These schools are to abstain from and shun any religious or anti-religious education. They are there solely to prepare children for citizenship. In short, their purpose is secular education with no promulgation or interference in the field of religion. Christians and other religious people have a right to be spared from the teachings of any theory or idea which weakens or destroys the faith of their children. And yet people who believe in the teachings of the Bible are subjected to unfairness, coercion and totalitarianism, in that they are forced to support, with their own tax money, government institutions of learning that undermine and ridicule their religious beliefs.

The idea of evolution destroys the Bible account of creation. If that is destroyed, the faith of the children in the rest of the Bible is also destroyed. Even if some teachers purposely avoid teaching evolution, the textbooks given are saturated with it. This teaching begins in the lower grades, and in the state universities the teaching of evolution is regarded as necessary to produce so-called educated and enlightend graduates. If the students are brave enough to resist the teachings of evolution, they are often held up to public scorn and ridicule before the class.

5. EVOLUTION AND HUMANISM ARE THE QUASI-OFFICIAL RELIGION OF PUBLIC INSTITUTIONS

John A. Moore of the University of California at Riverside said in a paper delivered in 1981 at the National Academy of Science in Washington, D.C.:

> If we do not resolve our problems with the creationists, we have only ourselves to blame. Let's remember, the greatest resource of all is available to us — the educational system of the nation.

It is quite obvious that students in our public schools are constantly being indoctrinated with evolution in one way or another, so that evolution, and many times with its accompanying humanism or idolizing of the achievements of mankind without God, has become the established religion of the public school, taught *under the guise of science*, and in the name of science. In this way the public schools have become the parochial schools of the evolutionists.

That such is the case is obvious from action taken in 1986 by the Florida State Board of Education, consisting of the governor and state cabinet members. Although according to polls, 80 percent of the people of Florida did not want evolution presented in schools as a fact, and several scientists spoke against biased textbooks that had been recommended, citing factual errors in them, the State Board of Education voted unanimously to approve the objectionable textbooks.

6. EVOLUTION DEFINITELY SHOULD NOT BE TAUGHT IN PUBLIC SCHOOLS

Dr. Colen Patterson, senior paleontologist for the British Museum of Natural History, in a public lecture before the American Museum of Natural History in New York City, November 5, 1981, said that he asked the geology staff of the Field Museum of Natural History this question:

> Can you tell me anything you know about evolution, any one thing that is true?

He asked the same question of evolutionists that met at the Evolutionary Morphology Seminar at the University of Chicago. The answer he received from both groups was silence, except that one member of the Morphology Seminar said:

> I know one thing — it ought not to be taught in high school.

How correctly Arlen Carlblom wrote in the Mankato, Minnesota, *Free Press*, January 23, 1985:

I have taught my children to believe that the Bible is the accurate Word of God. When public schools promote evolution, it undermines my children's faith in me. If the atheist child has the right not to be indoctrinated with Christian ideas, my child has the right not to be indoctrinated with the anti-Bible views supported by the theory of evolution.

Supreme Court Justice Abe Fortas summed it up correctly when he stated in connection with the Supreme Court ruling (1981) regarding the Arkansas antievolution law:

Government in our democracy . . . state and federal . . . must be neutral in matters of religious theory . . . It may not aid, foster, or promote one religious theory as against another.

This includes the evolutionary idea or belief over against any other belief. Teaching evolution over against the teaching of the Bible is worse than, and as unconstitutional as Lutherans teaching their belief in public schools over against Roman Catholicism, or Jews teaching their beliefs over against Christianity, and vice versa. Above all, simple elementary justice demands that tax money paid by Christian citizens should not be used by schools to destroy the Christian faith of the children of these taxpayers.

7.   TEACHING EVOLUTION IN PUBLIC SCHOOL IS VERY EVIDENTLY A VIOLATION OF THE FIRST AMENDMENT

The Supreme Court of the United States in 1971 in the *Lemon vs Kurtzman* case set up a three-part or threefold test for religion and state problems. To meet constitutional standards, a government action:
   a. Must have a secular purpose.
   b. Its primary effect must neither advance nor *oppose* religion.
   c. It must not excessively entangle religion and state.

   a. Falsely claiming to be a scientific fact, evolution may claim to have a secular purpose. But since evolution is a nontestable and nonproven idea, and many ideas of evolution have been proven false or falsified, and because of the ardor that evolutionists assume in clinging to their assumed right to teach the evolutionary belief, and because of the almost intense hatred they show over against the creation belief, teaching evolution is not serving a *secular purpose* but an antireligious purpose.

   ` b. It is very evident that evolution *opposes* religion. In the June 19, 1987 Supreme Court's Louisiana decision, Justice Brennan in writing the majority opinion stated:

Families entrust public schools with the education of their children, but condition that trust on the understanding that the classrooms will not purposely be used to advanced religious views that may conflict with the private views of the student and his or her family. Students in such institutions are impressionable and their attendance is involuntary.

There is no question that the anti-creation, anti-God, and anti-Bible views of evolution *oppose* and *conflict* with the private beliefs of the student and his or her family.

Dr. Robert Maddox, executive director of Americans United for Separation of Church and State, July 1987, p. 23 of *Church and State* stated correctly as a comment to Justice Brennan's statement:

Thus, public school teachers must exercise great care to be sensitive to the various religious viewpoints held by students in their class . . . The government must maintain an attitude of appreciative neutrality toward religions and non-religion.

Above all, the government and its institutions must not assume antireligious attitudes.

c. Government action must not excessively entangle religion and state. There can hardly be any question that the teaching of evolution in the schools entangles religion and state. Why do we have all these complaints against the teaching of evolution in the schools? Why all these court cases? Why all this turmoil between believers in evolution and believers in creation? Why all these state laws passed trying to prohibit the teaching of evolution or trying to get creationism into the schools to counteract the teaching of evolution? Why all these laws to get evolution into and out of the school textbooks?

8.   IF EVOLUTIONISTS WANT EVOLUTION TAUGHT, THEY SHOULD ESTABLISH THEIR OWN PRIVATE SCHOOLS, AS CHURCHES DO

There are many different beliefs regarding evolution. Let each evolutionary belief build, maintain and support its own schools. For evolutionists to insist that their evolutionary beliefs and antireligious views should be subsidized by taxes of all people is wrong and unconstitutional. Christian parents spend thousands of dollars to teach their children the way they want them taught according to their religious beliefs, and above all, so that their children may not be misled by the teachers of evolutionary beliefs. So also the evolutionists should provide their own schools if they want their children taught this belief.

9.   LIKEWISE CREATIONISM SHOULD NOT BE TAUGHT IN PUBLIC SCHOOLS

Creationism should not be taught, not only because it is a violation of the First Amendment of our Bill of Rights, but for many other reasons. Teaching creation in public schools would only harm Christianity. What fun an evolutionist like Isaac Asimov and others of his belief could have, twisting the meaning of the Bible account of creation, as he has done in his interpretation of Genesis, in his book *In The Beginning Science Faces God In The Book of Genesis*. Atheistic evolutionists could really destroy the Christian faith of children more effectively in this way than by teaching evolution directly.

Furthermore, creationism should not be taught in public schools because not all Christians have the same belief regarding different statements of creation, such as the length of the days. Some may believe in theistic evolution.

Considering what many theologians have done in interpreting Genesis chapters one and two according to their way of thinking, what kind of treatment would the Bible account receive at the hands of public school teachers who are not Christians, or whose knowledge of the Bible is weak, or who have become ardent believers in humanism and evolution? Yes, what would happen if the average teacher trained in a secular college were to teach the Bible account of creation? We know that to have creation taught by teachers who do not believe in it, do not want to teach it, or do not know how to teach it, would result in God's Word being degraded or ridiculed; and it certainly would do only harm to the account of creation and most likely to the trust of a child in all the rest of the Bible.

10.   TO BE FAIR EVOLUTION SHOULD NOT BE TAUGHT BY CREATIONISTS

What has been said regarding creation being taught by people who do not believe in it, are against it, or are uninformed about it, also holds true regarding evolution being taught by people who believe in creation.

11.   NEITHER EVOLUTION NOR CREATION SHOULD BE TAUGHT

Attorney Clarence Darrow in the Scopes Trial of 1925 in Dayton, Tennessee, was correct when he said:

It is bigotry to teach only one view of origins.

He meant the creation point of view. Likewise it is bigotry to teach only the evolution point of view. George Herscher in *Letters to Church and State* magazine in September 1987 was right in declaring:

> You say that you heartily agree with the United States Supreme Court decision that creationism should not be taught in the pubic schools. I should like to say if this is the case then evolution should also be prohibited from being taught. If creationism is considered a religion, then evolution, its antithesis, is also a religion. If the Supreme Court is denying the teaching of creation, then it should also deny the teaching of evolution.

The public schools of the state have only one purpose and that is to train and educate young people for good citizenship. In order to do this it is not necessary to teach about origins, because there is such a wide conflict of opinion on that matter and because it involves religion. However, religion in training young people to live morally right and according to the laws of government does train young people for good citizenship. This is not usually the case with the teachings of evolution. Yet although religion trains for good citizenship, it should not be used in public schools to train for citizenship, not only because such religious training is contrary to the First Amendment, but also because there are conflicts of opinion as to what is morally right.

The study of origins should not be taught in public school because it is not necessary either for the study of science or for the sake of good citizenship. The subject of origins should be totally removed from public school education, as School Superintendent Rich Langton of Medford, Oregon, stated wisely in declaring:

> Evolution is not taught in any of the schools of Medford, neither is creation for that matter. Down through the years, educators have learned that this is such a controversial subject that it is for the better not to deal with it at all than to try to deal with it, even on a fair basis, pointing out the claims of both sides. At appropriate levels, where it is understood, we do teach simple genetics, but we in no way get into the question of the evolution of man.

That is doing it right, constitutionally and in the truly American way. In fact there would be many fewer church schools today if Christian parents had not been forced to start their own schools to avoid the teaching of evolutionists, who have turned the public schools into their own anti-creation, anti-religious schools.

12.   IS IT ACADEMIC FREEDOM AND LIBERTY, OR IS IT ACADEMIC LICENSE?

Granting schools the right to teach evolution does not belong in the field of academic freedom and liberty, but is assuming a *license* it does not have. It is assuming a license to teach something that harms others. Liberty ends as soon as it infringes on the rights, liberty, property and possessions of others. According to *Webster's New World Dictionary*, license is:

An undisciplined freedom, constituting an abuse of liberty.

True freedom, and this includes academic freedom, is not anyone's exclusive right and does not give him and her absolute liberty to do as they please, but it involves a respect for the rights and beliefs of others.

In a number of cases teachers have complained and made court cases charging that they lost their freedom of speech and were deprived of their academic freedom in not being allowed to teach their ideas of evolution. In 1966 Susan Epperson of Arkansas claimed she lost her freedom of speech in not being allowed to teach evolution. In 1967 a teacher in Tennessee claimed that the anti-evolution law under which Scopes was convicted in 1925 interfered with his academic freedom. Under such reasoning a Christian teacher could claim his so-called academic freedom also is interfered with. If it is wrong for a Christian teacher to practice so-called academic freedom to foster and estabish religion in public schools, as the United States Supreme Court has rightfully ruled, then it is equally wrong to foster and establish antireligion, anti-creation through the evolutionary idea.

Teachers have all the liberty and academic freedom in the world to teach their ideas of evolution elsewhere, outside of public institutions. The fact that the public would not be paying the salary and providing utilities and a lecture room for them would not be depriving them of "academic freedom." If public teachers and institutions wish to teach their religious and antireligious ideas, let them build their own buildings and pay their own expenses, as the churches rightfully should be and are doing.

Restraints on freedom of speech have been held legal in other fields. The Hatch Act forbids federal employees from active participation in partisan politics. Likewise public schools and their teachers should not be allowed to participate in partisan religious and antireligious teachings. Because one is a teacher does not give one the right or the license to teach anything one wants and ride roughshod over the convictions of others, and especially the religious convictions protected under the First Amendment.

13. **EVOLUTIONISTS ALSO CONTROL SCIENTIFIC JOURNALS, POPULAR MAGAZINES, NEWS MEDIA, TV STATIONS, PUBLIC BROADCASTING SYSTEMS, LIBRARIES, GOVERNMENT PARKS, UNIVERSITY PROFESSORSHIPS AND GOVERNMENT RESEARCH PROJECTS**

The teaching of evolution permeates not only the public institutions of learning but also all the above mentioned sources of information. How many times do we hear: "Millions and billions of years ago" this and that happened, without any positive scientific proof! In this way, the evolutionists try to convince people that evolution is a fact. Scientific journals print only that which favors evolution and the contrary views of creation are ignored. Most large publishing houses will print only that which favors evolution, because most of these printing houses are under the control of leaders who are evolutionists.

Regarding university professorships, Dr. Henry Morris wrote in *The Twilight of Evolution,* p. 27:

Similarly, it is almost an impossibility for a convinced creationist to obtain or to retain an influential position on a university faculty in the various disciplines now dominated by the evolution concept, such as anthropology, geology, biology, psychology and psychiatry.

Also libraries, both school and public, are filled with books favoring evolution. Books presenting the creation point of view are extremely scarce as I found in the local library. There is an abundance of books on evolution.

And how many millions and billions of dollars have been provided by the government to directly and indirectly foster and promote evolutionary research? Dr. Robert Gentry in *Creation's Tiny Mystery* (1986), stated:

[M]illions of dollars are granted annually by government agencies to fund a variety of evolution-oriented research projects. [page 6] Each year the Federal Government through the National Science Foundation, grants millions of dollars for research based on evolutionary ideas, and over the years of its operation possibly hundreds of millions have gone for the same purpose. [page 126] Over the last several decades countless millions of government funds have been spent on incredibly "far-out" ventures specifically designed to test a number of evolutionary predictions-one prime example being the costly unmanned space mission to Mars to look for evidence of the evolutionary beginning of life. This mission failed to find any trace of even the most primitive forms of life. Despite this failure, evolutionists continue to obtain funds for almost any experiment which they feel is important. We must conclude that until now evolutionists have not been inclined to launch a full-scale effort to perform the falsification test. [page 182-183]

The last three words are important. To be real scientists they should do all in their power *to see if evolution can be falsified.* And much of evolution has been falsified, by others.

14.   SCOPES "MONKEY" TRIAL

14 A. WHO AND WHAT WAS INVOLVED IN THE TRIAL

That trial began July 10, 1925, in Dayton, Tennessee. John Scopes, a high school teacher, was accused of teaching evolution in violation of the Tennessee law forbidding such teaching in the public schools. Acting as special prosecutor was William Jennings Bryan, who had been a former Secretary of State under President Woodrow Wilson and had been nominated three times for the presidency by the Democratic party. He was a Bible-believing fundamentalist Christian. He was not a scientist and did not have up-to-date scientific knowledge regarding evolution, and he did not realize that the American Civil Liberties Union and its main attorney, Clarence Darrow, were setting a trap for him.

Darrow was a famous liberal criminal lawyer in Chicago. He was also an agnostic. Darrow cleverly maneuvered the trial so that instead of evolution being placed on trial, Bryan and his fundamental beliefs were tried and Bryan was made to appear ridiculous by the sarcasm and insults of Darrow. The news media, deeply involved in evolution as they are today, were present in vast numbers.

14 B. DARROW'S WRONG LOGIC

In a statement Darrow made at the time of the trial he expressed some important *wrong* thinking and logic. He stated Sprague de Camp *In The Great Monkey Trial*, 1968, p. 223:

The fact that any theory or scientific view may be contrary to any religious idea furnishes no right for a state to prohibit it. If this were true, then most astronomy and geology would fall under the ban.

First of all, evolution has no proven scientific foundation, and because it cannot be proven or falsified it is not a scientific theory.

Secondly, although a state may not prohibit an idea that is contrary to some religious idea, it does have a right and duty to prohibit it in its governmental institutions. Any religious or antireligious idea that opposes the religious convictions of others should not receive government *establishment.* Thirdly, astronomy and geology would not be banned if evolution is banned. Only the false assumptions of origins taught in astronomy and geology would be banned. Fourthly and above all, the fact that people may disagree in a wide variety of religious subjects does not give evolutionists the license to teach their antireligious and religious idea on origins as something superior to or as not contradicting the religious ideas of others.

Sprague de Camp in *The Great Monkey Trial,* 1968, p. 224, expounds on Darrow's false logic. He wrote that Darrow:

pointed out that there are many different interpretations of the Bible. Therefore evolution could not, *ipso facto* be taken as a contradiction of the Bible.

The different interpretations of origins given in Genesis came not from people who believe in the literal wording of Genesis but from people who believe in theistic evolution. Theistic evolution finally is in the same class as atheistic evolution regarding the origin of things, and therefore there is no "contradiction" between the two.

Using false logic Darrow said with "his voice rising to a roar", p. 257:

If today you can take a thing like evolution and make it a crime to teach it in the public school, tomorrow you can make it a crime to teach it in the private school and the next year. .in the church.

He should have known that, according to the First Amendment, *the free exercise of religion* cannot be prohibited outside of public institutions.

Darrow continued: p. 257

Soon you may set Catholic against Protestant, and Protestant against Protestant, and try to foist your own religion upon the minds of men.

And that is exactly what the evolutionists are doing: the teaching of evolution is set against the teaching of creation. In public institutions no religion or antireligion should be allowed that sets one belief against another.

Since the time of Darrow in 1925 the poor logic of evolutionists has not improved. Fred Edwords, who has lectured and debated widely on the creation-evolution question and is administrator of the American

Humanist Association, wrote in "Why Creationism Should not be Taught as Science" (1980):

> Evolution, as normally taught, does not require the student's allegiance.

On this basis a Roman Catholic could teach his belief to a Protestant in school and vise versa, as long as allegiance is not required.

Edwords continues:

> Only his or her understanding of the objectively presented concepts is sought. Therefore the teaching of evolution is neither a threat to nor an imposition on the religious freedom of any child. Students are always free to disagree with any theory they learn. . .
> If they are offended by evolution, they can send their children to private religious schools. .

In other words, a teacher, practicing a license to teach anything he or she wants to teach, could subject a child to any kind of indoctrination, and the child becomes subject to the risk of ridicule. And in still other words, like in Nazi Germany and Russia, the child belongs to the whims and fancies of the teacher and the state. This moves us a long, long way from religious liberty.

The total arrogance of the humanist and evolutionist Fred Edword is shown in these words:

> . . .this is hardly sufficient to justify all the rest of the pupils. an inferior education.

Children do not need unproven evolution for a superior education. The arrogance continues:

> It would seem there is a state interest in teaching this material, and teaching it exclusively. This is made clear by the fact that evolution is the one great unifying principle of all science. Students cannot be adequately prepared for scientific careers if they are left in the dark about its existence.

Most sciences would be more accurate if they were not misled by the unproven assumptions of evolution. Evolution is not a unifying principle and it is not a proven science. And so Edwords rambles on and on with one wrong, illogical statement and argument after another.

14 C. BRYAN MISLED INTO A TRAP

It is truly amazing how Bryan was led into a trap that was laid for him by Darrow. Toward the end of the trial Darrow told the Unitarian minister Potter, S. de Camp *In The Great Monkey Trial*, p. 346:

I'm going to put a Bible expert on the stand. . . No, not you; a greater expert than you, greatest in the world — according to him.

Potter replied:

"You mean Bryan himself? You're going to put him on the stand and question him? That would be a master stroke!"

Darrow told Potter to find some possibly unscientific spots in the Bible. Toward the end of the trial Bryan agreed to be placed on the stand and questioned by Darrow. Bryan was later to question Darrow, but the trial never got so far that Bryan could question Darrow.

Darrow began questioning Bryan on numerous parts of the Bible, especially the miracles recorded in the Bible. By letting himself be placed on the stand Bryan let himself and the miracles of the Bible be put on trial instead of evolution. Darrow started out by asking Bryan if the Bible should be literally interpreted. Then Darrow questioned Bryan on Jonah and the whale, on the sun standing still, the Flood, the time of the Flood, the Tower of Babel, the age of the earth, etc. All during this questioning Darrow insulted and humiliated Bryan. Finally Darrow moved in for the kill.

Darrow knew about the tooth that was found in Bryan's home state of Nebraska, the tooth that I referred to in Chapter XI, Part 4: Hoaxes and Frauds of Evolutionists. That tooth was developed by the evolutionists into an ape-man who was proclaimed by them to be millions of years old. At the trial in Dayton, Tennessee, so-called experts, such as Professor H. Newman of the University of Chicago, ridiculed Bryan and laughed him to scorn because they claimed that the proof of that tooth being millions of years old could not be contested. The claimed age of that tooth became a weapon in the hands of Darrow. It is very likely, because Bryan could not give an answer to the supposed age of that tooth, that he gave answers regarding the age of the earth and the length of the creation days which he would never have made otherwise. Darrow's devastating question to Bryan was: "Do you think the earth was made in six days?" Bryan replied: "Not six days of twenty-four hours."

After more questioning, Darrow lured him into answering how long the days were. He replied, periods of time, covering millions of years. People in the court gasped in unbelief and shock that Bryan would make such a statement. Some claim that Bryan got this idea from some theologians who also had begun to accept millions of years.

Only two years later, in 1927, it was admitted by the evolutionists that that tooth came from the jaw of a pig. But the evolutionists in the meanwhile gained ground throughout the world, for reports of that trial were spread by the news media all over the world. Darrow gained two objectives in the meanwhile: First, that the Bible should not be accepted literally and that its teachings were questioned by evolutionists. The other objective was that propaganda was gained for the idea of evolution to the effect that evolution was accepted as a fact by many scientific people.

In the meanwhile the news media abused and ridiculed Bryan's Bible beliefs, and the testimony of these so-called evolutionists experts was broadcast all over the world. The day after the questioning, in a crafty move by Darrow and others on the evolution side in declining to argue the matter further, Bryan was robbed of his chance to make a defending speech.

14 D. EVOLUTION WAS NEVER PUT ON TRIAL

Evolution was supposed to have been on trial, but Darrow manuevered the trial so that creation and the Bible were placed on trial. The fallacies and the nonscientific basis of evolution were not discussed. And if they had been discussed, no court could have settled the question and declared that either evolution or creation was a proven scientific fact.

In at least two other court cases since 1925, creationists again let themselves, instead of evolution, be placed on trial. Discussions of the errors of evolution were avoided or circumvented to a great extent in those trials: Arkansas 1981 and Louisiana 1985.

14 E. BRYAN'S DEATH

Just a few days after the end of the trial, Bryan quietly died at the age of sixty-five while lying down for a nap. There is little doubt that the highly disturbing, emotional ordeal that he underwent in the cross-examination by Darrow had much to do with his sudden tragic death. One sympathetic journalist of that day wrote regarding this: (de Camp 413)

> Darrow's cross-examination of Bryan was a thing of immense cruelty. . . I have no doubt that the humiliation of being called "an ignoramus" and a "fool and a Fundamentalist," and of hearing his beliefs referred to as "your fool religion" cut Bryan to the quick. Four days after the trial ended I talked to him at some length and he was even then quivering with hurt at the epithets which had been applied to him. He was a crushed and broken man.

For all this Darrow was rebuked by many people throughout the land. Some declared his treatment of Bryan was wantonly brutal. He was rebuked also for using the court trial for making propaganda for evolution and for doing this in a circus atmosphere. He was scolded by liberals as well as conservative theologians and by many others. If Bryan would ever have cross-examined Darrow, he would have been right in calling Darrow's evolution ideas: "Your damned-by-God, nonscientific, illogical, fool evolutionary ideas."

14 F. EVOLUTION GAINED A RENEWED FOOTHOLD IN AMERICA AND ITS EDUCATION SYSTEM

Although there was no examination of the evolution idea during the trial, Darrow managed to have the ideas of evolution spread. He arranged to have his so-called "expert" scientists give their assumed scientific evidences for evolution, especially regarding that "tooth" found in Bryan's home state of Nebraska being millions of years old. The reports of these so-called scientific evidences were spread to all parts of the world as is still being done today.

Dr. Robert Gentry, in *Creation's Tiny Mystery* (1986), p. 88, states regarding the effect this has had on the world:

The perceived outcome of the trial among scientists was both pervasive and self-perpetuating. From henceforth any scientist who openly professed any belief in a literal interpretation of Genesis became suspect among his peers. This disdain for creation was passed on to each new generation of university students by both scientists themselves and educators, many of whom knew no better than to echo their scientific colleagues. Since the Scopes trial, three generations of college-educated Americans have been indoctrinated with the view that evolution represents scientific truth.

However, since then evidences against evolution have increased tremendously, so that evolutionary professors are now trying to avoid debates with creationists. Today much more can be said against evolution than at any time in the past century because there are now more facts against evolution, and more anti-evolutionary evidences are constantly being found and brought to bear against the evolutionary idea.

15.   OTHER COURT CASES

15 A. ARKANSAS ANTI-EVOLUTION LAW (1966)

Susan Epperson, a biology teacher in Little Rock, Arkansas, claimed in 1966 that the 1928 Arkansas law banning the teaching of Darwin's theory of evolution caused her to "lose part of her freedom of speech." According to the *Minneapolis Tribune* (September 1966):

Murray Reed, a Chancery Court Judge one step below the Arkansas Supreme Court, held in May that the law must go because it tends to restrain the quest for knowledge by banning a theory that poses no hazard to the community. . . Reed said the freedom to teach and freedom to learn must be unrestrained except when they involve a doctrine hazardous to the community. He decided that the evolution theory as not so dangerous. . . [Notice the word: *unrestrained.*]

The *Minneapolis Tribune* continues in regard to the United States Supreme Court:

. . .The Supreme Court has made it plain that freedom of speech is neither absolute nor totally unrestrained. For example, in 1927 the Supreme Court held that "the teaching of what is immoral or inimical to the public welfare may be forbidden by the state, even though taught as moral or religious duty. [Notice the words: *nor* totally *unrestrained.*]

Inimical means not friendly, adverse, hostile, unfavorable.

On the other hand, the *Minneapolis Tribune* reports:

Arkansas Attorney General Bruce Bennett argues that the Darwinian theory of evolution — like polygamy — is inimical to the public welfare. . . Bennett emphasized that some restraints on freedom of speech have been held legal — including the Hatch Act, which forbids federal employees from active participation in partisan politics. Similarly, he said, Mrs. Epperson is subject to restraint by the evolution law because she was a state employee, hired by a state subdivision. . .and paid with state funds. Mrs. Epperson's personal view is that a reasonable restraint would not conflict with academic freedom.

Throughout the whole AP account runs considerable faulty reasoning. First of all, there were in the law no restrictions on freedom of speech. Mrs. Epperson has the right to preach and teach all she wants in regard to evolution, but not in public institutions and not sponsored by the state with tax money. Then Judge Murray Reed was totally wrong when he assumed that teaching evolution poses no hazard to the community and is not so dangerous. Naturally, it poses no hazard if you are an evolutionist and atheist, but it poses an extremely great hazard to parents who do not want their children taught such anti-Christian doctrines. Many Christian parents have been compelled to pay for the education of their children in private schools because of the evolution taught in public schools. If it is wrong to foster and establish religion in public schools and institutions, as the U. S. Supreme Court has correctly ruled, then it is equally wrong to foster and establish anti-creation views and antireligion through the evolutionary idea. Public servants are totally out of line in fostering any religious or antireligious ideas in the public institutions they are working for.

The United States Supreme Court has rightly declared:

the teaching of what is immoral and inimical to the public welfare may be forbidden by the state.

The teaching of evolution is extremely adverse and hostile and inimical to what Christian parents believe, except those who have been misled by evolutionists into belief of theistic evolution. Teaching evolution is also "inimical to the public welfare", because it causes constant friction, factions, and antagonism among its citizens.

To Arkansas Attorney General Bruce Bennett's statement that Mrs. Epperson was subject to restraint by the evolution law because she was a state employee, should be added this: that she was teaching ideas that were hostile and antagonistic to the beliefs of many Christian parents.

Above all, throughout the entire court case evolution was assumed to have a proven scientific basis. The AP according to *The Free Press* (Mankato, Minnesota), October 24, 1967, stated:

Mrs. Susan Epperson claimed she could not teach biology properly...without explaining the Darwinian concept of evolution.

First, in teaching biology it is not necessary to teach the origin of life, of plants and animals, since origins cannot be proven scientifically and it is not necessary for a study of the present structure and propagation of life. Secondly, if she wanted to teach the origin of life properly in biology, she would also have had to teach the *other* explanations of origins, such as creation.

But in contrast to all this the Supreme Court on November 13, 1968, according to the *Minneapolis Tribune*, ruled that:

state laws prohibiting the teaching of evolution in public schools are unconstitutional.

The [Mankato] Free Press, according to AP report stated:

The United States Supreme Court struck down a law on Tuesday saying the prohibition against the teaching of evolution in Arkansas public school was an establishment of religion by the state and unconstitutional.

How prohibiting evolution, that has never been proven to be scientific, is establishing the literal teaching of the Bible is beyond comprehension. All this does is remove all discussion of unproven origins out of the classrooms. Saying that prohibiting evolution is establishing the literal teaching of the Bible is using inverse or inverted logic. This is about the same as saying the creation belief is established by prohibiting the belief in evolution. Prohibiting the teaching of unproven evolution neither establishes creation nor rejects evolution.

Justice Abe Fortas, in writing the unanimous decision of the Supreme Court, in regard to the prohibition of establishing religion as given in the First Amendment, stated according to *Church and State* magazine of May 1981, p. 10:

The State may not adopt programs or practices in its public schools or colleges which aid or oppose any religion. This prohibition is absolute. It forbids alike the preference of a religious doctrine or prohibition of theory which is deemed antagonistic to particular dogma.

Here evolution is referred to merely as a "theory" with no antireligious or religious connotation. The false assumption made by Justice Fortas in writing the opinion of the Supreme Court was that evolution is considered a scientific theory. However, evolution, as has been shown before, is not a scientifically proven theory or fact, but is an idea that has an antireligious and religious connotation. Evolution is in essence anti-creation and is either atheistic (anti-God) or theistic (associated with God). The term "evolution," like all other terms and ideas, is the sum of all the attributes thought of as essential to its meaning; and anti-creation and atheistic and theistic are part of the attributes associated and connected with evolution.

Evolution and anti-creation and anti-religion are so intertwined, entangled and involved with each other, that anti-creation and antireligion are part of the connotation and implication connected with evolution. Evolution in essence is both antireligious and a religion in itself. Because of their close implication and connection, Christians are right in claiming that all three (evolution, anti-creation and anti-religion) are party to the same violation of the First Amendment. All three work together in misleading the children in their religious beliefs and in the beliefs of their parents.

Declaring that the First Amendment:

forbids. . .the prohibition of theory which is deemed antagonistic to particular dogma.

elevates evolution to a proven science and places the atheistic and theistic attributes of evolution in a class separate from all other religions. However evolution is not scientific and not a science and therefore is not a scientific "theory" as Justice Abe Fortas implied. It is a religion. Therefore by permitting evolution to be taught in public institutions it is giving "preference" to the evolution religion and is "establishing" the religion of evolution. See p.p. 328-340, 349-359.

15 B. ARKANSAS AGAIN MAKES NATIONAL HEADLINES IN 1981

This time is it *The Balanced Treatment for Creation-Science and Evolution-Science* act which states that if schools teach evolution they must teach creation on a scientific basis, without religious connections. At the time of this court case Professor Stephen Gould of Harvard University brought forth the old unproven idea of evolution that:

Evolution is a fact, like apples falling out of trees.

Here *unproven* evolution is placed on the same level as *proven* gravitation. This is poor and false logic. As we have seen before, there is no proof that evolution is a fact. In like manner creation cannot be proven scientifically, although it is at least logical and reasonable, having at least a reasonable explanation of *The First Cause.* Since creation-science has a religious connotation just as evolution has, it was struck down by the courts as a violation of the First Amendment. So also religious and antireligious evolution should have been prohibited in Arkansas in 1966.

15 C. THE KELLY SEGRAVES CASE IN CALIFORNIA 1981

In 1981 again, another evolution court case arose, in California this time, in the Kelly Segraves case in which three San Diego high school students sued the state of California for violating their rights by teaching Darwin's theory of evolution as the sole explanation of the origin of species. According to the *Wall Street Journal* (February 21, 1981):

The plaintiffs say California is teaching evolution as a fact rather than a theory, which excludes alternative views about man's origin from science courses. They also maintain that evolution is the central doctrine of a particular religion: secular humanism. That, they say, violates their rights because they are taught views that conflict with their own religion. . .The state says no rights are being violated because it claims there aren't any credible scientific alternatives to evolution. It contends that the view that man was created by God doesn't constitute science, and therefore doesn't belong in the science classroom.

But on what basis does the state declare evolution a scientific fact, in that it declares evolution has no "credible scientific alternatives"? There is no way in which origins can be proven scientifically, either by evolutionists or creationists. Again, on what basis, outside of the false basis that evolutionists have assumed, can it be declared that an outside nonmaterial force or being cannot be the first cause of all natural material things? Both the state and evolutionists are assuming something that has no scientific basis. True science may ignore the supernatural in studying and evaluating the present process of things, such as science has developed in the two laws of thermodynamics and the theory of biogenesis, but true science cannot explain *the origin* of these laws. If evolutionists wish to study and teach origins, they cannot ignore the possibility of a nonmaterial first cause creating material things.

15 D. LOUISIANA 1982

In 1982, Louisiana also passed a balanced treatment of evolution and creation law. During the course of legal litigation Senator William Keith, author of the law, said (Mankato, MN) Free Press, July 9, 1985:

> They say that creation science is a religious belief, but evolution also is a religious belief. It is the cardinal belief of Hindu, Buddhists, Unitarians and theological liberals.

He might have added secular humanism. This case finally reached the Fifth Circuit Court in Louisiana. Of the fifteen judges involved, eight of them declared:

> Irrespective of whether it is fully supported by scientific evidence the theory of creation is a religious belief.

The seven other judges stated that the fact, that creationism is a religious belief, does not preclude the possibility that the theory may also be scientifically true. This close vote shows what might happen some day to reverse a Supreme Court decision like Arkansas of 1968, as more and more judges and others realize that evolution is not a science.

Finally the case was taken to the U. S. Supreme Court. The *Church and State* magazine of July 1987, stated, p. 6:

In a June 19 decision, the United States Supreme Court ruled 7 - 2 that a Louisiana statute mandating the teaching of "creation - science" violates the constitutional separation of church and state. The court majority found the measure to be a thinly veiled effort to require religious instruction by public schools.

The decision of the Court was correct in disallowing the teaching of creation - science on the basis of the First Amendment. But some question the statement that it was "a thinly veiled effort to require religious instruction," as the *Church and State* magazine reported.

15 E. ALABAMA 1987

In March of 1987 United States District Judge W. Hand banned forty-four textbooks from virtually all Alabama public classrooms in a class-action lawsuit filed by 600 parents and teachers. Judge Hand stated, according to *News Service*, March 5, 1987:

With these books the state of Alabama overstepped its mark and must withdraw to perform its proper nonreligious function.

In a two and one-half week trial before Judge Hand in October 1986, it was argued:

. . .that secular humanism was being taught as a religion in numerous books. Fundamentalists say secular humanism is the elevation of transient human values over eternal spiritual values and secular humanists believe that humans can handle their own affairs without divine intervention.

Judge Hand was off course when:

He cited the history books as "deplorable" not so much for what they contained but for what they omitted such as the history of the Puritans and early revival movements.

The religious history of the many different denominations is not a necessary part of history instruction in public school or even in a church school.

On August 26, 1987, the U. S. Eleventh Circuit Court of Appeals in Atlanta overruled Judge Hand. However, this court refused to decide whether secular humanism is a religion within the definition of the First Amendment. Judge Frank Johnson Jr. of that court stated that the Supreme Court has always avoided setting up a comprehensive test for what constitutes a religion because it is such a very "delicate question."

Regarding the forty-four books, the circuit court claimed they found nothing in the books that promoted any particular religious perspective.

15 F. TENNESSEE 1988

On February 22, 1988, the AP reported:

The Supreme Court threw out an appeal [from the circuit court of Atlanta] by seven Tennessee families who say their religious freedom was violated when their children were exposed to "godless" public school books. . .The justices without comment let stand a ruling requiring the fundamentalist Christian children to read the books was constitutional.

However the AP also reported:

In seeking Supreme Court review, lawyers for the families said the case "represents a classic confrontation between parents and public school officials over the education of children." They said children should not be required to read religiously offensive books as a condition of remaining in school. . .The appeal likened the families' objection to those made by Jehovah's Witnesses families that sparked the Supreme Court 1943 decision striking down a West Virginia law that required all public school students to participate in the daily reciting of the pledge of allegiance. The appeal added, "The rule emerging from the Sixth Circuit ruling is that children can be forced to read books which violate sincere religious beliefs so long as they are not forced to believe the contents of what they have read."

Forcing children to read books contrary to their religious beliefs is a violation of their constitutional rights. It is as wrong as forcing a conscientious objector to go into the battlefield. Children belong to parents and children should not be taught anything offensive to them and their parents. Children are sent to school not to be taught anything and everything a teacher or state want to teach but merely to be taught subjects that are necessary for good citizenship.

Certainly all parents should be deeply concerned by what is taught to their children in school, and it should not be left to the state and teachers alone to decide. School boards and teachers should work in unison with the parents. If the state and the teachers insist on deciding what is to be taught, contrary to the desires of the parents, we are on the way to the government having absolute control of what is taught children, as has happened in Russia.

THE POSTLUDE

XXV.   A TRIBUTE TO OUR CREATOR-REDEEMER GOD

1.   CAUSE AND EFFECT

Having seen that the evolutionistic attempt to explain the origin of all things has no possible scientifically testable foundation, I shall in the last part, in the postlude, give credit to the only possible *First Cause*. The universe is here, the earth is here, life on earth is here, mankind is here. They are *the effect*. Every effect has a cause. What is the cause of all the above mentioned effects? It is totally irrational, illogical and nonscientific to believe that these effects could have gotten here without a superior greater cause.

Science has a law of cause and effect on which much of science is built. This law states that like causes produce like effects, and that every effect must have an adequate greater cause. No effect can be, as far as quantity and quality is concerned, greater than the cause.

The trouble that evolutionists have is that they totally ignore the primary first cause of all things, without which there can be no effect, no universe and everything that goes with it. If everything in the universe is due purely to natural causes, then there must have been a series, a chain of natural causes reaching back to the beginning, to eternity. If the chain is broken off at the beginning without scientific foundation, it leaves the entire idea of evolution dangling and unexplained.

Evolutionists claim that the universe and life are without an initial nonmaterial cause. But since the universe operates with cause and effect, how can it be explained from science that the universe itself is without an initial cause? The Big Bang idea certainly does not explain origins. And if the evolutionists allege that matter is eternal in itself, they still do not explain cause.

Since evolution deals only with natural, material causes, a beginning that is due only to a natural material cause is impossible. It is a self-contradictory idea, contrary to scientific logic and therefore false and absurd. It is an oxymoron — a contradiction.

There must be a primary cause, a force of some kind that is greater than material causes and above material causes. There must be a nonmaterial cause, a Creator, a God, above and beyond all material things. But as far as the evolutionists are concerned the name of *"God"* dare not be considered, lest the whole idea of origins become supposedly unscientific, philosophical, religious or even superstitious. But science is not scientific if it ignores a nonmaterial first cause, just as a man is illogical if he says a car or any manmade invention got here without the brains and thinking of man.

Dr. John Petrie, an Episcopalian pastor, correctly summed up the entire matter by stating:

Science is strictly limited to the physical universe. How did that universe come into being? Again science has no means for answering the question. Science studies a universe already in existence, already in operation. That it can study. That it does study with ever increasing discoveries of new truth.

Where did the universe come from? Science cannot know. Its theorists have talked of an original nebula out of which by a process of evolution the world we now have has come into being. But science cannot account for the nebula, nor for the existence of laws whereby the inorganic is supposed to have given birth to the organic, and the vegetable is supposed to have changed to the animal, and the animals into the thinking "animal," man. When scientists give us theories as to how these miracles occurred they speak not as scientists but as philosophers.

Philosophers using their logical reasoning should clearly recognize that there must be a first, nonmaterial cause. And if they are honest they will have to become theologians who recognize a God that they must be responsible to as their Creator, as many of the greatest scientists of the past and present have done.

Even ancient Aristotle deduced that reason and logic insisted on the existence of a Being who had no beginning. Later thinkers amplified Aristotle's thinking. There had to be something that was self-existent, nonmaterial. The entire universe, all material, all creation, including life itself was dependent on something else, on something nonmaterial.

And yet we still have today, more than ever before, people with the silly ideas that this whole universe just evolved. James Trefil in *The Moment of Creation*, p. 215, states:

From this point on, the stages of the Big Bang that we described earlier will simply replay themselves in reverse — nuclei dissociating into protons and neutrons, protons and neutrons dissociating into quarks — until we are back to the original state that started the Big Bang. This scenario leads inevitably to the most fascinating question of all: Will the universal contraction (which cosmologists half jokingly call the Big Crunch) be followed by another expansion (the Big Bounce)? In other words will the universe arise phoenix-like from its ashes and repeat the entire cycle? The picture of a universe that is reborn every hundred billion years is very attractive to some people. The main advantage of an eternally oscillating universe is that the question of why it all started and where it all came from simply do not have to be asked.

Those last words may satisfy evolutionists, but they do not satisfy men who are scientists. Scientists ask questions and seek answers that can be proven scientifically before they make conclusions that are only assumptions and guess-work. Where did the material of the universe and the power of oscillation come from?

James Trefil concluded his book on page 223 with these words:

My message, then, to those who feel that science is overstepping its bounds when it probes the early universe is simple: don't worry. No matter how far the boundaries are pushed back, there will always be room for religious faith and a religious interpretation of the physical world.

For myself, I feel much more comfortable with the concept of a God who is clever enough to devise the laws of physics that make the existence of our marvelous universe inevitable than I do with the old-fashioned God who had to make it all laboriously piece by piece.

Since the old-fashioned God made it all in six days, He certainly did not work at it laboriously piece by piece. And so after all this silly nonsense, Trefil and other evolutionists have to come back to a God as the Prime Cause, Creator and Designer.

Regarding all such thinking, I must repeat a great statement made by Dr. Alfred Rehwinkel in *The Wonders of Creation*, p. 182:

To say that all this just happened by itself, but required millions of years to develop, is no answer. It is cheap and dishonest evasion of the real issue. And to wrap that kind of an answer in bombastic scientific verbiage is merely resorting to the tricks of the magician to deceive the naive and the credulous who delight in being deceived. . . .This is not science. It is nothing less than the world's greatest hoax and fraud — sheer scientific quackery. Every normal, intellectually honest person knows that every effect must have a corresponding cause; that is science and is also common sense.

2.   WHO CREATED THE CREATOR?

Some evolutionists, as a last resort, ask: "Who created the Creator?" Some atheists claim that they *never saw God*. A French astronomer (Lalande) who died 1837 is said to have pointed his telescope to the heavens and, not seeing God, said: "There is no God," as though the nonmaterial God could be seen with a telescope. One of the first Russians in space also said he looked around and he could see no God out there in space. But God cannot be perceived by our five senses. To do so is similar to a blind man claiming there is no light and a deaf man saying there is no sound and to a man saying that there are no sun, moon or stars because he cannot hear or smell them.

August Berkshire, Director of the Twin Cities chapter of American Atheists reported January 11, 1986 in the *Minneapolis Tribune* in ridicule of news columnist George Will:

The first-cause argument for a god is inherently flawed. The premise is that something as complex as the universe needs a creator. However, that creator must be at least as complex as his creation - and by the Christian description, is much more complex. Who could create that Creator? If a god could have always existed, then it is much more likely that the universe, being simpler, could have always existed.

At the end he tries to ridicule Mr. Will by stating:

He should stick to politics, economics, and perhaps science fiction, and leave science to those who know the meaning of reason and evidence.

But it is Mr. Berkshire who should learn the meaning of reason. As far as the origin of God or of the universe is concerned, it is not a question which was the simpler or the more complex, but which had the power, knowledge and know-how to create the other. Matter could not create a creator, but a Creator could create matter.

Dr. Henry Morris in *Scientific Creationism*, p. 19, answers this question of God and matter and which was first in these words:

"But, then, who made God?" But such a question of course *begs* the question. If the evolutionist prefers not to believe in God, he must still believe in some kind of uncaused First Cause. He must either postulate matter coming into existence out of nothing or else matter having always existed in some primitive form. In either case, matter itself becomes its own Cause and the creationist may well ask: "But, then, who made Matter?"

For matter to come out of nothing, without an adequate cause, would be the greatest of all miracles. Secondly, for matter not only to evolve by itself, but above all, for such an immense, such a magnificent and such a complex universe as we have, to evolve by itself without a still greater cause or miracle worker would be the *miracle of miracles.*

Two such impossible and immense miracles are scientifically impossible. William King stated correctly:

> There is much difficulty in believing in God. There is a much greater difficulty in *not* believing in a Creator God.

3.   ONLY GOD COULD CREATE

Since matter cannot be the cause of its own existence, there must therefore be a superior, powerful, nonmaterial and supremely intelligent Being who was before and above matter and the laws inherent in matter. This Being must be in the last analysis the Cause and Creator of all existing material and animate things and the Originator of time and space. Sound reason, logic and philosophy insist on such a conclusion. This is also the teaching of Divine Revelation given in Romans 1:20, which I repeat here for emphasis:

> For since the creation of the world *His invisible attributes* are clearly seen, being understood by the things that are made, *even His eternal power and Godhead,* so that they are without excuse. [Emphasis Added] NKJV

Evolutionists try to circumvent this truth but they cannot prove creation false or illogical.

4.   WHAT WAS THERE BEFORE CREATION, OUTSIDE OF GOD?

An African creation myth gives an idea of the total nonexistence of anything before creation and of the inconceivable emptiness everywhere:

No stars were there — no sun,
Neither moon nor earth;
Nothing existed but darkness itself —
A darkness everywhere;
Nothing existed but nothingness.
For how long this nothingness lasted
No one will ever know,
And why there was nothing but nothing is something
We must never try to learn.

Yet God is eternal and He was active. He was before time, space and material.

Psalm 90 says of God:

Before the mountains were brought forth Or ever You had formed the earth and the world, Even from everlasting to everlasting You are God. NKJV.

Man just cannot understand the eternal existence of God, having neither a beginning nor an end. Dr. Alfred Rehwinkel in *The Wonders of Creation* states, p. 50:

. . .it would not seem irreverent or presumptuous to assume that He was active then as He is now, but in some other sphere of which we know nothing. The very nature of God would seem to demand this. God is life and the source of all life and energy. That means activity.

5.   WHAT DID GOD CREATE?

Jeremiah 33:22 declares:

As the host of heaven cannot be numbered, nor the sand of the sea measured, so will I multiply the descendants of David. NKJV

And all these stars and planets are totally different from each other, as I Corinthians 15:41 states:

There is one glory of the sun, another glory of the moon, and another glory of the stars; for one star differs from another star in glory. NKJV

What a grand, magnificent, awe-inspiring spectacle the stars of heaven present to man! The seemingly limitless space of heaven is filled with many galaxies of countless stars. The number of them and their diversity stagger the imagination of mankind.

The astronomer Sir James Jeans said:

Put three grains of sand inside a vast cathedral, and the cathedral will be more closely packed with sand than space is with stars.

The movement of the sun, the moon and the stars is so accurate that our watches can be set by them. Genesis 1:14 declares that they serve "for signs and for seasons, and for days and years." How correctly Psalm 19:1 declares: "The heavens declare the glory of God And the firmament shows His handiwork." NKJV The stars of the heavens declare that God was before all matter, before all time, before all space, before all stars, before all galaxies, before the solar system and before the earth. With His almighty power and with his infinite wisdom and creative design He brought the universe, the heaven and earth into existence.

However, God created not only a wondrous heaven that can be viewed through a telescope. He also created another world that is just as marvelous. All around us are marvelous animate and inanimate tiny things that can be viewed only with a microscope. The waters of the earth are filled with living creatures that can be viewed only likewise. Here men have seen creatures of many different shapes and forms. Some are so small that millions of them might be contained in one cubic inch of water. Because of their tiny size they are called animalcula or small animals. They have mouths, stomachs, muscles, nerves, glands, eyes — in short all the important features of large animals. Paradoxically as it may seem, the universe is as small as it is large.

A man by the name of Chalmers said regarding the created worlds of God that the telescope and the microscope have revealed:

> The one led me to see a system in every star; the other leads me to see a world in every atom. The one taught me that this mighty globe, with the whole burden of its people and of its countries, is but a grain of sand on the high fields of immensity; the other teaches me, that every grain of sand may harbor within it the tribes, and the families of a busy population. The one told me of the insignificance of the world I tread upon; the other . . . in the waters of every rivulet, there are worlds teeming with life.

6.   MATTER AND THE ELEMENTS

(In Chapter XII, 6, I wrote regarding the essence of matter, here about its origin.)

Evolutionists like Heinz Haber, in *Our Blue Planet* (1965) believe:

> [T]hat in its original state matter consisted only of one kind of basic building block: hydrogen atoms. Imagine that the volume of the universe was filled with an exceedingly rarefied gas consisting only of hydrogen atoms. A fundamental force was exerted between these particles — the force of gravity.

But where did the hydrogen, and where did the force of gravity come from? Evidently hydrogen has become the Cause and God for some of these people.

Men like Fred Hoyle once believed:

From time to time people ask where the created material comes from. Well, it does not come from anywhere. Matter simply appears. . .At one time the various atoms composing the matter do not exist, and at a later time they do.

In this way evolutionists have substituted faith in matter for faith in a nonmaterial first cause. Faith in God at least provides a first, elementary cause.

In the first few words of the Bible, God gives the origin of all matter: "In the beginning God created the heaven and the earth." This includes all the materials that the universe consist of. God created not only hydrogen but all the other elements of matter: gold, silver and about 92 elemental substances. Why are all these elements different from each another? Why are they found in different parts of the earth and in different layers of the earth as they are? And why would they all flow out of hydrogen, *if they do?*

Matter has no life as plants and animals have. Yet in a piece of so-called dead matter there are billions of atoms, each one filled with movement, action energy and force, each one an active universe in itself. We know what an active piece of matter uranium is and what it does in an atomic bomb. Within matter is force and the cause of that force is a creation of God.

Professor John Monsma, professor of philosphy and theology at the Catholic University of America, Washington, D.C., wrote in 1962 in *Science and Religion:*

Creation may be defined as the production of something from absolutely nothing that is preexistent. . .for every effect there must be a corresponding cause. . .Positive or empirical science is that branch of knowledge which is concerned with phenomena and their immediate *causes.* It includes physics, chemistry, biology, astronomy, astrophysics, radio astronomy, and the like. The only method used in positive science is the *experimental* method, no matter whether its tool is the most refined microscope or the newly perfected radio telescope. What does not fall within the realm of sensible experience is not an empirical datum and cannot constitute the object of empirical investigation. Thus understood, positive science has definite limits which the scientist himself implicitly admits. . .It is our contention that the doctrine of creation is completely beyond the reach of positive science, and that any rejection of it in the name of science is inconsistent and fallacious. . .Science may tell us *what* the world is once the world has been made, but not *how* it came about to be, since this is not a problem whose answer is subject to empirical verification. . .Our contention is that evolution is not self-explanatory and that it demands a cause. That cause cannot be matter, which is itself in need of an explanation and is subject to the laws of evolution. . .It must therefore be a superior and supremely intelligent being which is above matter and its laws and in the last analysis, the cause and creator of all existing things. This is the teaching both of Divine revelation and of sound philosophy. Against it the attacks of science are absolutely groundless. . .We may rightly conclude that the doctrine of creation, and religion in general, have nothing to fear from science. . .One of the most formidable temptations of contemporary scientists is that of erecting a proud citadel, a modern Tower of Babel, as a challenge of human intelligence to the Divine Creator.

7.   TIME AND GOD

What is true of matter and space is also true of time. Before creation there was no time. Time and space and matter are all tied to creation. St. Augustine stated that the world was not created *in* time but *with* time.

8.   THE LAWS OF NATURE AND GOD

What is true of matter, space and time is also true of the natural laws that coexist with matter. The laws of nature require a lawgiver who is all-powerful and all-wise. It is for this reason that these laws of nature are a problem to the evolutionists. Saying that these laws came into existence without a lawgiver does not explain how these laws came into existence.

The laws of nature are the orderly way in which things happen in matter, in nature, in the universe, time and again. But the question is why do these things happen in such an orderly sequence. Why, for example, does gravity always exert the same downward influence on all objects? Why do the earth and other planets move around the sun as precisely as they do? Why does each species or kind of plants and animals produce only its own kind and not something else? Why do seeds from a certain plant sprout and grow only into the same kind of plant? Why do cells of males and females develop and multiply and grow, time after time, until another human being is produced?

Men have delved into these mysteries of nature and tried to find the cause of these laws of nature, but the origin of these laws is the same as that for matter, space and time. Without an all-powerful and all-wise Creator and Designer it is impossible to account for these laws. Physicist Stephen Hawking said:

> The more we examine the universe, we find it is not arbitrary at all but obeys certain well-defined laws that operate in different areas. It seems very reasonable to suppose that there may be some unifying principles.

Rocket expert Wernher von Braun stated:

> The natural laws of the universe are so precise that we have no difficulty building a spaceship to fly to the moon and can time the flight with the precision of a fraction of a second. These laws must have been set by somebody.

Yes, it would be impossible for scientists to understand things and make things operate and do things as they do, if the laws of nature had not been created by an all-wise, orderly, designing God who caused all things to continue to operate in an orderly way day after day and time after time.

9.   GOD IS ABOVE AND NOT BOUND BY THE LAWS OF NATURE

Although God created and designed the laws of nature, He has caused many *super*natural things to happen. He caused things to happen outside the normal experience and knowledge of man, such as the miracles mentioned in the Bible. God is also *super*natural in that He is not limited to and bound by the laws of nature, but is over, above and beyond these laws. Above all, God is *pre*natural in that He existed before the universe and the laws of nature were created.

God's *supernatural* character and activity are evident in the miracles He performed, which went above the laws of nature. He showed that He is above the natural law, when Moses saw the bush that did not burn up; when the three Israelites walked in the fiery furnace of Babylon without being injured; when the lions refrained from harming Daniel when he was put into the den with them; when Christ walked on the water; when Christ turned water into wine; when He raised Lazarus from the dead; and when Christ was conceived without a human father.

10.   THINGS THAT HAVE BEEN MADE ARE EVIDENCES OF GOD'S NATURE AND ESSENCE

I must repeat Romans 1:19-20 once more:

> Because what may be known of God is manifest in them, for God has shown it to them. For since the creation of the world His

invisible attributes are clearly seen, being understood by the things that are made, even His *eternal power* and *Godhead.* [Emphasis Added]

From the things that have been created there are all kinds of evidences of God's attributes: that whoever *caused* the universe and all that is in it was an *eternal* being existing before creation; was an *all-powerful being* who could create such a vast, immense creation; and was also a *nonmaterial, spiritual* being who was before, above, beyond and greater than all the material things we can see in creation. The words "being understood by the things that are made," show and stress that the things that are made have certainly not been made by themselves, *but by God.*

Astronomer Robert Jastrow stressed the opposite side of this truth when he declared:

> Scientists have no proof that life was not the result of an act of creation.

In fact, scientific evidences verify creation.

11. CREATION WAS PERFECT

As God looked at what had been created each day, He declared that "it was good." At the end of the sixth day, as He looked at *"everything that He had made,"* He declared that indeed *"it was very good."* God had created a perfect world, perfect in every detail, totally, absolutely good, including Adam and Eve, who were our *masterpiece* forefathers. Today the wisest, the most adept, the most skilled, the most beautiful woman and the most handsome man are mere *degenerates* of the masterpiece. When God finished the creation nothing was missing for perfect animals or mankind. See the first part of this book as to what the earth must have been like in its perfection (Chapters IV and V).

12. THE EARTH: THE ONLY ONE OF ITS KIND

The earth is the only known place in the universe that can support life. Genesis 1:14-15 state that God made the sun, moon and stars for the sake of the earth and man. Even Preston Cloud, head of the School of Earth Science of the University of Minnesota and no creationist wrote in *Cosmos, Earth and Man* (1978), p. 2:

> Planet Earth. . .is the only object in the solar system, indeed in the universe, that is *known* to be capable of supporting life. . . Only a thin atmospheric blanket shields us from the lethal radiation beyond, and from equally lethal extremes of heat and cold. Only a

little film of water moderates our climate and provides the solvent in which our life stuff is suspended. Earth's interior is forever sealed to entry beyond a few kilometers in depth, whether we start our penetration on land or at sea. It is worth our while, therefore, to try to understand our. . .fragile life-support system, and the necessity of treating it with care.

13. THE EARTH AND THE UNIVERSE CREATED IN SIX DAYS

The Hebrew word for *day* in the Old Testament may have one of three possible meanings. First, it may mean the period of light that passes between sunrise and sunset, as it is used in Genesis 1:5: "And God called the light Day." Secondly, it is used to refer to an ordinary day of 24 hours. Thirdly, it is used in the sense of age or era as in Isaiah 11:15: "like as it was to Israel in the *day* that he came up out of the land of Egypt." In this third sense the meaning is simply an era without a long, extended period of time and above all not millions of years. The Bible nowhere speaks of millions of years. The word *day* as used in Genesis chapter one is without doubt a normal 24 hour day.

This is the obvious meaning as is evident in the words used in Genesis: "And the evening and the morning were the first day," said of all six days. That six ordinary days were meant is evident in Exodus 20:9 and 11:

Six days you shall labor and do all your work. .For in six days the LORD made the heaven and the earth. NKJV

If the evolutionary idea of days meaning millions of years were true this would mean "six days," each lasting millions of years, "You shall labor." Such an interpretation is ridiculous. If it were not for the idea of evolution, there would hardly be anyone who would doubt that Moses meant a 24-hour day. Ages, eons and millions of years do not consist of mornings and evenings.

The idea that the days mentioned in chapter one of Genesis consisted of millions of years is ridiculous for other reasons. If the third day consisted of millions of years, then the plants that were created on that day would have had to live millions of years without the sun which was created the fourth day. God said on the first day "Let there be light, and there was light." If the first day was millions of years long, it would have taken that long to create light, which also is ridiculous. If God could not create light instantly throughout the universe as He created other things instantly, then the light from the stars that are claimed to be millions of *light years* away would not yet be visible to us. God has performed many miracles instantly — not only at the time of creation but also at other times. Overnight "the rod of Aaron . . . had sprouted and put forth buds, had produced blossoms and yielded ripe almonds" (Numbers 17:8). NKJV Christ turned water into wine instantly. Adam and Eve were created the sixth day. If the seventh day was an era of millions of years, then Adam and Eve lived through millions of years, totally unreasonable.

Some people think that such passages as Psalm 90:4 "For a thousand years in thy sight are but as yesterday," and II Peter 3:8, "one day is with the Lord as a thousand years," show that the Hebrew word for day, "yom," is here used for a period of a thousand years or more. But these passages merely show that God is not limited to time, as is the case with mankind, and that with God there is only timelessness or no time.

14.   GOD'S CREATIVE ACT CAN BE FULLY GRASPED ONLY BY FAITH

Although Roman 1:18-20 tells us that natural man can learn of the existence of God by virtue of his human reasoning, and that he can know "by the things that are made" that there is a Creator, yet Hebrews 11:3 declares: "Through *faith* we understand that the worlds were framed by the word of God." These two passages do not contradict each other. The Romans passage merely tells us that the vastness and the complexity of the universe could not have developed by itself, by accident, by chance. All these supernatural things must have had a *supranatural*, wise, almighty Creator and Designer. This is as far as human reasoning can go. How this universe was made, human reasoning cannot understand. That it was made by the Word of God reason cannot discover and comprehend. It is only through faith created in us by the Word of God that we can fully grasp the creative act of God as presented to us in Genesis. Yes, only through the knowledge given in the Bible and by faith created through the Bible do we know how the universe was created.

15.   WHAT KIND OF BEING IS GOD?

Although a description of God and His essence is impossible, we can gain a glimpse of what He is by referring to what he is *not*. We cannot confine God to time and space and the material universe because He is above, beyond and before time, space and matter. The best we can do is to compare Him to a spirit. But even here we cannot develop a mental image of a spirit, because we have never seen a spirit. We can refer to the spirit of man. But just as we are not able to locate the spirit of man anywhere in his body, so also we cannot locate the spirit of God anywhere in His universe. He is both everywhere and yet entirely in our presence, just as our eyes can see millions of miles out into space and yet be entirely where we are. Because God is so much greater and different from what we are, we really cannot compare the spirit of man with the Spirit of God. Man's spirit is confined to his body, whereas God in His Spirit is above and beyond the universe He created. The only thing we can do is accept God as he presents Himself to us in His Word. He is a Triune God, Three in One, Father, Son, and Holy Ghost. He is almighty, omniscient, omnipresent, unchangeable, eternal, perfect, gracious, just, etc. In short, the entire Bible is a description of God. And He asks us to read and study His Word to learn about Him and us.

16.   ATTRIBUTES OF GOD

16 A. God is *eternal* and *incomprehensible* from eternity to eternity, from everlasting to everlasting. He always was and always existed. He has no beginning and no end. He was before time and creation began. Psalm 90:2 declares:

> Before the mountains were brought forth or ever thou hadst formed the earth and the world, even from everlasting to everlasting thou art God.

Psalm 102:27 states:

> Thou art the same, and thy years shall have no end.

All this is incomprehensible to us. So also the thought of His eternal activity (apart from the existence of the material universe) is incomprehensible. The infinite God is beyond the comprehension of finite mankind.

Hand in hand with God's infinity goes His *immensity*. Because of His immensity our puny reason and intellect cannot comprehend God. "His greatness is unsearchable!" (Psalm 145:3) Because of His infinity and immensity, God cannot be confined to any definite space such as this universe. God is above and beyond space, as Solomon declared at the dedication of the Temple in Jerusalem (I Kings 8:27):

> [W]ill God indeed dwell on the earth? Behold, the heaven and heaven of heavens cannot contain You; how much less this house!" NKJV

Although God does enter into time and space, He always remains above and beyond time and space.

16 B. Because of this God is also *omnipresent*. In Jeremiah 23:24 God declares:

> "Can anyone hide himself in secret places, So I shall not see Him? says the LORD. "Do I not fill heaven and earth?" says the LORD. NKJV

Although God is present and active in the universe, he transcends all space. Since God is everywhere at the same time, nobody can hide from Him. He fills heaven and earth, but not in a manner that a part of God is in one place and a part at another place. The entire God is everywhere at the same time. God is present with us in every need. At the same time we cannot hide our sins from God. His grace also surrounds us.

16 C. God also is *omniscient* in that He *knows all things*. Psalm 147:5 declares:

> Great is our Lord, and mighty in power; *His understanding is infinite*. NKJV

He knows the thoughts within a man's mind. Psalm 139:2 states:

> Thou knowest my downsitting and mine uprising, thou understandest my thought afar off.

God knows not only our thoughts but also our emotions, our feelings and the intents of our hearts as Hebrews 4:12 states: "[He] is a discerner of the thoughts and intents of the heart."

16 D. Together with the infinite knowledge of God goes His great and glorious *wisdom*. Psalm 19:1 states: "The heavens declare the *glory* of God and the firmament shows His handiwork." NKJV. Yes, the heavens, the universe, the earth and all that is therein declare the great wisdom of God in creating all things. Romans 11:33: "Oh, the depth of the riches both the *wisdom* and *knowledge* of God!" Here a destinction is made between the wisdom and knowledge of God. The two words are not synonymous when applied to God. The wisdom of God refers to his great skill, expertise, and know-how that He showed in creating the universe and in ruling and preserving it today. Man too easily criticizes God in His past and present work, and man loves to elevate his puny wisdom above God's unsearchable wisdom. Man loves to ignore, reject and criticize the wisdom of God.

The wisdom of God is shown in perpetual motion. Men have tried for centuries to develop a device that would move forever in perpetual motion. But God created such a device when he created the universe and especially the solar system of which our earth is a part. Our solar system and all its parts (the planets and their moons) float through space in constant perpetual motion with no strings, ropes, or rods attached as they spin through space in unison and in precision of timing that no man-made device could match. Certainly God is an Architect of supreme wisdom in devising such a creation.

Astronaut Eugene Cernan in 1972 summed it all up beautifully. I must repeat his statement, *The Free Press*, Mankato, MN, Nov. 30, 82:

> When you look at the earth from the moon and you see the perfectness and beauty of it and the logic of it all, you know it didn't happen by accident. It is moving with beauty and you get a feeling that you are looking at our earth as a God, whoever that God might be, envisioned it when He created it. I'm anxious to get back and get the feeling again.

In spite of all that the evolutionists tried to prove to the contrary in those trips to the moon, astronaut Cernan and other astronauts saw the superb *wisdom* of the Creator behind the entire universe.

Then consider the way in which God perpetuates all the plants and animals of this world so that the different kinds continue to propagate and how God provides the food needed for all the different kinds.

Then consider man, the crowning creature of all creation, who has a body "fearfully and wonderfully made," which body, although now a degenerated descendant of the masterpiece, is still a majestic and beautiful creature in design. Every part of the human body is superbly suited to the purpose for which it was intended and created. Look at the human hand, for example, with its four fingers and a thumb. The hand is equally well created for doing house and yard work, for writing, for typing, for lifting an object, for skimming over the keys of a piano, for many different types of sports and for a thousand other purposes.

Consider also the wisdom shown in the creation of the eye and thousands of other creations. The eye can be adjusted so that it can see distances varying from a few inches to many miles. It can see tiny objects and read a book at a distance of a few inches. The eye can see a landscape stretching over many miles and bring it into the focus of a space only half an inch in diameter. Yet it can distinguish extremely large objects like mountains and small objects like a bird at the same time. It can distinguish objects of different sizes, colors, shapes and positions in the landscape.

One more example of design, creation and wisdom. Look at a watermelon. William J. Bryan wrote many years ago:

I was eating a piece of watermelon and was struck with its beauty. I took some of the seeds and dried them and weighed them; I found that it would require about 5,000 seeds to weigh a pound. . . One of these seeds put into the ground, when warmed by the sun and moistened by the rain, takes off its coat and goes to work; it gathers from somewhere 200,000 times its own weight and, forcing this raw material through a tiny stem, constructs a watermelon. . . What architect drew the plan? Where does that little seed get its tremendous strength? Where does it find its coloring matter: green, white, red and black? How does it build a watermelon?

Then look at the beautiful flowers that God in His supreme wisdom created and designed, and through self-propagation perpetuated for centuries. No matter where one looks in nature, in vegetables and fruits of all kinds, in the animal world and even in insects one must marvel at the wisdom shown in their creation. Only a fool would deny that there was Supreme Wisdom and a Designer behind all this.

16 E. In regard to the attributes of God that describe His nature as given in the Bible much could also be said in regard to His *omnipotence* or almighty power, His loving concern for all creation and especially for mankind, His goodness, His mercy, His grace, His loving forgiveness as shown in providing forgiveness through the atoning sacrifice of His Son, Jesus Christ. Much could also be said in regard to His holiness, justice, righteousness, His faithfulness, unchangeableness, truthfulness, patience and His benevolence.

17.   WHAT IS WRONG IN THIS WORLD

But in spite of all these beautiful and marvelous attributes of God, all is not right between man and his all-wise Creator. Ever since the first people, there has been rebellion by mankind against its Creator. It started with Adam and Eve, it showed up again in their first children, Cain and others. It continued in their descendants, so that finally in total disgust and righteous anger God wiped out billions of mankind except for a remnant in the Flood. This remnant was needed to provide a Redeemer — Savior that God promised mankind through Adam and Eve.

This rebellion against God continued shortly after the Flood in a manifest way at the Tower of Babel. It showed up again and again in the descendants of Abraham, and it has continued unto this very day. It has continued to a greater degree today not only in those who rebel against God and the moral law that He has instilled in every person, but above all in those who even try to deny His existence, in spite of all the evidence that He exists.

Rebellion against God, *sin*, has always been, since the days of Adam and Eve to this day, the problem in this world. That all people are sinners is clearly declared in Romans 3:10: "There is none righteous, no, not one." Because of sin, the rebellion against God and his law and will, there is evil and wickedness in this world. There is covetousness, hatred, fighting, corruption, lust, deceit in the hearts of men. Above all, because of this rebellion against the Creator, the evil in mankind causes men to worship and serve "the creature more than the Creator" (Romans 1:25).

18.   A REDEEMER — SAVIOR

But in spite of all this rebellion and sin, God in grace, mercy, kindness and loving forgiveness has provided a way, a means of deliverance from sin and its results of eternal separation from God. He has provided a Redeemer — Savior in His Son, Jesus Christ. Through Him and Him alone God has provided forgiveness and restoration in God. II Corinthians 5:21 declares:

> For [God] made Him [Jesus Christ] who knew no sin to be sin for us, that we might become the righteousness of God in Him. NKJV

This Redeemer — Savior was promised immediately after mankind fell into sin. While still in the Garden of Eden, God said to Satan, Gen. 3:15: "I will put enmity between you and the woman, and between your seed and her seed; He shall bruise your head, and you shall bruise His heel."

Regarding man's Redeemer — Savior, the Son of God, Bernard Bell of Columbia University many years ago wrote in *A Book For Tired Machinists:*

> Some day it flashes over us that the saints of all the ages have not been fools, and that the Christian Church in her creeds has not been uttering the arrant nonsense that many clever people say she has; that this Jesus is really God Almighty come among us men; that he is alive forevermore; that in very truth he does reveal God in all His power and friendship to us mortals.
>
> Jesus is not some vaguely recognized abstraction which may be acknowledged and then put out of one's mind, like gravitation and the ether; but God is Jesus, walking still among us men, hearing us pray, blessing us in sacraments, our compassionate friend,

touched with every feeling of our infirmities, but at the same time God of God, Light of Light, Very God of Very God.

This is a most beautiful declaration of what God has done for us in and through Jesus Christ. This statement is so sorely needed today in an age when so many people claim themselves to be *scientific geniuses (Homo sapiens, sapiens)* and at the same time are *spiritual ignoramuses.* The wisest thing the most learned man can ever learn is that "The fear of the LORD is the beginning of wisdom" (Psalm 111:10). Fear here means a humble awe of the all-wise Creator and the Word of His will and wisdom. The worst ignoramus is what another Psalm declares, 14:1:

The fool [no matter how well educated he thinks he is] has said in his heart, "There is no God." NKJV

Man today, as he is by nature without the God of the Bible, is spiritually discerned, blind, ignorant and dead, a spiritual corpse, I Cor. 2:14 states: "The natural man does not receive the things of the Spirit of God, for they are foolishness to Him, nor can He know them, because they are spiritually discerned." NKJV

In short, a man is saved by faith in Jesus Christ, his Redeemer - Savior. Man, on the other hand, is lost because of his own logic, for logic condemns his foolish false idea — the origin of the universe, the earth and man by way of evolution.

Why did God choose such a simple way to heaven — alone by faith in Christ? God just does not want rebellion in heaven again, as happened when the evil angels rebelled against Him. Nor does He want people in heaven like the *children of men* in the days after Adam and Eve, who denied and rejected Him and whom He had to destroy in the Flood. The beauties, splendor, magnificence and glories of heaven are so beautiful and wonderful that God does not want anything there that will mar its blessedness. People sing in heaven out of sheer joy in the salvation God has provided, through the saving atonement made by Christ. Therefore boasting and glorying in man's own efforts are totally out of place in heaven. It is as the Apostle Paul so clearly expressed it in Ephesians 2:6-9:

[He] made us to sit together in the heavenly places in Christ Jesus, that in the ages to come He might show the exceeding riches of His grace in His kindness toward us in Christ Jesus. For by grace you have been saved *through faith,* and that *not of yourselves; it is the gift of God, not of works,* lest anyone should *boast* (italics by author). NKJV

How much clearer could it be put? Above all God does not want any *boasting Homo sapiens, sapiens* people in heaven to mess up heaven.

19.   HEAVEN

The Bible refers to three different heavens or kinds of heaven. The first heaven is the atmosphere surrounding the earth, in which the birds and airplanes fly and the clouds move (Genesis 1:8 and 20). The second heaven mentioned (Genesis 1:14-17) is that in which the sun, moon, planets and stars move — outer space. The third heaven, the one we all hope to reach, is that glorious place that the Apostle Paul refers to in these words:

> I know a man in Christ who fourteen years ago. . .was caught up to the third heaven. . .how he was caught up into Paradise and heard inexpressible words, which it is not lawful for man to utter (II Corinthians 12:2-4). NKJV

Here the Apostle Paul tells us that the glory of Paradise or heaven is so great that it cannot be described in human words. This is the heaven where God is present in all His glory and where hundreds of millions of angels are in the presence of God (Daniel 7:10).

19A. *What* is heaven? According to the Bible, heaven is a real, objective place. Speaking of heaven, Christ said: "I go to prepare a place for you," and He refers to it as "My Father's house." In Revelation 21:23 the Apostle John spoke of heaven as "the holy city," that has "no need of the sun or of the moon to shine in it, for the glory of God illuminated it, and the Lamb [Christ] is its light." NKJV

19B. *Where* is heaven? This is a question which we cannot answer because God has not revealed its location. According to the language of the Bible, we may however think of it as being above us somewhere. In Psalm 103 heaven is spoken of as "high above the earth." When Jesus left this earth, we are told: "He was taken up and a cloud received Him out of their sight." Acts 1:9. For this reason, with the disciples we think of heaven as being "up there somewhere," beyond the azure blue. Scripture speaks of heaven as the place where the saved children of God "shall see God" and where "we shall be like Him, for we shall see Him as he is." In short, heaven is beyond this earth.

19C. *What kind of place* is heaven? Here is where human words become even more inadequate because there is nothing on earth that can be compared with it. Whoever has been to Yellowstone National Park and other very scenic places in the western part of our country stands amazed at the beauties and glories that the hand of God wrought there. And when a man comes back from his trip there and his friends ask him to describe some of the things he saw, he cannot, for some of those things are too stupendous and beautiful. Words cannot describe them. You have to see it yourself. If this is true of some things on earth, how much more so must it be true of heaven, the place where Christ has gone to prepare a place for us. All we can do is wait until He takes us to heaven, and then we shall see it as it really is.

However, heaven with all its glories is referred to us as our home. Jesus said:

Let not your heart be troubled; you believe in God, believe also in Me. In My Father's house are many mansions, if it were not so, I would have told you. I go to prepare a place for you. . . that where I am, there you may be also (John 14:1-3).

Jesus here compares heaven to a large home place with many mansions. Heaven is presented to us as our family residence, our home town or our home country where we will live happily undisturbed with our fellow saved believers together with the angels of heaven. The heavenly home is where the angels and the saved believing children of God sing, out of sheer gratitude to God, in music too beautiful for human ears to comprehend, because of all the wonders that God has provided for us.

19D. *Who is in heaven?* What a place heaven must be since it is the home of God and the habitation of Christ, the Savior - Redeemer, the King of kings, the Lord of lords! The fact that Christ, our Savior, is there makes it a place of bliss and supreme joy. He who loved us with an everlasting love, who sacrificed Himself and gave His life as ransom for us, is in heaven, waiting for us, longing for us. When the believers in the Savior get there He will welcome them before the large assembly as his brothers and sisters. If the President of the United States would take us before a large assembly and proclaim us as his friends, his brothers and sisters, what an honor that would be for us! But in heaven Jesus, the King, the Creator of heaven and earth, will take the believers before the vast assembly of all the angels and the blessed and will declare: these are my friends, my brothers and sisters. Indeed, any honor that famous men of this earth can bestow upon us dwindles into insignificance compared with the honor and glory which Christ in heaven will bestow upon us. What a place of ceaseless activity heaven must be with all those angels, serving God, worshipping Him and carrying out His commandments for the promotion of His purpose.

Above all in heaven are the uncounted people beginning from the days of Adam and Eve who have been permitted to enter. The Apostle John says concerning the vision of heaven which he saw:

After these things I looked and I behold, a great multitude which no one could number, of all nations, tribes, peoples, and tongues, standing before the throne and before the Lamb, clothed with white robes, with palm branches in their hands (Revelation 7:9). NKJV

From these words it is evident that there are so many saved people in heaven that no man can ever count them. All these people came from all the nations, races and tongues of this earth, for wherever the Gospel of Christ is preached, there are always some who believe these *Glad Tidings* and thus inherit the glories of heaven. *Think of it!* We shall meet Abraham, Isaac, Jacob, Job, David and all the rest of the believers of the Old Testament. Also the New Testament saints, the Apostles, all the followers and disciples of the Lord and all the believers of the past centuries will be there to meet us. There will be people from Europe, Asia, Africa, Australia, and all other parts of the world. People often like to know about their ancestors in Europe. You will meet these saved in heaven. Christ said: "Many shall come from the east and west and shall sit down with Abraham, and Isaac, and Jacob in the kingdom of heaven." Mt. 8:11. What wonderful company and companions await us in "Yonder shining regions!" Some consider it quite an honor to be admitted into the society of the elite here on earth. But what is that compared with admission into the society of God's elect in the "City fair and high"?

With this conglomeration of people in heaven from all nations, languages and ages, the question arises, shall we know one another in heaven? Here on earth, especially in larger cities, people often do not know the people living with them in the same block, yes even in the same apartment house. But in heaven such a condition will not exist. There we shall meet and recognize many believers in Christ, including the patriarchs of old, the prophets and apostles, whom we never had occasion to meet personally here on earth.

The Bible tells us that when Jesus took three of His disciples to the Mount of Transfiguration, these disciples at once recognized Moses and Elijah even though they had never seen these two before. In like manner we most likely will know all other Christian people in heaven. And if we will be able to know all the saved people of the past and of other nations, then we surely will know and recognize those whom we knew and loved on earth. In heaven Christian parents will know their Christian children and the children their parents, and friendships formed on earth will be renewed and continued in heaven, for those who are saved through faith in their Savior, Jesus Christ.

Regarding the saved in heaven we are told, Revelation 7:9, that they are clothed with white robes and have palms in their hands. The Apostle John does not mean to say that those in heaven wear royal robes woven in white silk, but their white robes mentioned here are a symbol of their purity and righteousness. Those persons whom John saw standing before the throne of God were pure and righteous. They were not so by nature, but were impure and unrighteous like all other people on earth. However, these people became pure and righteous after they had been washed in the blood of the Lamb of God. The blood of Christ is sufficient to cleanse even the greatest sinner from his guilt, sin, impurity and unrighteousness. David murdered Uriah and the Apostle Paul shed the blood of the disciples of Jesus, but they both repented and by faith washed themselves in the blood of Christ, and now they are in heaven clothed in the white robes of innocence. "Though your sins be red as scarlet, they shall be as white as snow," Is. 1:18 if they are washed in the blood of Christ.

But regarding the great multitude which John saw in heaven, did they have the same bodies which they had on earth? The answer is no, for only their souls were there. When a believer dies, his body is placed in the grave where it molders away into dust and decay, but his soul which never dies is taken immediately to heaven. While Christ hung on the cross, he said to one of the malefactors: "Today shalt thou be with me in paradise." Luke 11:43. As far as the body of the malefactor is concerned it was laid in the grave, but his soul was at once taken to the glories of heaven. In II Corinthians 5:8, the Apostle Paul triumphantly exclaims: "We are confident, yes, well pleased rather to be absent from the body and to be present with the Lord," that is, according to the soul. NKJV What a comfort it is to know that the souls of our loved ones who have died in true faith are already enjoying the glories of heaven.

19E. But the question arises: Will their bodies and our bodies be ever reunited with our souls in heaven? Yes, the same bodies which we had on earth will on the last day be reunited with our souls. Job writes: "In my flesh shall I see God: Whom I shall see for myself and mine eyes shall behold, and not another" (Job 19:26-27). On the last day our body will be gathered together and be reunited with the soul. We shall see our loved ones, who have been saved through faith in Christ, with the same bodies, the same features in all respects; and yet we all will be changed.

The Bible tells us that our bodies, although they will be the same we had on earth, will undergo a glorious change. The Apostle Paul writes: "The dead shall be raised incorruptible and we shall be changed." (I Cor. 15:52) Just what this change will consist of, the Apostle Paul tells us: "So also is the resurrection of the dead . . . It is sown in dishonour, it is raised in glory . . . it is sown in weakness; it is raised in power; It is sown a natural body, it is raised a spiritual body . . . As we have borne the image of the earthy, we shall also bear the image of the heavenly" (I Corinthians 15:42-44, 49). Paul also tells us that Christ "shall change our vile body, that it may be fashioned like unto his glorious body" (Philippians 3:21). According to these words, our bodies are to experience a great change when we shall rise from our graves, just as a great change was wrought in the body of our Lord when He rose from the dead. Christ's body was the same after His resurrection and yet it was different, it was identical and yet changed, it was recognized by the disciples and yet, in some mysterious way, it was no longer subject to the limitations, the restrictions, and material wants of His former state. He ate with His disciples, but not to satisfy bodily hunger. He merely wanted to show to them that He had risen from the dead. He appeared to them even though the doors were locked and bolted. He appeared suddenly and just as suddenly disappeared. He told His followers to meet Him in Galilee, but He did not travel there with them. In some mysterious, supernatural, miraculous way He appeared there.

The resurrected body of Christ is a type of what our own resurrected body is to be like. As His body was no longer subject to the restrictions and limitations of his former state, so shall also our body no longer be restricted to time and space. As His body was no longer mortal, so shall also our bodies no longer be subject to death. No more tears, no more decay, no more degeneration, no more second law of thermodynamics, no more sickness, no more death. Revelation 21:4 triumphantly exclaims: "And God will wipe away every tear from their eyes, there shall be no more death, nor sorrow, nor crying; and there shall be no more pain, for the former things have passed away." What a glorious prospect awaits us in heaven and what bliss and happiness our loved ones in heaven already enjoy!

19F. *What do the people of heaven do* or what kind of life do they lead? The Apostle John says in Revelation 7:10 and 15 that the great multitude of people he saw in heaven:

cried with a loud voice, saying, Salvation to our God who sitteth upon the throne and unto the Lamb. . .Therefore are they before the throne of God, and serve him day and night in his temple: and he that sitteth upon the throne shall dwell among them.

Uppermost in the minds of the people in heaven is the thought that their salvation is due entirely to God. If God had not prepared salvation for them they would not be enjoying the glories of heaven that they now enjoy. And with this salvation uppermost in their minds, they out of pure appreciation to God thank and praise Him continually as if they can never sufficiently thank Him for it.

After the saved people sing their hymn of thanksgiving, the angels also cannot be silent but take up the refrain. The angels sing:

Blessing and glory and wisdom, Thanksgiving and honor and power and might, Be to our God forever and ever (Revelation 7:12) NKJV

We notice a great difference between the hymn of the saved people and that of the angels. The angels say nothing about salvation because they are not in need of salvation, while the saved people place the word "salvation" at the head of their song. If God had not provided salvation for mankind through faith in Christ, they would not be in heaven now. Nevertheless perfect harmony exists between the hymn of the saved and the refrain of the angels. Together they acknowledge the glorious work and attributes of God.

19G. *What are the blessings that the saved people in heaven enjoy?* First of all, we will be delivered from all the evil that is present in this world. Revelation 7:16-17 declares:

They shall hunger no more, neither thirst any more, neither shall the sun light on them, nor any heat. For the Lamb which is in the midst of the throne shall feed them, and shall lead them unto living fountains of waters, and God shall wipe away all tears from their eyes.

Revelation 21:4 continues:

And God shall wipe away all tears from their eyes, and there shall be no more death, neither sorrow, nor crying, neither shall there be any more pain: for the former things are passed away.

Thus the people in heaven will be free from every pain, heartache, and sorrow to which we are subject here upon earth. This world is often at best a vale of tears. The poor clamor for food and raiment, the blind grope in darkness, the sick yearn for relief from pain, those in debt worry about their bills, and worry drives many to an untimely death. But in heaven such evils shall no longer exist but all shall be different. They shall hunger no more, neither thirst any more. These words probably mean very little to the average well-fed person, but there are times and places where it is full of meaning. Speak to people in parts of Africa, southern Asia and other parts of the world, where millions never know a day that isn't spent without the gnawing pain of hunger, and tell these people that "they shall neither hunger anymore nor thirst anymore"; that means something to them, in addition to enjoying all the bliss and grandeur of Heaven.

Yes, in heaven there will be continuous, uninterrupted happiness for all who are fortunate enough to enter. All the sufferings and evils of this life will then be put away. In eternity no tear shall dim our sight, and nothing shall cause us to sorrow or weep. The saved person who has been crippled throughout his earthly life shall in heaven enjoy the use of all his members. The poor in this world who were saved shall then no longer hunger and thirst. The saved sick will not feel the slightest pain, for there is no such thing as sickness in heaven. The despised and rejected of men will wear a crown of glory and be respected by all the inhabitants of heaven.

Furthermore there will be no more death in heaven. Death is a merciless enemy that spares no one. For centuries it has been stalking through the world, slaying unnumbered millions. Children as well as adults are snatched away by it. But in heaven "death is swallowed up in the victory." (I Cor. 15:54) The saved in heaven are beyond the possibility of dying, for Jesus tells us, Luke 20:36: "Nor can they die anymore, for they are equal to the angels and are the sons of God, being sons of the resurrection." NKJV

19H. In short, the entire second law of thermodynamics, degeneration, decay and entropy will be removed. Above all, we will be free of the greatest of all evils, of *sin*. We will be free from *original sin*, the root and beginning of sin and rebellion against God. We will also be free of all *actual sin*, so there will be no more need to lament as the Apostle Paul did: "For the good that I would, I do not: but the evil which I would not, that I do. . .O wretched man that I am: Who shall deliver me from the body of this death?" (Romans 7:19 and 24). Even the temptation to commit sin will not be there.

19I. Not only shall all misery, grief, pain, sickness, death and sin be put away, but also *nothing but joy and happiness will prevail in heaven*. All the thinking of the wise men of this world and all the schemes of utopian dreamers have not thought of anything like this. And what the Apostle John writes in the book of Revelation about heaven is not an idle dream or a fairy tale but a fact, a fact assured by the Almighty God in heaven. The Bible declares that heaven is a place of unspeakable joy. "In thy presence is fulness of joy; at thy right hand there are pleasures for evermore" (Psalm 16:11). Jesus said to his disciples: "Blessed are ye that weep now: for ye shall laugh." (Lk. 6:21) Yes, there will be laughter in heaven, pure heavenly laughter. There will be no more sour faces, no downcast spirits, no worry, no gloom or sadness. There will be no more ups and downs. A perpetual smile of joy will light up the countenance of the saved.

The greatest joy will be to see God and Christ in their full splendor, glory and love for saved mankind. What great joy it will be when we shall see face to face Him who loves us with an everlasting love, who provided for us the way of salvation, who graciously kept us to the end, so that we might receive the crown of eternal life in heaven! "And God Himself shall be with them and be their God!" God is the source of endless joy. Therefore to be in His presence gives the inhabitants of heaven boundless bliss and joy!

19J. Above all, we shall enjoy the glories of heaven *forever*. The bliss of heaven will never be interrupted or ended. "So shall we *ever be* with the Lord" without any interruption (I Thessalonians 4:17). Saint Peter tells us that our inheritance in heaven will be "incorruptible, undefiled and that does not fade away" (I Peter 1:4). Our stay in our earthly home, "Our Home, Sweet Home," is uncertain; we may have to give it up at any time, but our stay in our heavenly Father's house will be forever. In John 3:16 Jesus declared in that most beautiful verse of the Bible: "God so loved the world, that He gave His only begotton Son, that whosoever believes in Him should not perish but have *everlasting life.*" NKJV

19K. Now the all-important question is *How do we get there?* Of what good will all our knowledge of heaven, its glories and blessed life be if we do not know how to get there? Think about this most important question! Few deny their desire for heaven. Most delight to hear about that bright and shining city on yonder shore. They hope to meet their loved ones there again. But the wish and the desire are not enough. We must know the way for sure! The Bible's language is so simple that all can understand.

19L. Between man and heaven, there is only one barrier to be removed, the barrier of *sin*. Man has forfeited the right to enter there. This applies to all without exception. The Bible says: "There is no difference for all have sinned and come short of the glory of God," (Rom. 3:22f) and "If we say we have no sin, we deceive ourselves and the truth is not in us." (I John 1:8) Sin makes us unfit for heaven. "The wages of sin is death." (Rom. 6:23) We do not deserve heaven.

19M. But thanks be to God, there is One who has removed the barrier. Jesus Christ atoned for the sins of all. He paid the penalty of sin by suffering and dying as our substitute. Jesus is the one and only way to eternal life. He tells us in His Holy Word: "I am the way, the truth, and the life: no man cometh unto the Father, but by Me." (John 14:6) As Noah's ark was the only place of safety at the time of the Flood, and as Joseph was the only man who could supply food at the time of the Egyptian famine, so Jesus Christ is the only way to heaven. Peter told the rulers of Israel concerning Jesus: "Nor is there salvation in any other, for there is no other name under heaven given among men by which we must be saved" (Acts 4:12). NKJV (I hope to write another book: "Behold YOUR man! *Behold Your King!* Behold Your GOD and CREATOR! BEHOLD YOUR SAVIOR!")

Our virtues, our morality and our outward good character before men will not get us there, for we have sinned by omission as well as by commission. The only way is by trusting in Christ as our Savior from sin. Yet many foolishly trust in their own works, believing that through them they may gain eternal life. Spurgeon once said to an old man, "I hope you have seen to it that yours will be a pleasant lot when your life comes to an end." "Yes," the old man replied, "I think I have seen to it, for as far as I know, I have never been drunk in my life, I have never used a profane word, and I also go to church occasionally." He seemed quite satisfied with himself and was much surprised when Spurgeon told him that he would never reach heaven if he should die in such a self-righteous state of mind. There are too many who build their hopes of getting there in that way. But heaven can never to attained by works. The Christian hymn expresses this truth most beautifully in the words:

> Not the labors of my hands
> Can fulfill Thy Law's demands;
> Could my zeal no respite know,
> Could my tears forever flow,
> All for sin could not atone;
> Thou must save, and Thou alone.

Truly, heaven cannot be bought. It can never be merited by sinful man. "The gift of God is eternal life through Jesus Christ our Lord (Romans 6:23). This fact is clearly stated also in Revelation 7:13-14. One of the elders in heaven asked the Apostle John in the vision of heaven which he was privileged to see: "Who are these arrayed in white robes and where did they come from?" John said, "Sir, you know." The elder replied, "These are the ones who come out of the great tribulation, and washed their robes and made them white in the blood of the Lamb." NKJV. The only way is by faith in Christ, in washing away our sins by the sacrifical blood of Christ. We are not saved by just any kind of faith, such as faith in ourselves, faith in someone else, or faith even in some kind of God, but alone by faith in Jesus Christ as the one and only Savior from sin.

What a wonderful picture of heaven the Apostle John has given us in his divinely inspired book of Revelation. If only ten percent, if only one percent, of all that the Bible says about heaven were true, would it not be worthwhile for us to use our time well in becoming prepared for it? In fact, the Bible truly describes only a small fraction of the glories and blessings of heaven. Human language can not fully describe it. If we only believed this more firmly, we would not set our affections so much on things of this world nor burden our hearts so much with the cares of life but look more toward yonder blessed state where joys shall never cease and where griefs and sorrows are no more. If we believed this more firmly, we would not look upon death so much with fear and trembling but with more joy and yearning.

20. WHAT WILL BECOME OF THIS EARTH AND UNIVERSE SOME DAY?

Hear the testimony of St. Peter: "But the day of the Lord will come as a thief in the night, in which the heavens will pass away with a great noise, and the elements will melt with fervent heat; both the earth and the works that are in it will be burned up" (II Peter 3:10). NKJV. From this it is evident that the universe, earth, stars and planets as they now are will be dissolved in the Day of Judgment. Will this be a total annihilation? Hebrews 1:11-12 says of the earth and heavens that "they shall be changed." So this does not give the impression that the "passing away" and melting and burning up of which Peter spoke is necessarily a complete annihilation. In II Peter 3:13 Peter adds: "Nevertheless we, according to his promise, look for new heavens and a new earth, wherein dwelleth righteousness." The apostle John stated about the same, Revelations 21:1: "I saw a new heaven and a new earth, for the first heaven and the first earth had passed away. Also there was no more sea." NKJV. God will carry out His plans for His creation!

21.   THE END OF THE EARTH AND UNIVERSE

According to Jesus and the apostles, the Flood of Noah's days was a prototype of the final judgment day.

> For this they willingly are ignorant of, that by the word of God the heavens were of old and the earth standing out of the water and in the water, Whereby the world that then was, being overflowed with water, perished. But the heavens and the earth, which are now, by the same word are kept in store, reserved unto fire against the day of judgment and perdition of ungodly men (II Peter 3:5-7).

On the basis of the Bible a day of worldwide judgment and perdition and damnation of ungodly men will come upon this earth once more as happened in the days of Noah. And the reason for it is the same as in Noah's day: the prevalent wickedness, godlessness, indifference to God and anti-God attitude of the people. Our twentieth century has reached highly advanced stages of technical and material progress, with all kinds of luxuries, comforts and leisurely living. But as in the first centuries, so also today fewer and fewer people are guided by what God teaches. Instead, our age has become one of indifference to God. Evolution with its accompanying atheism, anti-God and anti-creation attitudes has gained control in many places and areas throughout the world.

Even some within the churches have become filled with the evolutionary concept, in that they try to harmonize the Bible with the evolutionary unbelief. As the children of God in the early centuries intermingled with and accepted the godless ideas of, the children of men, so also today some in the churches have accepted the godless ideas of the evolutionists.

The world is moving to its final judgment and a condemnation more severe than happened in the days of Noah. It is therefore very important that we heed the warning of the Apostle Peter given in following his words which were quoted at the beginning of this section:

> Therefore, since all these things will be dissolved, what manner of persons ought you to be in holy conduct and godliness, looking for and hastening the coming of the day of God, because of which the heavens will be dissolved being on fire, and the elements will melt with fervent heat? Nevertheless we, according to His promise, look for new heavens and a new earth in which righteousness dwells (II Peter 3:11-13). NKJV

22. THE CLOSING DOXOLOGY AND DEDICATION

Using the first four words of the Bible, "In the beginning G O D," as a doxology to God we must recognize that He is not merely the King of kings and the Lord of lords, but that He is the indescribable and incomprehensible "I AM WHO I AM" who appeared to Moses in the desert of Horeb (Exodux 3:14). This incomprehensible "I AM" is the Great All-Knowing Being, the Omniscient One; the Almighty, the All-Powerful Being, the Omnipotent One; the One Present Everywhere, the Omnipresent One; the Great Creator and Wise Designer who was before all material, before all the energy that exists in atoms and gravity, before all time and space; the Being who is spiritual and nonmaterial. Without *Him,* science, which is bound to the things that He created, can never explain the origin of the universe, of the earth, of life and of mankind. True, full, complete *science* begins with a knowledge of *I am who I am* and His word and work. This *I AM* has revealed Himself in the Bible as a Being who is three in one and one in three: Father, Son and Holy Ghost - indescribable and incomprehensible!

To Him Be All Honor and Glory!

To this

Indescribable, Incomprehensible, Non-material

I AM WHO I AM

The Creator Of All Material and All Living Things

This Book Is Dedicated.

THREE MAJOR STRIKES AGAINST EVOLUTION

THIRTY TWO REASONS WHY EVOLUTION IS NOT SCIENTIFIC

In considering the evolution problem we must consider why evolution is not a scientific theory or a science or, above all, a fact as the evolutionists repeatedly claim.

Evolution has three major strikes against it: I. there are at least eight reasons why evolution goes contrary to a number of proven laws of science, II. there are at least ten reasons why evolution is scientifically not possible and III. there are at least fourteen reasons why evolution is not a science or a fact. See p. 324.

I.   STRIKE ONE: EVOLUTION GOES CONTRARY TO A NUMBER OF PROVEN LAWS OF SCIENCE

1.   Evolution goes contrary to two basic laws of science called the **first and second laws of thermodynamics.** According to the first law, nothing has been created or annihilated (totally destroyed) since the beginning. This law can be summarized in the scientific words: from nothing comes nothing. In other words the big bang, the universe, the solar system, the earth and life on it could never have happened by themselves.

2.   According to the second law everything is degenerating, deteriorating, decaying, dissipating, going to pieces or going downwards and not evolving upwards to greater complexity. This law stands in direct opposition to the belief of evolution that the universe and the things of this earth evolved and progressed upwards and are still doing so today. See pages of book 253-266.

3.   Evolution goes contrary to the **theory of biogenesis** (origin of life), which states that life comes only from life. Every living thing comes only from some other living thing. According to this law of science, life could never have evolved by itself. See pages 211, 218, 254.

4.   Evolution goes contrary also to the proven evidences of **geology** as is evident in the sedimentary rock of the higher elevations all around Mankato, Minnesota, in the Grand Canyon of Arizona and elsewhere on this earth and also in the sedimentary rocks in Africa that evolutionist Richard Leakey is digging around in for fossils of human beings and animals.

It is obvious that these **sedimentary rock layers,** formed from extremely muddy waters, were not laid down either here or in Africa or anywhere else gradually over millions of years, as the evolutionists claim. Otherwise there would be only a layer of dust as there is on the moon. In these sedimentary rocks are found the fossils of plants and animals that are heaped and entwined with each other in masses, which show that they did not die gradually here and there but were buried quickly and deeply in very extremely muddy waters. See pp. 71-92, 291-295.

5.   Evolution goes contrary to scientific evidences, because it goes contrary to evidences in the **polar regions.** The polar plates did not move there gradually as some evolutionists claim, in order to explain the tropical plants and animals that once thrived there. The animals there died suddenly and violently in masses. See pp. 104-108.

6.   Evolution goes contrary to the scientific law of **cause and effect:** every effect — everything that exists or happens in this universe — must have a superior cause that is greater than life on this earth and greater than the material things of the universe. **Evolution has no superior cause.** More and more scientists are declaring that a nonmaterial force, power, intelligence or nonmaterial Being must be considered that is greater than the material things of this universe. See pp. 373-375.

7.   Evolution goes contrary to proven laws of science also because it ignores and rejects **the history** given in the first eleven chapters of Genesis. These chapters show that the people who lived before the Egyptians, Babylonians, Indians, Chinese, Incas, etc. were highly advanced and skilled. Science demands that every bit of information be considered, including the historical and scientific statements made in religious books. See pp. 21-85.

8.   Evolution also ignores the **geological statements** and other facts given in the book of Genesis, which explain many of the geological features and evidences of this earth. Also the two laws of thermodynamics, the origin of life, cause and effect, and many facts of science are expressed in these chapters of Genesis. There is more factual science regarding geology, in one brief statement in connection with Noah's Flood, **"all the fountains of the great deep were broken up,"** than can be found in all the geology books of the world. See pp. 61-98.

II.   STRIKE TWO: EVOLUTION IS SCIENTIFICALLY NOT POSSIBLE

1.   Evolution does not consider the extreme **complexity that exists in the cells** of plants, animals and human beings. According to men of science, who have studied these cells, there is zero possibility that they could have developed by themselves. Medical doctor Michael Denton in his book "*Evolution — A Theory In Crises*" p. 249 stated: "Between a living cell and the most highly ordered non-biological system, such as a crystal or a snowflake, there is a chasm as vast and absolute as it is possible to conceive." See pp. 211-212, 222-223, 256.

2.   Evolution also does not consider the **complexity of the human body.** We know that cells are extremely complex, but when we consider the organs of the human body we are stunned still more by the complexity of all the different organs: the brain and the nervous system, the eyes and how they work and how impossible it is for eyes to form themselves. Then consider the complexity of the brain, the ears, voice, throat, tongue, nose, skin, touch, lungs, heart, blood, stomach and digestive system. Above all there is the amazing reproductive system where two single cells can develop into all these parts again in only 270 days. To believe that all the thousands of species could simultaneously evolve similar male and female counterparts that could reproduce future generations is scientifically absurd, ridiculous and even asinine. See pp. 218 and 223-234.

3.   Evolution does not consider the vast difference between the **different kinds of animals** — from small ants and bugs to huge elephants and whales. They could not have evolved one from another. The different species arose **not like a tree** with branches of evolution, but they rose as a **grove of trees.** No kind or species has ever evolved into another kind or species. There is no evidence anywhere in this world as far back as evolutionists want to go that any real evolution from one species or kind to another has ever taken place. Instead all evidence among the fossils show that all species appeared on the earth at the same time in much the same form as they exist today. Charles Darwin said: "It must be said today that in spite of all the efforts of trained observers not one change of a species into another is on record." See pp. 200-206.

If our bodies and the bodies of animals depended on mutations or changes taking place by chance and running wild, as the evolutionists believe, to evolve different kinds of animals, we could be seeing all kinds of freakish people and animals evolving. You would never know what your next descendant might look like if it depended on chance.

4. Evolution is scientifically not possible because there is no evidence that any animal — and above all, that apelike animals — ever evolved into a higher form such as man. There just has been no crossing over from one kind to another and above all there is no evidence of any evolution moving upward. The changes have been horizontal, in varieties within species or kinds, but not vertically upward toward more complex and advanced kinds. See pp. 194-218.

5. Evolution is not possible because the flow of energy from the sun has never created life in any form as Dr. James Birx and Professor Keith Kline claim. Believing this is as non-scientific as believing that living things could arise from non-living matter, by spontaneous generation. See pp. 212 & 256.

Although the sun helps life in seeds of plants to start and grow, yet the sun cannot design and arrange the millions of nucleotides in the DNA that now exist in all living cells. On the other hand the sun is finally destructive to the life that has been designed and exists in plants. They degenerate and die according to the second law of thermodynamics.

Also even if man could some day design some form of life, life still could never have evolved by itself and become reproducible in descendants. A house, car, computer or any other machinery could evolve by itself and reproduce itself easier and more readily than life could ever have evolved.

6. Evolution is also not scientifically credible, plausible and possible because of the evidence in the clocklike, precise orbit that the entire solar system is revolving in. A big bang would create only disorder and not order. (p. 175)

7. The sun, the planets and their moons are so different from each other in substance and form that they could not have evolved from a single mass of materials. The same is true of the sun and all its sister suns or stars. They too are vastly different from each other, so they could hardly have resulted from one evolutionary process. See pp. 166-193.

8. The sky or expanse surrounding the planets would be the same if they had evolved. Earth, Saturn, Jupiter and others are all different. See pp. 175-188.

9. Evolution is not credible also because there is no air and water on the other planets and moons. There most likely would be if they all had evolved.

10.   All the planets would not be round, but irregular and jagged from the explosion of a big bang and from bumping into each other, while flying around in space if they had evolved.

III.   STRIKE THREE: EVOLUTION IS NOT A SCIENCE

1.   Because there are no evidences for evolution in spite of all the claims of evolutionists. See pp. 311-312.

2.   Because evolution has given many explanations which are not scientific as to why **dinosaurs** became extinct. On the other hand they have given no scientific explanation regarding why and how the fossils of dinosaurs and other creatures were **preserved.** See pages 140-142. At the end of this book see the letters I wrote to the news media and answers I received from them. See p.p. 427, 428, 429.

3.   Because there is no evidence for a big bang which runs counter to existing laws of science and nature which have proven that out of nothing comes nothing. See pp. 154-160.

4.   Because evolution has no scientific explanation for the sudden rise of advanced civilizations all over the world 5000 years ago. The Neanderthal and Cro-Magnon people are very likely a part of the people who were buried in the sediments laid down at the time of the Flood. See pp. 120-123 and 137-138.

5.   Because primary evolution or the first origins of the universe or of life cannot be tested, proven, disproven or falsified on the basis of scientific observations and experiments. See pp. 303-307.

6.   Because most claims of recent, secondary evolution that animals and mankind have evolved have been falsified. There is no evidence of animals and plants ever evolving from one species into another. Also the technical abilities of the first people in recorded history and many of the sciences falsify evolution. See pp. 307-308.

7.   Because the entire idea is based on **chance** that things evolved by themselves, which is totally impossible. See pp. 166-167 and 321-324.

Already 50 years before I wrote this book I, as a young pastor, wrote in the introduction to a sermon on Psalm 136:25:

Again we are being blessed with bountiful rains and crops to sustain us and all other creatures. But to what or to whom are we responsible for all these things? Some say it is due to chance, others to the laws of nature and others to God.

Suppose that this world were ruled merely by chance. Then there would be no such thing as law and order in this world. Everything would be topsy-turvy and things in this world would be in a pitiful condition as is illustrated by the man who was dissatisfied with God and the laws of nature laid down by God and who one night in a dream found himself in a world ruled by chance. There he saw men with their heads next to their feet without any bodies, some had their ears on their shoulders, and others had their eyes on top of their heads, etc. One year a tree would bear apples and the next year lemons. It all depended on chance. Sometimes the sun would set at noon and perhaps it would be gone for weeks or months, or perhaps it would return in a few minutes. Sometimes the sun would be so far away that everything would freeze and then again it would be so close to the earth that everything would be scorched. It all depended upon chance. It is needless to say that when the man awoke he was glad to find that not chance but God governed the universe.

Furthermore this world is not ruled merely by a set of blind laws of nature with nothing else behind them. If that were the case then everything would be alike upon earth and there never would be a change but a monotonous sameness and regularity in all events. Then rain and sunshine, wind and weather would be as regular as a clock. In short, everything upon earth would run in unchangeable ruts. It is true that this earth is ruled by certain laws called the laws of nature but behind these laws is a lawgiver. One can find laws only where there is a lawgiver. And the giver of the laws of nature is someone greater than nature, the almighty Creator. And since He is behind the laws of nature and is not bound by them, He changes and varies them, so that there is a continual change upon earth.

8.   Evolution is not a science because it falsely claims scientific basis for its beliefs without providing any proven facts to back them up. Evolutionists again and again claim that evolution is a fact but they never provided any facts. See pp. 303-321.

9.   Because evolution is totally irrational and unreasonable from beginning to end: starting with the big bang idea, then an immense universe with its billions of stars that in no way could have gotten here by itself, then the precise solar system with its varied planets and some

planets and moons rotating in reverse direction from the rest. Then there are the multitudes of different kinds of life on this earth, both among plants and animals to the various very complex life cells. Consider all the different kinds of plants, animals, fish, birds and living cells in all forms of life. It is not scientific to believe that the millions of different kinds of plants and animals could ever have developed and continued to propagate all by themselves. How could cucumbers, potatoes, trees, strawberries, corn, wheat, weeds of all kinds ever have developed by themselves and acquired the ability to reproduce themselves? How could also all the different kinds of animals, cats, dogs, pigs, horses, lions, elephants, snakes, bugs, flies ever have developed and acquired the ability through males and females to reproduce? Then consider all the different kinds of birds and also the fish and all the different kinds of cells in plants and animals. On the basis of the evidences available on earth and in the universe, the probability and possibility of evolution happening by chance is zero. The whole idea is like so much childish prattle or foolish talk. See pp. 304, 313-314.

10.   Because many evolutionary claims are mere story-telling and **fiction.** The fairy tales for children are more reasonable than the evolutionary beliefs and stories. Children at least know their fables are fables. See pp. 325-328.

11.   Because in essence evolution is a fable that has been turned into an anti-religion and at the same time it is a **religion in itself.** How many times have children and older students been ridiculed by evolutionary teachers for their religious beliefs and for not believing "the millions and billions of years" idea of the evolutionists? If belief in God (theism) is a religious belief, dogma or teaching, so also the denial or rejection of God (a-theism) is a religious belief or dogma. Because evolution is being constantly taught in many public schools, evolution has become the established religion in these schools, contrary to the First Amendment to the United States Constitution. Neither evolution nor creation belong in public institutions because both are religions, as well as for other good reasons. What devastating effects some evolutionists could have in teaching creation, ridiculing what we believe regarding the Bible, creation, the fall of man, and Adam and Eve, referring to them as being mere myths.

Because evolution is a religion in itself and has no scientific basis, it is more religious than creation. Listen to Dr. Philip Johnson, a law professor in the University of California, Berkeley who, after intensive study of it, wrote in his book DARWIN ON TRIAL: "Evolution is fundamentally a religious position . . . and it's being taught in the schools as a fact when it isn't even a good theory . . . It is religion in the name of science, and that means that it is misleading people about both religion and science." In fact, evolution is a religious cult — the way they unjustly denounce and degrade their unbelieving peers and students in schools and universities. See pp. 328-340, 349-359, 368.

12.   Because no efforts are made by them to falsify their basic belief of uniformitarianism or gradual evolution. Although evolutionists are continually finding fault with each others ideas and arguments, yet most cling to gradual evolution as its basic foundation in which they try to claim millions and billions of years for their other ideas and claims, especially that man evolved from an apelike creature. Instead, fundamentally, they cling to their evolutionary ideas even after they have been proven false. See pp. 289-295, 307-308.

13.   Because of the many fraudulent claims and misrepresentations that were propagated for years after they had been proven false. Skulls and skeletons have been manipulated and pictures have been made and touched up to bring out the desired effect as occurred in the NATIONAL GEOGRAPHIC Nov. 1985 and March 1992. See also TIME Magazine March 14, 1994. Piltdown man in England, Nebraska man, Java man and Peking man proved to be false, hoaxes and misrepresentations. Teaching children evolution is mental and spiritual rape of our children. This kind of rape is worse than physical rape because it effects their eternity. See pp. 124-153, 352, 372.

14.   Because of many other reasons that could be given. Evolution does not have even one guess, supposition, assumption or hypothesis on which to build a scientific theory or much less on which to establish a law of science or to prove that it is a scientific fact. It is a false science, a science so-called, a pseudoscience, a counterfeit, a sham, a fraud. See p. 315. One man stated that evolution will go down in history as the biggest fizzle and laugh of the twentieth century. See pp. 303-306.

A lawyer stated that he would hate to defend evolution in a court of law.

ADVICE FOR CREATIONISTS

Do not let yourself be drawn into a debate between evolution and creation. That is not the problem. If I would have let creation be brought into my secular radio talk shows and debates or into my letters to the news media they would have ridiculed my creation position and torn my presentation to pieces as Christ warned in His Sermon on the Mount, where He said: "Do not give what is holy to the dogs (i.e. the Bible, creation, Adam and Eve, the Gospel of Christ, etc.); nor cast your pearls before swine, lest they trample them under their feet, and turn and tear you to pieces." Christ also warned: "Behold, I send you out as sheep in the midst of wolves. Therefore be wise as serpents and harmless as doves." (Matthew 7:6 and 10:16).

Discuss with evolutionists only the fact that evolution is not scientific. By making the secular world face the fact that evolution is not scientific, they can be made to consider that the ideas of evolution are wrong and not facts as many of them falsely believe. See my contacts with National Geographic and others further on.

In Addition the Religious Fable of Evolution Has Brought
SIX VERY EVIL, HARMFUL, DEVASTATING EFFECTS UPON MANKIND
(See pages 341-348 of this book)

In this connection ecology should be considered. Ecology is the branch of biological science that deals with the relations between living things and their environment and the evil effect that some environment has on plants and animals. However we should also be concerned about mankind and its evil environment. One evil environment for mankind is the devastating effects that evolution has on the beneficial morality of mankind, on the sciences, the Christian religion, the young people, the First Amendment, the news media, etc.

1.   It has destroyed THE BENEFICIAL morality of mankind.

2.   It has corrupted, degenerated, misled, harmed and caused confusion in many of the SCIENCES of the world.

3.   It has corrupted and degenerated THE CHRISTIAN BELIEFS of many Christian pastors, churches and denominations.

4.   It has CONFUSED many of THE YOUNG PEOPLE and has harmed their welfare, so that "they are trying to find themselves" their origin, their place in society and their destiny.

5.   It has become "THE ESTABLISHED RELIGION" of the United States, contrary to the First Amendment of the United States Constitution.

6.   It has misled **the news media**, so that they believe and propagate the evolution story without checking to see if the entire idea is factual and scientific.

First, evolution with its anti-God belief that there is no God and no creation has led to the demoralization, corruption and degeneration of the BENEFICIAL morality of the world, the morality that benefits and does not harm mankind. Already 2000 years ago in the days of the Apostle Paul most people even though they knew that there was a Creator on the basis of the things that were made, did not worship and glorify the God of creation.

In Romans 1, verse 20 Paul states that the attributes of God, that He is eternal, all-wise, all-powerful and that He is above all material and living things, are clearly seen by the things that are made. But the

Romans like so many others of that time did not believe in this very evident God, so they were without excuse. Instead they worshiped gods of their own fabrication, just as theistic evolutionists today in rejecting the God of the Bible worship a god of their own making in the New Age, in fabricating other religions of their own today, and in not accepting the creator God of Genesis. Because of this, God let them go their evil ways and worship idols and themselves. As a result of this idolatry they lost their **beneficial** morality, which God permitted as a well deserved punishment. Romans 1, 28 states: "God gave them over to a debased mind, to do those things which are not fitting."

The apostle Paul in writing to the assumedly wise people of Rome and others of that time wrote Romans 1:22: "Professing to be wise they became fools and changed the glory of the incorruptible God into an image made like corruptible man . . . and worshiped and served the creature rather than the Creator." And that is what humanism (the worship of man and his abilities without God) is all about today. Humanism, which goes hand in hand with evolution, is not one bit more advanced than ancient people who idolized and worshiped their leaders and ancestors.

And what evil effects has all this FOOLISH thinking brought to the world today? Listen to the apostle Paul as he preaches his 20TH CENTURY SERMON for today about sexual promiscuity, herpes and AIDS. Listen as Paul continues his sermon, verse 26: "For this reason God gave them up to vile passions. For even their women (lesbians) exchanged the natural use for what is against nature. Likewise also the men, leaving the natural use of the woman, burned in their lust for one another (gays), men with men committing what is shameful, and receiving in themselves the penalty of their error which was due (herpes, AIDS, even death, etc.) The Family Research Institute in Washington DC found that homosexuality reduces an individual's life span by half (40 years) according to **Omega** a scientific journal that focuses on death and dying, 1994. The Bible, always correct, stressed **beneficial** morality correctly 20 centuries ago.

Let Paul finish his TWENTIETH CENTURY SERMON, verses 28-32: "And even as they did not like to retain God in their knowledge, God gave them over to a debased mind, to do those things which are not fitting, being filled with all unrighteousness and immorality, wickedness, covetousness, maliciousness, full of envy, murder, strife, deceit, evil-mindedness; haters of God, who, knowing the righteous judgment of God, that those who practice such things are worthy of death, not only do the same but also approve of those who practice them." This is a scorching sermon for all times.

From all this it is evident that the primary evil in this world is the idea that there is no creation and therefore no God, that all took place by mere chance, by evolution. And out of this primary evil flows all the other evils of mankind today. One wonders if things like this were not also prevalent in the days before the Flood, so that God in righteous anger tore up the entire crust of the earth.

Some of the writings of Carl Sagan, the archbishop of the evolution religion, are not only not scientific but also have very poor reasoning, beliefs and assumptions.

On top of all that they are foul, rotten, using coarse, vulgar four letter words repeatedly that are highly X-rated. All this in a book that is supposed to be highly scientific. I hope that is not what is used in the classes of universities. Such talk and writing is highly out of place in classes and university books. But language like that could easily flow out of a religion like evolution.

Evolutionists proudly proclaim and insist that man is just another animal. If one is only another animal why not live like an animal and some do. With the idea that man is only another animal ingrained in children, no wonder there is so much violence today, that people are being murdered right and left, women are being raped and one is not safe in his own car or home.

Numerous grandparents are ashamed of and disappointed in the sassiness and disrespect shown by their grandchildren as a recent newspaper report revealed. Christian parents who do not believe in evolution would not tolerate such disrespect.

The world famous attorney, Clarence Darrow, who defended evolution in the famous Scopes trial, defended two young men, Loebs and Leopold, for murdering a 14 year-old boy. He appealed to the judge: "Your honour, it is hardly fair to hang a 19 year-old boy for the philosophy that was taught him at the university." (From CLASSIFIED SPEECHES, edited by W. Brigans).

See to it that your children, grandchildren and great grandchildren etc. are not taken in by SATAN'S EVOLUTION RELIGION, that there is no God and Creator.

Secondly, evolution has corrupted, misled and caused confusion in many of the SCIENCES of the world. It has fouled up, messed up and harmed sciences such as geology, history, biology etc. See p. 313, 346.

Dr. Michael Denton, a medical doctor, stated in regard to this in his book EVOLUTION: A THEORY IN CRISIS, p. 358: "The influence of evolutionary theory on fields far removed from biology is one of the most spectacular examples in history of how a highly speculative idea for which there is no really hard scientific evidence can come to fashion the thinking of a whole society and dominate the outlook of an age."

One science that has been gravely harmed and misled is GEOLOGY — the science that deals with the structure of the earth's crust and with the fossils of plants and animals that were buried in extremely muddy sedimentary waters. These muddy waters were turned into sedimentary rock with fossils of plants, animals and even fish encased in them. Failing to read these sedimentary rocks correctly has caused the evolutionists to give a wrong interpretation regarding these rocks as well as the length of time it took for them to be formed — certainly not over millions and billions of years. If they were laid down over millions of years there would be only a fine layer of dust as there is on the moon.

Evolution has also fouled up, misled and corrupted the science of ARCHEOLOGY: the science that deals with the study of the life and culture of ancient people. Where did those highly advanced and technically inclined people of Egypt, Babylonia, India, China, Peru, Greece, Asia Minor, Crete, etc. come from that suddenly appeared in history like a sunrise? Advanced mankind could not have developed suddenly from some apelike creature to Homo sapiens, sapiens (wise smart man) as they like to call man in their ideas of the origin of man. See pages 39-60.

The science of HISTORY has also been messed up. History deals with the origin of all things and especially with the origin of man. The history books of the world begin with the Egyptians. The Bible gives the history and names of people who lived 2000 years before that. But evolutionists refuse to consider that. A true scientist must consider all facts, including what is recorded in religious books.

The science of PALEONTOLOGY has also been botched up. This is the branch of geology that deals with prehistoric forms of life in the plant and animal fossils. The same forms of life exist today as they claim lived millions of years ago, so there is no evolution in plants and animals.

BOTANY is the science that deals with plants, their life, structure, growth, classification.

ZOOLOGY is the science that deals with animals, their origin and classification.

BIOLOGY is the science that deals with the origin, history and characteristics of plants and animals. The sciences of botany, zoology and biology have all been fouled up and corrupted by the evolution fable.

ASTRONOMY is the science that deals with the study of the stars and galaxies, their origins and ages. The evolutionists claim of billions of lightyears for the galaxies very likely is as wild as their statements that the earth, the solar system and the universe are billions of years old or that a big bang took place in billionths of a second from a tiny nucleus of matter. We just do not know how vast God created this universe.

The billions of years for the earth and the universe are based on a false reading of the sedimentary rock of this earth which very evidently were laid down in a very short space of time, in a massive Flood of extremely muddy water as mentioned before, when the crust of the earth was torn up with violent earthquakes and volcanoes and storms howling at hundreds of miles an hour. There is no way of measuring the universe, the billions of lightyears, the billionths of a second, and the billions of degrees of temperature such as the evolutionists wildly claim. God did say to Abraham that his descendants would be as numerous as the stars in the heaven and the dust of the earth.

Then also evolution has misled the GOVERNMENTS and THE NEWS MEDIA of the world, so that they do not realize that evolution is not a science but merely a fable that has been turned into a religion and even a religious cult, the way they treat their peers and students.

However the book of GENESIS corresponds with all the above sciences and with fossils found in the crust of the earth. Although creation cannot be proven scientifically by actual tests, yet creation by a superior, nonmaterial power greater than the things of this earth is logical, reasonable, has a NONMATERIAL FIRST CAUSE greater than the MATERIAL universe and has never been proven false.

But EVOLUTION is not scientific, logical or reasonable and secondary evolution has been proven false, for there is no evidence that plants or animals ever turned into another kind of plant or animal. Biology falsifies evolution with its scientific law: life can only come from life.

Thirdly, evolution has corrupted, messed up and degenerated THE CHRISTIAN BELIEFS of Christian churches, believing that creation, Adam and Eve, the Flood in Noah's day, the fall of man into sin, the Tower of Babel and Jesus Christ are only myths. With that goes the breakdown of other fundamental beliefs of Christianity; namely that man is saved by his works and not by the grace of God through faith in Jesus as our Savior. On top of that many of the clergy of a number of Christian denominations just do not seem to realize what damage evolution has done to other fundamental beliefs of Christianity and above all to misleading members of their churches. Christian churches, denominations, colleges and universities have given away their Christian birthright for a mess of pottage, Gen. 25:29-34. And it has resulted in the development of new anti-Christian, man-made religions such as humanism (the worship and idolizing of man) and the New Age religion. This kind of idolatry is running wild in the world today, so that idolatry is rampant not only in what has been called heathen lands but is prevalent throughout much of the civilized world of today.

To reconcile their beliefs in evolution with creation and the Bible some of the clergy have accepted the idea of theistic evolution. Atheistic evolution on the one hand rejects the God of the Bible or even any gods that may have been devised. However the theistic evolutionists reject not merely the God of the Bible, but worse they fabricate a god of their own imagination by rejecting the Creator God of the Bible.

It is as Harvey Wegner stated in Christian News April 19, 1993: "Theistic evolutionists like to have the best of both worlds. They aspire to be Christians and unbelievers at the same time. They go with what is fashionable in their day as 'scientific' truth, and sacrifice the eternal truths of Scripture. They think they are demonstrating superior intellect and regard with contempt . . . Christians who take the divine revelation seriously. In fact, they are the fools and . . . they are unfaithful shepherds who lead the sheep astray."

When one reads in the *Christian News* and elsewhere how far some Christian pastors and denominations have drifted from the Bible since the days of their parents and grandparents, we all should be highly shocked and alerted. Most of this flows out of the evolution religion into which children of the past two generations have been indoctrinated from many different sources.

Fourthly, and very sadly, evolution has confused the YOUNG PEOPLE of today. They are wondering whether they are monkeys and animals or human beings responsible to a Creator and Designer. They are "trying to find themselves" as they say. They are wondering what their place is in this world. During the tax season I had a young man in my office who was very little interested in his tax work but when he saw a copy of my book lying there, he became very interested in regard to his place in life.

Professor H. Enoch wrote in his book EVOLUTION OR CREATION, p. 98 that evolution has caused, "the universal spread of atheism among the educated. Thousands of young men and women have lost their faith in God as a result of studying the theory of evolution." He quoted Professor Huxley, saying: "The doctrine of evolution, if consistently accepted, makes it impossible to believe the Bible."

Fifthly, evolution has become "THE ESTABLISHED RELIGION" of the United States, contrary to the United States Constitution. If belief in a God (theism) is a religious belief, dogma or teaching, then so is a denial of God (a-theism). Evolution and atheism go hand in hand. Evolution has become the established religion of public schools, taught UNDER THE GUISE OF SCIENCE, and in the name of science. In this way the public schools have become the religious schools of evolution.

Sixthly, it has misled **The News Media**, so that they believe and propagate the evolution fable without checking to see if the entire idea is factual and scientific. See following pages 420 to 445.

CONTACTS I HAVE HAD WITH PROPAGATORS (PREACHERS) OF THE EVOLUTION RELIGION

EVOLUTION IS A RELIGION.
See pages 331-340.

One of my first major contacts with evolutionists was with NATIONAL GEOGRAPHIC. They have been one of the foremost propagators and sponsors of the evolution idea. I wrote to their Forum on March 21, 1992:

> I want to refer to a few quotes from your latest March 1992 issue where you state page 14, "Some 17 million years ago, during the Miocene epoch, there were at least three times as many ape genera as today. Their descendants are the lesser apes, or gibbons, to which we are only distantly related . . . We are the apes' sole modern success story." No evidence is provided that apes and humans are related, no more than dogs and cats or cows and horses are related to each other.

> On page 24 top you state: "WHAT HAD HAPPENED by roughly five million years ago to cause Africa's tree-living apes to descend to the ground . . .?" One of the problems with such fuzzy, illogical thinking is: how did those creatures get up into the trees in the first place?

> Then in the same sentence you continue: "then develop into divergent lines — modern apes and humans? And what did the progenitors look like? A century of paleontology has failed to turn up fossil bones from the critical period, . . ." Certainly if different kinds or species of living things (either plants or animals) ever evolved into another kind, one would find transitional forms all over in the "SEDIMENTARY rock" of this earth. But how correctly you confess: "A century of paleontology has failed to turn up fossil bones from the critical period."

> On pages 24 to 32 you try to show how brains developed in apes (and finally in man) so that today apes can do some reasoning and perform some acts at the suggestion of men. This is not something marvelous that is limited only to apes. Other animals also will respond to words spoken to them. I know of a dog who responded to things we said to him, even though no one tried to train him. All one has to say was: "Do you want to go for a walk" and he would run to the door.

On page 36 you correctly sum up the whole issue by quoting an animal trainer, "People think chimps are like humans, but they are wild animals." How correct! Referring to man as being just another animal does not make mankind related to any animal.

Your ideas about evolution taking place over millions of years have no scientific backing as is evident from the SEDIMENTARY rocks that were laid down all over the earth. These sedimentary rock layers are especially evident in the higher ground levels in Mankato, Minnesota and also in Wisconsin areas, as well as in the Grand Canyon and in other areas.

Sedimentary rocks in which the fossils are buried were not laid down over millions of years in the form of dust like on the moon but suddenly in violent turbulent waters in which animals, that turned into fossils, were encrusted in HEAPS all over the earth as is especially evident in the Badlands of South Dakota and other western areas.

That infamous, illogical, nonscientific November 1985 issue of NATIONAL GEOGRAPHIC that tried so hard to expound the belief in the idea (not a theory) of evolution is what finally caused me to write my book, which shows that evolution has no scientific foundation.

When you write articles that are truly factual, you have an excellent magazine that serves a good purpose. But your beliefs in regard to evolution are insulting to true science, reason, logic and intelligence.

You people are rapidly becoming the laughing stock of the world with your evolution propaganda. In spite of all the efforts of evolutionists via the public schools and news media, the biggest percentage of American people do not believe in evolution, above all that mankind evolved out of an ape stock of some kind.

The fairy tales for children are more reasonable than your evolutionary beliefs . . . The idea of evolution has simply become ridiculous in the eyes of most people.

* * * * * * * *

Mr. Robert Booth, Senior Assistant Editor, of NATIONAL GEOGRAPHIC replied April 8, 1992:

Thank you for your recent letter to the National Geographic Society regarding our March 1992 article on apes and humans.

As a scientific and educational organization, we report on the consensus of the world's scientists, a vast majority of whom see compelling evidence supporting the gradual evolution of life over the course of billions of years, including a common ancestry shared by apes and humans. We recognize the wide variety of beliefs that exist in the world, and we respect our readers' right to incorporate scientific knowledge into their personal beliefs in any manner they deem appropriate. Our role is to present those findings as objectively as possible to our readers for their evaluation.

Thank you for your comments. I will see that they are circulated among my colleagues, Sincerely, Robert L. Booth

No evidence of any kind is provided for their evolutionary beliefs for "supporting the gradual evolution of life over the course of billions of years, including a common ancestry shared by apes and humans." The whole idea as they state is based on "beliefs" without any scientific evidence.

✿ ✿ ✿ ✿ ✿ ✿ ✿ ✿

In PARADE magazine of September 20, 1992 excerpts were presented under "Science on Parade" from Carl Sagan's and Ann Druyan's book SHADOWS OF FORGOTTEN ANCESTORS. The question is raised "What makes us different?" I wrote to PARADE magazine:

The old efforts are made that it all lies in evolution when you make remarks like: "Pulling together a vast body of scientific information to trace the origins and evolution of life on Earth . . . Why are we so different? Or are we? . . . difference between our species and others are only differences of degree."

You mention how chimpanzees can go termite-fishing which an anthropologist couldn't do. Why should that be so unusual? Humans also cannot climb trees like chimps or smell like dogs. But humans can do immensely many and extremely more highly complex things than what animals can do. So there is a vast difference between apes and humans.

Toward the end of those excerpts it is stated: "Knowing how closely we're related to monkeys and apes, why should we be surprised that the differences are of degree and not of kind?" This seems to be your main arguments for your whole evolution idea.

Here you missed the entire scientific differences between humans and animals, including ape animals. As far as DEGREE of differences is concerned there are multitude of differences between humans and apes. As far as KIND of differences is concerned there are again multitudes of differences. There are all kinds of things that animals, including apes, can do that humans cannot do and there are endless kinds of things that humans can do that animals cannot do. No evidence is provided that apes and humans are related, no more than dogs and cats or cows and horses are related to each other.

The entire article by Carl Sagan and Ann Druyan was far from being brilliant new ideas and scientific. Your heading stated that the article was for "SCIENCE ON PARADE." But it was far from proving evolution to be scientific or a science.

I am constantly amazed at the illogical, nonscientific reasoning, fallacies and falsities of evolution, which fails above all to read the geology of this earth correctly. If the evolutionists cannot read the geology of this earth, that is before their very eyes, correctly, how can Carl Sagan and others read the heavens correctly?

The fairy tales for children are more reasonable than your evolutionary beliefs. It is time that the news media quit making "monkeys" of themselves before the world. The idea of evolution has simply become ridiculous in the eyes of most people, because it is a ridiculous idea WITHOUT ANY SCIENCE. The beliefs in regard to evolution are an insult to true science, reason, logic and intelligence.

Kindly send copies of this response to Carl Sagan and Ann Druyan and it would be only fair if this response were printed soon in the PARADE magazine.

I received no reply from either PARADE magazine or from Carl Sagan.

Someone said to me: You cannot make a man out of a monkey, but you can make a "monkey" out of some people who believe in evolution and that they are descendants of monkeys. They believe this no matter how many doctor's degrees and Nobel prizes they may have.

Carl Sagan and PARADE Magazine Again

I wrote to the Mankato, Minnesota FREE PRESS for their "Reader's Points of View," which they printed:

In the March 7, 1993 issue of PARADE magazine Carl Sagan wrote an article as a "distinguished scientist" about little space aliens appearing in the sleep or dreams of some people. He refers to these as alien "extraterrestrial invasions" or as "an epidemic of hallucinations." Hallucinate according to the dictionary means "to wander mentally — which may occur in certain mental disorders."

He also stated: "Hallucinations are common . . . are part of being human. But this does not make hallucinations real . . . There's considerable doubt whether extraterrestrials exist and frequently visit our planet."

And then he opens himself wide open to the "mental wandering" of his pet nonscientific idea of evolution: "No one would be happier than I would if we had real evidence of extraterrestrial life." In the United States space program he is backed with millions of dollars of taxpayer money to try to find life out in space, not finding it in the solar system.

In his closing paragraph he summarizes his evolution beliefs correctly in stating: "If indeed the bulk of the alien abduction accounts are really about hallucinations, don't we have before us a matter of supreme importance — touching on our limitations, the ease with which we may be misled, the fashioning of our beliefs and perhaps even the origin of our religions?" [especially the evolution religion.]

I have at least 32 reasons why Carl Sagan's and other evolutionists' ideas about evolution are not scientific. Their assumptions are mere hallucinations, not one bit better than the hallucinations regarding the existence of extraterrestrial aliens.

By far the largest percentage of people in the United States do not believe in the idea of evolution. May the news media spare all of us from more such nonscientific, religious beliefs of Carl Sagan and others of like beliefs.

No reply was received.

To Articles, PARADE magazine
750 Third Ave.
New York, NY 10017
    and
Carl Sagan Professor of Astronomy and Space Sciences
at Cornell University
Ithaca, NY 14850

CARL SAGAN AND MORE EVOLUTION ASSUMPTIONS

In the Sept. 19, 1993 issue of Parade magazine Professor Carl Sagan again comes forth with more evolution beliefs without scientific basis, this time on alien civilizations. On March 7, 1993 it was on extraterrestrial beings.

This time he writes about: "Hypothetical civilizations on planets of other stars . . . The NASA program is developing new technology, stimulating ideas and exciting [misleading] school children. In the eyes of many, it is well worth the $10 million a year that's being spent on it . . . We would be hearing from other beings independently evolved over billions of years . . . The knowledge that such other beings exist and that, as the evolutionary process requires, they must be very different from us would have a striking implication . . ."

Here Carl Sagan again "goes off the deep end" or as the dictionary puts it "rashly plunges into it" by assuming that life evolved on this earth. The evolutionists again and again make all kinds of predictions and assumptions in regard to millions and billions of years, billionths of seconds, billions of degrees and outer space being billions of light years but they cannot read correctly the evidences prevalent in the crust of this earth: that this crust was formed catastrophically in a short period of time and not gradually over millions of years as they falsely claim. Laid over millions of years there would only be a layer of dust as there is on the moon and not layers and layers of SEDIMENTARY rock as we have in the higher elevations of Mankato and elsewhere on this earth.

On the basis of the complexity that exists in the cells of plants, animals and human beings and the complexity that exists in the 6,000,000 different species of plants and animals on this earth, life could never have evolved in trillions of years, much less in millions and billions of years. These facts come from two outstanding scientists, one a medical doctor.

If Carl Sagan cannot correctly read the evidences in the crust of this earth that is before his very eyes, how can he read the very distant heavens correctly? Too many of the previous assumptions and guesses regarding the planets in the solar system have been proven totally wrong. See p.p. 172-193.

Please, Parade magazine, and please, Carl Sagan, spare our gullible children from more such nonscientific foolishness! Evolution has 32 reasons why it is not scientific and 6 very evil, harmful, devastating effects upon mankind, including most sciences. Please cease and desist.

                                        from a great grandpa, Albert Sippert

No Reply.

                    ✣ ✣ ✣ ✣ ✣ ✣ ✣ ✣

A year or two ago Carl Sagan, before an assembly of intelligentsia, notoriously called scientific creationism an oxymoron (opposite or contradictory ideas). But so-claimed scientific evolution is also an oxymoron. Although primary evolution cannot be proven scientifically, secondary evolution however has been proven false. Creation also cannot be proven scientifically but it at least is logical, reasonable, has a first cause and has never been proven false.

To provide a basis or explanation for origins that lies in the study of geology, biology, botany, zoology, archaeology, astronomy, history, etc. of this earth and universe, there are more solid evidences, scientific possibilities, foundations, facts and hypotheses in the first eleven chapters of Genesis than can be found in all the secular books of the world.

The Minneapolis Minnesota STAR TRIBUNE

December 1, 1990 I wrote to the Minneapolis STAR TRIBUNE regarding an article they printed Nov. 22, 1990 from the New York Times by Walter Sullivan, entitled "Dinosaurs probably roamed in polar regions near end of reign." The article states:

"Discoveries of dinosaurs and plant remains in near-polar latitudes are revolutionizing concepts of how dinosaurs lived toward the end of their reign, 65 million to 100 million years ago."

"The find suggest that some dinosaurs . . . lived in great herds, exploiting the rich flora that flourished in the constant daylight of polar summer."

"The fossils that have led to this new view have been found in Alaska, Canada, Greenland, the island of Spitzbergen in the Artic Ocean and Soviet Union, as well as in Antarctica and southern Australia."

"The evidence indicates that dinosaurs were not just sedentary [fixed to one location], tropical creatures. Great numbers inhabited both polar regions."

"At the time dinosaurs thrived near the poles, conditions were radically different from those today. The entire planet was warmer, especially in the polar regions, although it apparently began to cool toward the end of the dinosaur era."

Judith Parrish of the University of Arizona, who has studied plant remains from the Alaskan deposits, has found an "unbelievably rich" fossil flora. "The productivity was just astonishing," she said. No place on Earth today has comparable vegetation.

"Many of the plants were vinelike cycads [tropical, palmlike plants] that grew rapidly and carpeted the landscape," she said. "In the continuous daylight of summer, the grazers were able to browse on them 24 hours a day."

Much of this conforms with what many believe regarding what the earth was like at one time. Within only a couple of hundred miles of the South Pole there is evidence of luxuriant plant and forest growth that thrived there at one time and within 800 miles of the North Pole, also subtropical forest and large fossil leaves of palm trees have been found. In the frozen ground of the New Siberia Island a large fruit tree with green leaves and ripe fruit has been found.

The only way such luxuriant and tropical plant growth could be explained in the polar regions, and also having warm-climate animals living there, would be if there had been at one time warm, tropical climate existing there year around.

But to have such climate year around the earth would have had to travel around the sun in a perpendicular manner without its present 23 ½ degree tilt. However with no tilt, the polar region would be continually cool to cold and the equator region extremely hot. However with a water vapor canopy surrounding the earth and no tilt, the temperature around the entire earth would be the same all year without any extremes in weather.

Under such conditions all the many different fossils of animals and plants that have been found in the polar regions are explainable. Scientists have wondered when, why and how this strange arrangement occurred that the earth revolves with a 23 ½ degree tilt around the sun. But upon examining the animal remains in the polar regions we find evidences that something very drastic must have happened to this earth at one time.

Not only dinosaurs but also mammoths, which were huge animals 13 feet tall, and many other animals such as lions, horses, bears, bison, moose, wolves and rhinoceroses have been found in Siberia and Alaska frozen suddenly and buried. Some of these mammoths have been found standing in an upright position as if they had sunk down where they were standing, surrounded and covered with muck and sedimentation. The carcasses of some of these animals have been thawed out and fed to sled dogs.

What could have killed and quick-froze these huge animals and others with such suddenness before they could even swallow or lie down? An extreme cold must have swooped down upon them instantly like lightning, and this happened over thousands of square miles all over the polar region. Sled dogs have been out in blizzard conditions for many hours and even for days in temperatures below minus 80 degrees without freezing, but these huge animals froze almost instantly.

One possible explanation for all this is that the earth could suddenly have been tipped to its present 23 ½ degree tilt, the icy temperature from above the earth plunged, crashed or collapsed upon the polar regions and the water canopy came cascading down, freezing almost instantly.

All this conforms to what Sir Henry Howorth, president of the Archeological Institute of Great Britain wrote in 1887 in his book: THE MAMMOTHS AND THE FLOOD, in which he tried to prove:

In the first place that a very great cataclysm and catastrophe occurred . . . by which that animal, with its companions, was overwhelmed over a very large part of the earth's surface. Secondly, that this catastrophe involved a widespread flood of water which not only killed the animals, but also buried them under continuous beds of loam and gravel. Thirdly, that the same catastrophe was accompanied by a very great and sudden change of climate in Siberia, by which the animals which had previously lived in fairly temperate conditions were frozen in their flesh under the ground and have remained frozen ever since.

The fact that these animals have remained frozen ever since and that the meat is still edible today proves that these animals could not have met "the end of their reign, 65 million to 100 million years ago," as is claimed for the dinosaurs. They would have disintegrated millions of years ago.

Also, the fact that this catastrophe "involved a widespread flood of water, which not only killed the animals, but also buried them under the continuous beds of loam and gravel" proves that they were killed in a recent massive flood such as is recorded and handed down in the histories of at least 200 peoples, nations and tribes. The READER'S DIGEST issue of September 1977, page 129 states:

With variations, the Bible account of a great universal flood is part of the mythology and legend of almost every culture on earth. Even people living far from the sea . . . have legends of a great flood washing over the land, covering the tops of mountains and wiping out virtually all life on earth.

No reply was received to this letter.

* * * * * * * *

In June of 1993 the Minneapolis STAR TRIBUNE had a big display about dinosaurs existing 230 to 65 million years ago. I wrote to them June 17, 1993:

DINOSAURS AND 65 MILLION YEARS AGO

In this month of June three big displays have appeared in the Star Tribune regarding dinosaurs and that they existed from 230 to 65 million years ago and then became extinct.

There is no question that dinosaurs roamed over this earth at one time but they did not become extinct for the reasons that evolutionists give for their extinction.

Many false explanations have been given in past newspaper articles: regarding the dinosaurs and their disappearance and for all the other fossils buried in the sedimentary rocks all over the world. What caused the dinosaurs and other animals to die suddenly in masses heaped together and sometimes appearing as if they died in a violent turbulence? Evolutionists have given all kinds of strange, non-scientific ideas why they became extinct, but they have not given any scientific explanation **how and why** their fossils were **preserved.**

Many explanations are given for their extinction and one disagrees with the other. One cause given is: A giant asteroid slammed into the earth millions of years ago and kicked up a cloud of dust that obscured the sun for three to six months which destroyed the plants on which the dinosaurs fed. But that would not preserve their fossils.

Another cause given is a change of weather made things rough for the dinosaurs and they died. But that also would not preserve their fossils. Other reasons given are: Volcanic eruptions covered a million square miles of India with lava; another cause is dinosaurs died out gradually over millions of years. Every few months more nonscientific fables about the demise of the dinosaurs are propagated by evolutionists in the news media.

Other reasons given: Comets hit the earth, then also a death star is mentioned, even though they say that they are not sure if there is a death star. Also acid rain is said to have caused gradual extinctions. BUT NOT ONE OF THESE KINDS OF EVENTS WOULD *PRESERVE* DINOSAUR OR ANY OTHER FOSSILS.

Sudden burial in the sediments of massive turbulent extremely muddy flood waters would preserve fossils, but that would put the evolutionists too close to a flood like in Noah's days. They avoid a logical explanation such as that like a plague because that brings them too close to the Bible. Anything in the Bible just cannot be considered by them, even if it agrees perfectly with historical events and explains many of the geological features of the crust of the earth. Science demands that every bit of information be considered, including the historical and scientific statements made in religious books.

If there had been no account of Noah's Flood containing the statement "all the fountains of the great deep were broken up," (Gen. 7:11), we would have to infer an event like that to explain the geology of this earth. There is no need to find Noah's ark to prove the Flood. There is too much other evidence.

When "all the fountains of the great deep were broken up," the mountains were lifted up, lava gushed forth in the northwestern part of the United States and in India and other places. Evidently most of the crust of the earth was torn up into boulders, rocks, stones, sand and soil while world-wide earthquakes shook the earth and volcanoes exploded even in ocean bottoms and while world-wide hurricanes and tornadoes acted in unison to mess up the climate of the earth.

It is only under conditions like this that the sedimentary rock that are evident all over the higher elevations of Mankato, Minnesota and in Wisconsin and the Grand Canyon of Arizona could have been laid down. Floods like Mankato experienced a number of times in recent years could never have laid down these kinds of sedimentary rocks. And it is in rocks like these throughout the world that the fossils of dinosaurs, other animals and plants are found.

So very evidently the dinosaurs became encrusted in sedimentary rocks like these not 65 million years ago but only a few thousand years ago. If all this had happened over millions of years there would be only a layer of dust as there is on the moon.

Refusing to consider what is presented in religious books is not scientific. Regarding origins and makeup of the earth's crust, there is more sound geology in the words "all the fountains of the great deep were broken up" than can be found in all the geology books of the world.

No response was given to this article sent to them for their COMMENTARY page.

* * * * * * * *

On the other hand the STAR TRIBUNE seemed to be quite upset about CBS's airing of "The Incredible Discovery of Noah's Ark" 4 ½ months before, claiming that part of is was "an apparent hoax" regarding the showing of "a chunk of Noah's Ark." They printed an article that appeared in the LOS ANGELES TIMES, which accused CBS with "the sloppiness of CBS." At the end of this article the statement is made: "If CBS cannot be trusted to be straight with America on its . . . . Noah's Ark' program, how can it be trusted . . ."

On July 15, 1993 I wrote to the STAR TRIBUNE regarding all this: "I believe the same holds true if you do not let the article I sent you June 17 appear in your paper."

No response was given also to this letter.

* * * * * * * *

I wrote to the Minneapolis STAR TRIBUNE again July 10, 1994

I see in the July 8, 1994 issue of the Star Tribune that you again printed the false religious idea of the evolutionists that the dinosaurs became extinct about 65 million years ago.

I have shown to you several times that the 65 million years ago is completely false but you have never printed the corrections I sent you on this matter or tried to prove that I was wrong.

Must you preach this false nonscientific religious idea of the evolutionists over and over again to gain and hold converts to the evolution religion? It has totally no scientific foundation.

Let's be honest and honorable and print corrections sent to you.

                                                                Albert Sippert

No response was received.

*   *   *   *   *   *   *   *

AN EVOLUTIONIST'S FAULTY ARROGANCE

Donald Kaul of the **Tribune Media** gave an excellent demonstration in The Free Press Oct. 2, 1993 of the faulty arrogance that exists among some evolutionists, under the title "Americans are so dumb, school ought to be voluntary."

He states: "Half of us are performing at the intellectual level of moss. Wait it gets worse. When they separate out the people who couldn't read or do arithmetic . . . 20 percent of them were high school graduates. Wait it gets worse . . . Nearly half of all Americans believe in creationism . . . Only 11 percent believe that man and woman evolved from other forms of life millions of years ago, unaided by the hand of God . . . In some ways, that's even more discouraging than the literacy rates, because a lot of these creationists can read, meaning they are members of society's shrinking elite."

Then he hits creation with a vengeance and arrogance: "What has creationism got going for it, in terms of salesmanship? One book [evidently the Bible] . . . a small, very small, group of pseudoacademics with some frail claim on intellectual respectability — maybe they went to college — who bend facts around to make it look like evolution is an iffy proposition and the Bible is word for word."

The faulty reasoning lies in that while creation cannot be proven and tested or falsified scientifically in repeatable tests, it however is logical, reasonable, has a non-material first cause and has never been falsified. Creation presupposes a designer for all the complex, complicated and precise things that exists in the universe, in the solar system and on this earth. Everything that exists is so complicated it could never have gotten here by itself without someone designing all things and above all the six million different forms of life on this earth, none of which has ever changed into something else.

Then he makes his grand faulty defense for evolution: "In support of evolution, we have virtually every public school textbook printed in the past 50 years, we have the nearly unanimous endorsement of scientists and intellectuals of every discipline, we have scores of public museums around the world that are storehouses of evidence testifying to the validity of the evolution theory."

But none of these 3 claims have one single piece of evidence that evolution has ever taken place in plants, animals and human beings. The most outstanding evolutionists have declared again and again: Evolution is a fact, a fact, a fact; but they never provide any facts.

There is no evidence of any kind of plant or animal ever changing into another species. All the fossils of plants, animals and human beings that are found in the sedimentary rock of this earth are the same as exist today. Some evolutionists claim the archaeopteryx, meaning "ancient wings," as proof some animals changed from a land animal to an air animal.

They claim that this partly reptile-like and partly bird-like creature proves evolution. But some ex-evolutionists claim this was a hoax. But even if a creature like this existed, it would be just another animal that became extinct, and there are many animals today who are partly sea and partly land animals and partly air and partly land animals.

Then Donald Kaul goes into "tracks left by millions of years." These tracks are found in sedimentary rock which were not laid down over millions of years. If they had been left over millions of years, they would have been wiped out of the dust in a few years.

Then he goes into "the documentation of an Earth millions of years old, assembled through high-tech carbon dating techniques." But carbon dating can go back less than 10,000 years. Then using the potassium-argon method, lava from Hawaii which was known to be 168 years old was dated by this method to be 2,960,000,000 years old. Quite a fable!

The question now is which Americans are dumb: the people who have been indoctrinated in evolution in schools, parks, museums and elsewhere for over a hundred years and can find no evidence for evolution or some of the highly educated who believe the fable of evolution without any scientific evidence.

Is it a matter of being dumb or a matter of being foolish? I have more respect for some people with an 8th grade education than some with doctors degrees and Nobel prizes. People who do not believe in evolution are neither dumb nor foolish. They have good judgment on their side.

A University of California professor of law, who made a study of the issue, said: "Evolution is a religious thing." Therefore evolution and the propagation of it does not belong in school textbooks, museums, parks and other government institutions. As one editor said: "**Get it out of here**."

Although THE FREE PRESS of Mankato Minnesota printed part of the above critique, no response was received from Donald Kaul or the TRIBUNE MEDIA.

Twin Cities Public TV
Attention Jack Willis

Dear Jack Willis and management:

Last night I watched the disgusting, non-scientific evolution idea that was presented by Dr. Donald Johanson on the origin of mankind on public TV. Not one bit of scientific evidence was presented for this foolish non-scientific, religious idea of evolutionists.

Like all evolutionists he threw around the millions of years without any evidence for these millions of years. From millions he dropped down to thousands of years in a very short while. At the very beginning of the program he shows a family of the supposed first of mankind. But where did this entire family with males and females come from? He showed pictures of fire and refers to primitive tools. Certainly it did not take such supposed aborigines millions of years to use fire and tools.

He showed pictures of skulls found in the sedimentary rock of this world. But a man with a doctor's degree should be smart enough to realize that these skulls were not encased in sedimentary rock over millions of years. These sedimentary rock were laid down quickly from very muddy sediments and not over millions of years. Over millions of years only a layer of dust would be laid down as is found on the moon today.

He showed pictures of Neanderthal people living without clothes for millions of years. Certainly it would not take these Neanderthals, with a brain-case larger than we have, to learn to use at least the clothing that they could get from the skin of animals that they could kill. The Neanderthal and Cro-Magnon people were mere different varieties of human beings just as we have different varieties today.

I have seen statements made by evolutionists with doctors degrees who say that creationists with doctors degrees should have their degrees taken away from them. It is the opposite that should be done. Any evolutionist with a doctors degree who believes in this foolish non-scientific religious idea of evolution should have his degree removed.

The evolutionists constantly say that evolution is a fact, a fact, a fact but they never provide any scientific fact.

I am deeply concerned about the welfare of mankind.

* * * * * * * *

Mr. Jack Willis responded to my letter but he provided no facts for the defense of evolution, although I sent him my brochure with 32 reasons why evolution is not scientific. However he presented a new thought: "Another public television series currently in production will examine the other side of the controversy. The series, presently titled SCIENTIFIC CREATIONISM, will look at the continuing debate over evolutionary theory and creationism, and the teaching of each in public schools."

I responded: "However from the American constitution viewpoint there is a third side: that both evolution and creationism are religious viewpoints, neither of which can be proven scientifically, therefore neither should be propagated in any form in public institutions, including the secular news media. This is the proper American viewpoint."

I also added: "Although I firmly believe that evolution is completely false and that a designer — creator viewpoint is the only thing left, I do not agree with those who try to sneak creation into public institutions along side of evolution, both under the guise of science."

"As far as origins is concerned I find more solid evidences, scientific possibilities, foundations, facts and hypotheses in the first eleven chapters of Genesis than can be found in all the science books of the world as far as geology, archaeology, biology, botany, zoology, astronomy, history, etc. are concerned. And yet I would not want this taught in public institutions. Let this be done privately — the American way. When I went to public school neither evolution nor creation were taught and that is the way it still should be. By doing it this way, my education was not shortchanged.

To the editors of the TIME magazine
Time and Life Building, Rockefeller Center
New York, NY 10020

Regarding HOW MAN BEGAN in your March 14, 1994 issue: All the
assumptions and presumptions in the nonscientific article listed under
SCIENCE is mere evolution babble without any scientific foundation.

The fundamental scientific error made in this article is stated in
three preliminary sentences, page 82, column three. Referring to fossils
being 2 million years to 200,000 years old the statements are made:
"Many specimens are found in sedimentary rock, laid down in layers
through the ages. By developing ways of dating the rock layers, scientists
have been able to approximate the age of fossils contained in them. But
these methods are far from foolproof."

But evolutionists, who claim to be scientists, should know that
sedimentary rocks are not "laid down in layers through the ages." If they
were laid down through the ages gradually, according to their
uniformitarian idea of geological changes taking place uniformly and
gradually, there would be only a layer of dust as there is on the moon.
But these fossils, including those of dinosaurs, are mixed in the
sedimentary rock which could be formed only when extremely muddy
waters covered the earth through a worldwide extremely violent
catastrophe.

These layers of sedimentary rock were not laid down over millions
of years for fossil tree trunks 80 feet tall have been found in England
standing through ten layers of sedimentary rock, so these layers were
not laid down in layers over millions of years. Otherwise these trees
would have decayed before the next layers was laid down.

Nowhere on this earth does the geology of this earth verify the
evolution belief of millions of years. And with this falls the idea that man
evolved over millions of years. Also there is no evidence anywhere that
any one of the millions of species of plants and animals ever changed
into another species of plants and animals.

You made some statements that were correct, page 82: "The fossil
record remains maddeningly sparse," and page 87: "The only certainty
in this data-poor, imagination rich, endlessly fascinating field is that
there are plenty of surprises left to come." The surprises are that
evolution has no scientific facts and is not scientific and will be the
laughing stock of the decades to come. Your imagination presented

under "science" is running wild. Why do you people continue to preach this nonscientific, religious evolution belief to the detriment of mankind? You ignore solid scientific evidences.

They replied in a postcard dated May 2, 1994, stating: "Thank you for writing to TIME. The sheer volume of our editorial mail makes it difficult to reply personally to every reader, but we can assure you that your comments were circulated among several editors for their information and consideration."

Certainly one of these editors should have tried to defend their religious beliefs in such a vital far-reaching subject that affects the wellbeing of all mankind.

DISCUSSIONS WITH EVOLUTIONISTS ON SECULAR RADIO TALK SHOWS

The most confrontational discussion was my very first appearance on a radio talk show. It was on the Spokane, Washington KXLY radio September 4, 1991. It was to be a debate with Dr. James Birx, Ph.D., professor at some university in New York state, who had a book published in 1991, INTERPRETING EVOLUTION.

But it ended up with me debating two evolutionists: Dr. James Birx and the host, Alex Wood, who was just as confirmed in evolution as Dr. Birx. There was much that these two evolutionists stated that was totally false. I could not correct all of it during the talk show but am mentioning some of the 27 errors here with my corrections.

The host, Alex Wood, opened the debate on the wrong foot by stating:

ALEX: I think that the evidence for scientific evolution is overwhelming: paleontology, anthropology, genetics, molecular biology, even astrophysics all go back to an evolutionary basis.

ALBERT: Paleontology, anthropology, etc. do not prove evolution but rather disprove it. These sciences have been harmed by evolution, because of their false evolutionary assumptions and conclusions.

JAMES: As far as Genesis goes and as far as the Noachian Flood goes and Adam and Eve etc., I think that modern theologians, and as well as most scientists and rational philosophers are concerned, would say that these are stories and myths . . . evolution is not based on a myth.

ALBERT: Where is the scientific evidence that Genesis, the Flood etc. are myths? Creation is not a myth. There is more sound geology, biology, botany, zoology, astronomy, history, etc., in the first eleven chapters of Genesis than can be found in all the libraries of the world. The evidence is that evolution is a fable and Genesis is a fact.

JAMES: The difference between scientific evolution and all the other stories is that scientists look for evidence.

ALBERT: But even evolutionists like Stephen Gould state that they have not found any evidence. That is why he jumped to the "punctuated equilibrium" idea to explain the sudden appearance of all kinds of different creations. (See this book page 147f.)

JAMES: (Right after previous statement) The evidence may be geology, chemistry, age of the earth, different dates for the different rock strata and fossil records.

ALBERT: Geology, dates for rock strata, and fossil records have been misread by the evolutionists. The facts are just the opposite of what the evolutionists claim.

JAMES: Millions of fossils have been found to support the idea that plant and animal species have changed in time. Life has changed through the millions and billions of years.

ALBERT: The millions of fossils do not prove that plants and animals have changed into different kinds or species, but merely that there have been some changes into different varieties of the same species. Professor Stephen Gould of Harvard University, a leader for the evolutionists today, stated: "All paleontologists know that the fossil record contains precious little in the way of intermediate forms, transitions between major groups are characteristically abrupt." See pages 145-146 of this book.

JAMES: Groups of plants and animals have been placed in an evolutionary sequence.

ALBERT: There is totally no scientific evidence for such evolutionary sequence, but it is merely another assumption or fabrication of the evolutionists.

JAMES: There are comparative studies in embryology, anatomy, physiology and particularly genetics and the DNA molecule.

ALBERT: Embryology, anatomy, physiology, etc., do not prove evolution but are just another disproven assumption. The idea of embryology has been disavowed by some evolutionists. On the other hand genetics and especially the DNA molecule have clearly proven that evolution is impossible by outstanding scientists, like I. L. Cohen in DARWIN WAS WRONG and Michael Denton in EVOLUTION: A THEORY IN CRISIS.

JAMES: I think why some people object to evolution, they do not seem to object to gravity, relativity, quantum mechanics or electricity . . .

ALBERT: Equating evolution with gravity, relativity, electricity, etc., is an old worn-out evolution trick to mislead people into believing that evolution is a fact without providing any facts. Evolution is not testable, provable and falsifiable as those other items are. See pages 316 to 319.

JAMES: I think the reason why people object to evolution . . . is that evolution has something disturbing to say about man. It means that man is related to other animals . . . that man cannot be separated from other animals especially from apes.

ALBERT: This false teaching has separated man from God to whom he is accountable.

JAMES: Many of the ecological and environmental problems can be traced back to man being separate from animals.

ALBERT: This statement is highly questionable. Much rather the problem is the moral decay and downfall of man, which is due to people being taught that man is just another animal, accountable only to himself, to do his own thing without regard to others. If you are just another animal why not live like an animal?

IN SUMMARY: Evolution is the primary evil of this world out of which has flowed endless other evils. See the section shortly before this section regarding the numerous evil effects that evolution has on mankind.

JAMES: Human beings have been evolving about five or four millions of years ago. Man has been evolving culturally for millions of years. We see the slow evolution of the stone tools and weapons.

ALBERT: There was no slow evolution of the stone tools and weapons. Evolutionists fail to consider that there have been people for centuries who have been highly advanced like many of the people before the obvious Flood in Noah's days, and the Egyptians, Babylonians and many others after the Flood. Then on the other hand there also have been people all these centuries that were almost in an what might be called an "evolutionary stone age," like some people in various parts of the world in recent centuries and the very backwards people that Charles Darwin found on the southern tip of South America and on islands throughout the world. There were many people who roamed around in different sections of the world and hunted and gathered food wherever they could and whose fossils, buried in Noah's Flood, are now what the evolutionists like to call the Neanderthal man and Cro-Magnon man. Some of these have skulls larger than ours.

JAMES: There are links like Homo habilis, Homo erectus, Homo sapiens.

ALBERT: In regard to these, some of them have had backward sloping skulls, but that does not prove that they were developing upwards. A few years ago I saw a man with an extremely sloping forehead and yet he was a very intelligent man. If some evolutionists find his skull some day, they would claim he lived millions of years ago as Homo habilis.

JAMES: (Referring to the sun and the second law of thermodynamics): There is plenty of energy on the earth from the sun to drive this process of organic evolution.

ALBERT: The energy from the sun could never design and create life in complex living cells. (See pages 212 & 256 of this book regarding OPEN SYSTEMS and also my debate with Professor Keith Kline further on.)

JAMES: There are millions of fossils of fishes, amphibians, reptiles.

ALBERT: They do not prove evolution. They prove that they were destroyed in a very turbulent muddy flood like in Noah's days.

JAMES: (He goes into myths again.) Genesis is completely a myth. Just a story.

ALBERT: Genesis is not a myth. It corresponds with actual history, geology, paleontology, biology, astronomy and DNA molecules. There are no Egyptian, Babylonian and Judean-Christian Flood myths. These accounts of a world-wide Flood prove the Genesis Flood was known world-wide.

JAMES: We must distinguish between myths on one hand and scientific evidence on the other hand.

ALBERT: Genesis is clearly established as shown not only in the Bible and other accounts but also from the crust of the earth and fossils found in them. It is evolution that is a recently developed fable, it has been devised to counteract and defy the facts given in the Bible and it goes contrary to a correct analysis of the crust of the earth.

JAMES: In conclusion evolution is supported by science and reason.

ALBERT: Evolution is not supported by scientific evidence and it is totally unreasonable. There is no evidence that evolution ever took place. Reason must say that there is a non-material force, power, intelligence or Being behind all the material things and the life that exists, just as there is a non-material mind and intelligence behind all the things that men have designed and made. Romans 1:20 states the case clearly: "Since the creation of the world His invisible attributes (that the Creator is eternal, all powerful, all wise, etc.) are clearly seen being understood by the things that are made, even His ETERNAL POWER and GODHEAD (non-material attributes), so that they are without excuse." A man must be totally foolish to disbelieve all the creation evidences around us. That is why the Bible also clearly declares: "The fool has said in his heart, 'There is no God,' " Psalm 14, 1.

KMSU,
Mankato [MN] State University Talk Show

In a debate January 20, 1993 on KMSU with Professor Keith Kline, who is a biology instructor at Mankato State and teaches a class on evolution, he said the second law of thermodynamics "pertains only to closed systems." He was surprised that I would bring up the second law. He said "the earth would have to be a closed system with no input from anywhere else" for the second law to apply. "Every day the sun shines we are getting input with a large amount of energy, which can be utilized to form self-organizing systems on earth."

I said the sun can do nothing without the life systems, etc. that have been built into the cells of plants and animals. In essence the sun can do nothing at all by itself to produce life. The sun does nothing except to get things going with the life that has been built into the seed, after the seed has been placed into moist ground. In the course of time when plants get old, they finally deteriorate and the sun helps the deterioration. The sun becomes destructive. And so it is also with animals and human beings. They finally degenerate in spite of the sun and go to pieces. All finally die.

KEITH: They leave offspring. They have not gone to pieces. There are still plants, animals and people in the world.

ALBERT: But they have been reproduced by the life that has been instilled into the different parent cells that reproduce life. These reproducing cells cause life to reappear and continue.

KEITH: He goes into the European corn borer which he claims "transported to America has become a new species incapable of breeding with progenitors."

ALBERT: It is still a corn borer, it is not a new species, but a new variety of corn borer that does not interbreed. (This corn borer could be similar to a mule which does not interbreed with progenitors — donkeys and horses.)

KEITH: Evolution is caused by the flow of energy which is an intimate consequence of the second law of thermodynamics, to get back to that thing again. One of the things of current interest of scientists (chemists, physicists, biologists and the like) is when energy moves, things organize in a self-organizing pattern. One of the hottest topics in science today is the chaos theory. And that sort of thing is exactly the sort of thing that seems to organize new forms out of the flow of energy. On earth we have demonstrated that there is a flow of energy . . . and if you have a flow of energy from the sun then you should have self organizing systems.

ALBERT: In essence this idea is not one bit better than the evolutionist's basic ideas that plants and animals evolve from one species into another. As I mentioned before energy from the sun in itself will never produce life or self organizing systems. (So here I tried to lead the discussion into the field of cells, showing how totally impossible it is for living cells to develop by themselves as Dr. Michael Denton stressed in his book, EVOLUTION: A THEORY IN CRISIS and I. L. Cohen in his book, DARWIN WAS WRONG.) Cohen stated, p. 206: "Chemical molecules are dumb, — they have no brains — they cannot design supersophisticated systems by their own volition . . . molecules cannot get together and agree among themselves to generate a sequence of 3,000,000 nucleotides, in a VERY SPECIFIC ORDER. Such meaningful action would be an expression of intelligence — which chemical molecules do not possess. This means that no amount of chemical mixing, with or without heat, with or without pressures, would ever result in a 3,000,000 nucleotide sequence. For as long as this does not occur, we have no living species. Consequently, the evolutionists concept of the origin of life is untenable . . . What Darwin considered as a simple cell is anything but simple — it is the most complex, and sophisticated chemical factory humankind has ever tried to analyze."

ALBERT: Particles of sand, dirt, mud and water can never be changed into living matter no matter what is done. Cohen p. 212: "There is no mathematical probability whatever for evolution to have been the mechanism that created 6,000,000 species [of plants and animals] on this world."

KEITH: goes into viruses and particles, that he says: "are sort of semi-animate, much more complex than crystals and snowflakes. We can and have synthesized extremely simple forms of life like viruses and the future holds no barrier to synthesizing entire cells.

ALBERT: But they cannot evolve by themselves any more than cars and airplanes or anything else can come together by themselves. Also viruses are harmful to cells.

At the beginning of the debate and during the course of it, the host, Marilee Rickard, gave me the opportunity to present a number of my 32 reasons why evolution is not scientific. Keith made reference to only one of them: the second law of thermodynamics.

OTHER TALK SHOWS

On other talk shows, of which there were a number, the hosts and call-ins asked if I have been questioned by evolutionists. They also asked: Do evolutionists have any arguments? These preceding pages are the answers to these questions. During each debate I get into and each talk show I get on, the evolutionists unintentionally give me more reasons why evolution is not scientific. Hardly any call-in tried to correct anything I said. Most of them agreed with me. For argument's sake some hosts have tried to play the devil's advocate, just to test my reasons why evolution is not scientific.

SEPTEMBER 6, 1992 GRAND RAPIDS, MI TALK SHOW

A man called in who had some interesting thoughts about the big bang idea. He said that when you take a stick of dynamite and put it in a rock, it will blow up into pieces and all will go in different directions. Now how do you explain our planet and all the other planets going around the sun in such precise order, so that we know when the sun is going to rise and set? If we had a big bang these pieces of planets would fly out and hit something to bounce into orbit. The earth is round. You take a sledge hammer and hit a rock, it is going to break into jagged pieces. Earth and other planets are almost perfectly round. Why wouldn't they be oblong and triangular if they came from a big bang? Where did the material for the big bang come from? You take your fossils. Take a fish and lay it out here in back. In 3 or 4 days it is rotten. Yet you can find a rock with a fish in it. That had to be buried quickly.

WARNING TO EVOLUTIONISTS with doctor's degrees. A lot of these humble lay people do not need a doctor's degree to know that evolution is totally false.

A Strong Recommendation of the Book

Just before this book was about to be reprinted the following article appeared in THE CHRISTIAN NEWS of October 3, 1994. It was written over 4 years ago by Mr. Tom Buege, a science teacher.

Review by Tom Buege

This new book by Pastor Albert Sippert of the CLC really does live up to its title. It is an excellent overview of the debate between evolutionists and creationists from the origin of the universe to the development of civilization, from the testimony of the fossil record to the evidence of space exploration. And then, unlike most books on creationism, Reverend Sippert finishes with a most eloquent and beautiful description of the experience of the world to come in which the Christian will know the joys of heaven which far transcend anything this magnificent, but sin-stained present world has to offer.

No matter what a person's special area of scientific interest, he should find the entire book fascinating. Who would not be angered by the cruelty and crudeness displayed by Charles Darrow against an elderly William Jennings Bryan at the Scopes Monkey Trial in the 1920s? Who can resist a discussion about what the pre-flood world was like or why advanced civilization just seems to have blossomed out of nowhere some 5000 years ago. Who would not enjoy being reminded of the wonders of the human body with all its magnificent design and its function controlled by a brain of such complexity that scientists can't even begin to describe it let alone duplicate it?

The wonders of the plant world, the animal world, the stars, the planets, and earth itself are all here in a language that a layman with a high school education can understand. The author has amassed a wealth of information but has deliberately presented it in as understandable a way as possible.

There is one area where even many creationists might criticize Pastor Sippert, although members of the Lutheran Science Institute would undoubtedly agree with him. Pastor Sippert very clearly shows that both evolution and creation as explanations for the origins of life are religious concepts and cannot be proved or disproved by scientific evidence. As such, neither should be taught in the public school system.
The author warns that efforts to have creationism taught side by side with evolution can only lead to trouble. His argument is summarized on page 356:

"Considering what many theologians have done in interpreting Genesis chapter one and two according to their way of thinking, what kind of treatment would the Bible account receive at the hands of public school teachers who are not Christians, or whose knowledge of the Bible is weak, or who have become ardent believers in humanism and evolution? Yes, what would happen if the average teacher trained in a secular college were to teach the Bible account of creation? We know that to have creation taught by teachers, who do not believe in it, do not want to teach it, would result in God's Word being degraded or ridiculed, and it certainly would do only harm to the account of creation and most likely to the trust of the child in the rest of the Bible."

FROM ETERNITY TO ETERNITY is a real blessing in many ways and it is the hope of this reviewer that a number of editions will need to be printed. This is an excellent book for church libraries and Christian school libraries. We would also do our community a real service by attempting to place Pastor Sippert's book in municipal and university libraries!

* * *

So glad to see that you are making Sippert's From Eternity to Eternity available to CN readers!

This book review (above) which I wrote for the May-August 1990 "Lutheran Science Institute Journal" may help your readers appreciate the wide range of topics covered. Sippert's negative view of teaching creationism alongside evolution in the public schools is almost unique in creationist literature.

Thank you, Mr. Tom Buege, for analysing the essence and purpose of the book so well and for the recommendation you gave it.

Thank God, that in spite of my age I am still able to be back again in the mission fields of the world and be a pastor (shepherd) in a different way through this book — of misled, wavering and unconcerned people, including some pastors of this world.

A SECOND BOOK

Another book may be published depending upon how many requests for the book may be received. The book Behold YOUR man, your King, GOD, CREATOR, and SAVIOR includes a series of Advent and Lenten sermons.

Some of the contents are: the announcement of His coming, the WONDERFUL Babe of Bethlehem, Jesus' royal road to greatness, the most important battle in the history of this world, behold the vestures of your King, His weapons, the kingdom of His spiritual enemy, His kingdom is not of this world, no neutrality in His kingdom, His subjects, His relatives, His earthly enemies, His homage, His attitude, His throne, His victory, His triumphal entry into the abode of His spiritual enemy.

These sermons are informative and instructive based on the work of Jesus Christ as OUR man, King, GOD, CREATOR and SAVIOR. Broken into paragraphs they can be used for family devotions or meditations for individuals as well as for sermons.

Also included is An Analysis of the Lord's Prayer and An Exposition of the 23rd Psalm. Both of these sermons have been highly rated by those who heard or read them. Also: One of the many reasons God permits Christians to suffer afflications of all kinds. Also: The second great, devastating evil of this world.

BIBLIOGRAPHY

THE ABIDING WORD, Concordia Publishing House 1955

Ackerman, Paul, IT'S A YOUNG WORLD AFTER ALL 1986

Andrews, E. H., IS EVOLUTION SCIENTIFIC 1981

Asimov, Isaac, IN THE BEGINNING 1981

Asimov, Isaac, THE COLLAPSING UNIVERSE 1977

Berlitz, Charles, MYSTERIES FROM FORGOTTEN WORLDS 1972

Broms, Allan, THUS LIFE BEGAN 1968

Carrington, Richard, THE STORY OF OUR EARTH 1956

Casson, Lionel, ANCIENT EGYPT 1965

Cloud, Preston, COSMOS, EARTH AND MAN 1978

Culp, Richard, REMEMBER THY CREATOR 1975

Cunstance, Arthur, CONVERGENCE: AND THE ORIGIN OF MAN

Cunstance, Arthur, SURVIVAL OF THE UNFIT, 1971

Dallman, William, EVOLUTION? 1925

De Camp, LeSprague, THE GREAT MONKEY TRIAL 1968

Dell, Jacob, I STILL BELIEVE IN GOD 1942

Drinan, Robert, RELIGIONS AND THE COURTS AND PUBLIC POLICY 1963

Eldredge, Niles, THE MONKEY BUSINESS 1982

Fagan, Brian, PEOPLE OF THE EARTH 1977

Fagan, Brian, IN THE BEGINNING 1978

Feldman, Anthony, SPACE 1980

French, Bevan, THE MOON BOOK 1977

Galstad, Martin, FINDINGS 1984

Gentry, Robert, CREATION'S TINY MYSTERY 1986

Gish, Duane, EVOLUTION - THE FOSSILS SAY NO! 1978

Graebner, Theodore, EVOLUTION - AN INVESTIGATION AND A CRITICISM 1921

Graebner, Theodore, GOD AND THE COSMOS 1932

Gustavus College, NOBEL CONFERENCE XVIII 1982

Hammerton, John, WONDERS OF THE PAST 1923

Handrich, Theodore, THE CREATION, FACTS, THEORIES AND FAITH 1953

Handrich, Theodore, EVERY-DAY SCIENCE FOR THE CHRISTIAN, 1938

Hawkes, Jacquette, THE ATLAS OF EARLY MAN 1976

Hiebert, Henry, EVOLUTION: ITS COLLAPSE IN VIEW 1979

Hotten, Nicholas, THE EVIDENCE OF EVOLUTION

Hyma, Albert, STREAMS OF CIVILIZATION 1977

Institute for Creation Research, ACTS AND FACTS July 1982 - Jan. 1989

Institute for Creation Research, IMPACT July 1982 through Jan. 1989

Jelinek, J., THE EVOLUTION OF MAN 1975

Johnson and Yost, SEPARATION OF CHURCH AND STATE 1948

Kofahl, Robert, HANDY DANDY EVOLUTION REFUTER 1980

Kownslar, Allan, PEOPLE OF OUR WORLD - A STUDY OF WORLD HISTORY 1984

Kupal, Zdenek, MAN AND HIS UNIVERSE 1972

Leakey, Richard, PEOPLE OF THE LAKE 1978

Life Magazine, THE EPIC OF MAN 1961

Macbeth, Norman, DARWIN RETRIED 1971

Menendez, Albert, CLASSICS OF RELIGIOUS LIBERTY 1978

Minnesota Association For The Improvement of Science Education, EVOLUTION AND PUBLIC EDUCATION 1981

Monsma, John, SCIENCE AND RELIGION 1962

Moore, Ruth, MAN, TIME AND FOSSILS 1953

Moore, Ruth, THE EARTH WE LIVE ON 1956

Morris, Henry, and others, A SYMPOSIUM ON CREATION 1968

Morris, Henry, CREATION AND ITS CRITICS 1982

Morris, Henry, HISTORY OF MODERN CREATIONISM 1984

Morris, Henry, STUDIES IN THE BIBLE AND SCIENCE 1966

Morris, Henry, THE TROUBLED WATERS OF EVOLUTION 1974

Morris, Henry, EVOLUTION IN TURMOIL 1982

Morris, Henry, THE TWILIGHT OF EVOLUTION 1963

Morris, Henry, CREATION AND THE MODERN CHRISTIAN 1985

Morris, Henry, THE REMARKABLE BIRTH OF PLANET EARTH 1978

Morris, Henry, THE BATTLE FOR CREATION 1976

Morris, Henry, SCIENTIFIC CREATIONISM 1974

Motz, Lloyd, THE UNIVERSE: ITS BEGINNING AND END

National Geographic, MYSTERIES OF THE ANCIENT WORLD 1979

National Geographic, THE ONCE AND FUTURE UNIVERSE June 1983

National Geographic, THE SEARCH FOR OUR ANCESTORS Nov. 1985

National Geographic, HOMO ERECTUS UNEARTHED Nov. 1985

National Geographic, THE PEOPLING OF THE EARTH: IN SEARCH OF MODERN HUMANS Oct. 1988

National Park Service, GLACIER NATIONAL PARK, DEVILS TOWER, BADLANDS and OTHER PAMPHLETS

Nelson, Byron, AFTER ITS KIND 1927

Nelson, Byron, THE DELUGE STORY IN STONE 1931

Nelson, Byron, BEFORE ABRAHAM 1948

Noorbergen, Rene, SECRETS OF LOST RACES 1977

Parker, Gary, WHAT IS CREATION SCIENCE 1982

Patten, Donald, THE BIBLICAL FLOOD 1966

Patten, Donald, A SYMPOSIUM ON CREATION II 1970

Patten, Donald, A SYMPOSIUM ON CREATION III 1971

Patten, Donald, THE LONG DAY OF JOSHUA 1973

Pelzl, James, AN UPDATE OF THE VELIKOVSKY STORY 1984

Pensee, Editors of, VELIKOVSKY - RECONSIDERED 1966

Pfeiffer, John, THE EMERGENCE OF MAN 1969

Pieper, Francis, CHRISTIAN DOGMATICS

Pigott, Stuart, THE DAWN OF CIVILIZATION

Reader's Digest, ALL ISSUES JANUARY 1964 THROUGH
    JANUARY 1989
Rehwinkel, Alfred, THE FLOOD 1951
Rehwinkel, Alfred, THE WONDERS OF CREATION 1974
Ridenour, Fritz, WHO SAYS 1967
Rimmer, Harry, THE THEORIES OF EVOLUTION 1929
Romanes, George, DARWIN, AND AFTER DARWIN 1892
Siegler, Hilbert, EVOLUTION OR DEGENERATION - WHICH?
    1972
Silk, Joseph, THE BIG BANG 1980
Silverberg, Robert, CLOCKS FOR THE AGES 1971
Silverberg, Robert, FRONTIERS IN ARCHEOLOGY 1966
Stock, Chester, RANCHO LA BREA 1972
Thorndike, Joseph, DISCOVERY OF LOST WORLDS 1979
Tillinghast, PLOETZ MANUAL OF UNIVERSAL HISTORY 1925
Trefil, James, THE MOMENT OF CREATION 1983
Unger, Merrill, ARCHEOLOGY AND THE OLD TESTAMENT
    1970
Velikosky, Immanuel, WORLDS IN COLLISION 1950
Weinberg, Steven, THE FIRST THREE MINUTES 1977
Welthy, Paul, MAN'S CULTURAL HERITAGE - A WORLD
    HISTORY 1969
Wenke, Robert, PATTERNS IN PREHISTORY 1986
West, Willis, EARLY PROGRESS 1920
Whitcomb, John and Morris, Henry, THE GENESIS FLOOD 1961
Whitcomb, John, THE EARLY EARTH 1972
Wilson, David, THE NEW ARCHEOLOGY 1974
(The) WORLD BOOK ENCYCLOPEDIA
Wysong, R. L., THE CREATION AND EVOLUTION
    CONTROVERSY 1976
Zimmerman, Paul, DARWIN, EVOLUTION AND CREATION
    1958
Plus NUMEROUS OTHER BOOKS AND MAGAZINES

INDEX - NAMES AND SUBJECTS

INDEX OF SCRIPTURE PASSAGES